Natural Environment Research Council
Institute of Terrestrial Ecology

Native Pinewoods of Scotland

Proceedings of Aviemore Symposium, 1975

Edited by
Dr. R.G.H. Bunce and
Mr. J.N.R. Jeffers

Printed in England by
Graphic Art (Cambridge) Ltd.

Published by Institute of Terrestrial Ecology
68 Hills Road
Cambridge CB2 1LA

ISBN 0 904282 082

First published 1977
Dr. R.G.H. Bunce
Institute of Terrestrial Ecology
Merlewood Research Station
Grange-over-Sands
Cumbria LA11 6JU
Telephone Grange-over-Sands 2264

The Institute of Terrestrial Ecology (ITE) was established in 1973, from the former Nature Conservancy's research stations and staff, joined later by the Institute of Tree Biology and the Culture Centre of Algae and Protozoa. ITE contributes to and draws upon the collective knowledge of the fourteen sister institutes which make up the Natural Environment Research Council, spanning all the environmental sciences.

The Institute studies the factors determining the structure, composition and processes of land and freshwater systems, and of individual plant and animal species. It is developing a sounder scientific basis for predicting and modelling environmental trends arising from natural or man-made change. The results of this research are available to those responsible for the protection, management and wise use of our natural resources.

Nearly half of ITE's work is research commissioned by customers, such as the Nature Conservancy Council who require information for wildlife conservation, the Forestry Commission and the Department of the Environment. The remainder is fundamental research supported by NERC.

ITE's expertise is widely used by international organisations in overseas projects and programmes of research.

Preface

The native pinewoods of Scotland have long been the subject of scientific research and the significance of their component ecosystem was emphasised in 1959 in the publishing of the book by Steven and Carlisle. Despite the extensive knowledge of the forests and their acknowledged significance in scientific and amenity terms, the resource continued to be under threat because of its high commercial value. The objective of the Symposium was to discuss the ecology of the native pinewoods and the measures needed to promote their conservation. The evidence since the Symposium took place is that both objectives were achieved. There has been considerable acitivity recently in the extension of areas under conservation agreements and at least one was a direct result of the Symposium. It is hoped that this report will further consolidate the progress already made.

The programme was developed by the editors in co-operation with David Morris and Rawdon Goodier of the Nature Conservancy Council. The Aviemore staff of NCC supervised the local arrangements and organised the Symposium exhibition, with the assistance of Basil Dunlop of the Strathspey estates and the staff of the Macaulay Institute for Soil Science and the Coylumbridge Hotel.

The discussions that followed the papers were recorded, but transcripts have not been included in these proceedings because of lack of space. Copies of the transcripts are available on application to the editors.

R.G.H. Bunce
Merlewood
February 1976.

Contents

Introduction to the symposium on Scottish native pinewoods

Jean Balfour Countryside Commission for Scotland

In 1972, the Verney Committee wrote in their report 'Sinews for Survival': "Trees are beautiful as well as useful, they are one of our country's renewable natural resources, too often they are taken for granted".

Unlike agricultural land, where man at least in northern Europe and certainly in Scotland soon learned to husband this resource by caring for the land and fostering and improving its crop, forests have been steadily exploited until the 20th century, (and, of course, in much of the world, exploitation continues at an ever faster rate). Efforts by the Scots Parliament, from as early as the 12th century onwards by law and charter, to encourage planting and punish over-cutting, failed to prevail against the needs of fuel, building, destruction of wolves and bandits and the English attempts at conquest, with its attendant destruction. Only the comparative inaccessibility of the Highlands, and the late discovery of the forests of the north have saved these relict woodlands which we see today, and even they have not escaped entirely the hand of man.

Let us at least be encouraged that today we are no longer taking them for granted.

Before continuing, I would like to make clear what I mean by natural forest or other terms. By natural forest, I mean forest unmodified by man. Such places, if they exist at all in Scotland, are rare, but perhaps the tree-line area on Craig Fhiaclach may be one. Rather, I prefer to use the term continuous forest which means, to me, an area continuously under woodland since boreal times, whether subjected to the effects of man to a greater or lesser degree over a longer or shorter period of time. This definition includes a changing pattern of open ground both within, and peripheral to, the forest. Practically all Scottish woodland belongs to this category.

The role of native pinewoods

The discussions this week centre on the Scottish native pinewoods, their future, their vegetation, their patterns of change and their management, and, in two of the papers, it is sought to set them in context with the Scandinavian countries. We should remember, however, that they are a part, a large and important part indeed, of Scottish continuous woodlands and that all such woodlands are decreasing and are in need of care and protection. They are all-important elements in the Scottish countryside, part of our heritage if you will, both scientifically and scenically. In the long term, they have a part to play in improving the degraded land in parts of the Scottish highlands and uplands. Therefore, in being concerned for the native pinewoods, we should not lose sight of the whole range. Why then are the Scottish pinewoods singled out for special consideration? Let us look at some of the reasons, and at one in particular which has, I believe, important implications for their future.

1. They are the largest component of Scottish continuous woodlands.

2. They are spectacular.

3. They have a wide range of wildlife and vegetation interest, more so than most of the Scottish mixed deciduous woodlands.

4. They are capable of producing saleable timber and therefore have an economic value.

Let us look then at these reasons which attract interest in the Scottish native pinewoods:

First, they are the largest component of continuous woodland in Scotland and also in the UK. This means that, even allowing for the variety of types within the native pine forests, and recognising them as relicts, there are still areas which are large enough to fill one's horizon. Consider Glen Affric or the vista looking out over Abernethy. Look across Loch Maree from Letterewe or stand in the Black Wood of Rannoch. In these places, there is still the knowledge and awareness of being within a forest with its lively silence. This awareness, I believe, applies to foresters, scientists, land managers, conservationists and countryside spectator alike, a seemingly natural forest, something which has always been.

Second, pine forests are spectacular. Even Thomas Pennant, travelling in Scotland over 200 years ago, remarked on the magnificence of the pine forest in Mar and described Glen Tanar as second to none. Today, visitors to Speyside or Deeside are still impressed by the native pines and the information centres at Loch an Eilan and Glen More both concentrate on aspects of the forest in interpreting the area for visitors.

Third, they have a very wide range of wildlife and vegetation interest, a good deal of which is peculiar to the pine forest. It is unnecessary for me, in this company, to try to elaborate on this fact or to quote from McVean and Ratcliffe or Steven and Carlisle. Suffice to say that the long term inter-relationship between the ground flora and the pine is an aspect of particular interest to biological scientists, as are the associated ornithological and other aspects, while the more casual visitor can enjoy the caper or meet the all-pervading deer, and even look with interest at *Goodyera repens!*

Last, (the one to which I referred as having important future implications) the pine forests can produce revenue in the form of valuable timber. This reason separates them distinctly from other remnants of continuous woodland. In this, I believe has lain, somewhat paradoxically, both a major reason for their decimation over the last 200 years, but also for their safe-guarding, albeit in a decreasing way. This paradox is still with us and the future of the pinewoods depends a great deal on how we manipulate it in the future.

I would now like to review briefly the area and structure of the pinewoods, the pressures upon them and their regenerative capacity.

Area and Structure

In 1959, Steven and Carlisle estimated the continuous pinewood areas at about 26,000 acres. The 1971 survey has now put this area at about 4,000 acres of fully-stocked forest. Part of this change is accounted for by the drawing of boundaries rather narrowly and the improved estimation of stocking levels, but certainly suggests a reduction in the total area. In addition, there has been planting with other species in the area that was once pine forest.

The structure of these forests, and, in particular, what this structure should be, causes considerable debate. It does, however, seem fairly clear that, in a great many of the forests, there is a high proportion of older trees from 124-250 years, that saplings are not plentiful, and that the number of seedlings and very young trees varies considerably between different areas. There is some disagreement as to whether the low percentage of dead trees has been affected by the past removal, and it is also pointed out that old age can persist for a long time before death!

Regenerative Capacity and Pressures

The capacity of large numbers of old trees to produce sufficient quantity of viable seed is perhaps still not clear and there is certainly no apparent uniform pattern. Growing conditions play an important part in the survival of seedlings. At Glen Tanar, it is considered essential to scarify and to get below the thick humus layer for natural regeneration to take place. In Glen Affric, different methods are used. On thin soils, or with light heather cover, regeneration can be plentiful.

Undoubtedly, grazing pressures by deer and sheep are of fundamental importance, and, in many places, their exclusion is an essential prerequisite for success. The increase in deer numbers generally, and their increasing pressure, must be viewed with concern, if we seek more natural regeneration.

Whatever the answers are, it seems clear that, both in the longer and shorter term, the pinewoods are at risk. That the crisis may not happen for another 10, 15 or 20 years seems to be no valid reason for not pursuing a positive course of action now.

Ownership

Before we consider what we mean by positive action, and the ways and means in which it can be achieved, let us remind ourselves of the pattern of ownership of the native pinewoods. Using the areas given by Steven and Carlisle, some 68 per cent was in private ownership in 1959. The 1971 survey shows the area in private ownership to be 82 per cent; conversely, the public sector has diminished from 32 per cent to 18 per cent. It must be remembered that these changes in percentages are worked out on areas which differ greatly between 1959 and 1971. It is not suggested that the public, rather than the private side have, during that period, planted proportionately a greater number of

exotics or ceased to care for the small scattered pine areas which they may own. What is important to recognise is that the future for about 80 per cent of our pinewoods is in the private sector, which is increasingly under pressure from financial burdens and uncertainty. Perhaps, too, the fact underlines the particular responsibility of the public sector, which faces neither discontinuity nor penal tax burdens, to husband carefully their 20 per cent of this important resource.

Let us now take stock of the present situation, before we consider the future. About a decade after Steven and Carlisle's book, a small group in Aberdeen, under the Chairmanship of Professor John Matthews, began to consider the future and it was decided to put in hand the 1971 survey. Though some may have questioned the need for this survey at the time, I am sure that it has, in fact, provided a valuable new baseline for considering the future. Following on from this survey, last year's discussion meeting took place in Inverness, and those present visited Glen Affric. This year we have the interesting programme which lies ahead this week. I welcome the work that is being done on pinewoods and the increasing knowledge which is being gathered about the whole ecosystem as well as about the various specialised aspects of flora and fauna and soils. The wide range of the papers being given this week demonstrates this knowledge very clearly.

Let us not delude ourselves, however; the increase of knowledge and study of our native pinewoods is of vital importance and must continue, but more important still is the continuance of the pinewoods themselves. They must cease to shrink with each decade; indeed, we should be looking for a dynamic and expanding native forest, and we should be seeking for positive ways to achieve this expansion.

So do not let us despise the hand of man too much, so long a factor in these forests, since man's hand can be used for the improvement of the situation.

A Strategy for the Future?

I should now like to put forward three broad objectives for the maintenance, safeguarding and management of our native pine forests for the future:

1. **Dynamic native pinewoods—including expansion in appropriate areas**

   A dynamic forest is one which is regenerating and not dying on its feet. To achieve regeneration today nearly always requires some help from man, although such help is not always essential, as parts of Rothiemurchus demonstrate. In very small areas, such as Crannach or Doirie Daraich (Loch Tulla), fencing, to reduce heavy grazing, is probably the greatest need. In certain of the large areas, some form of ground treatment may also be required — such as at Glen Tanar. In others, again, hand planting may be necessary, as the Nature Conservancy found at Ben Eighe. But we should also seek an expanding rather than a shrinking forest by encouraging the forest, in appropriate places, to recolonise lost ground. Crannach is perhaps an example of where recolonisation is feasible, particularly when comparing old maps with the present-day area. Other examples are Shieldaig, recently partially destroyed by fire, and the remnants of Megernie in Glen Lyon.

Today, the only native pine forest with a plan for expansion is the Black Wood of Rannoch, where current proposals allow for a trebling of the forest in the long term, to a plan worked out by the Forestry Commission with help from the Nature Conservancy Council.

2. **Forest management which takes proper account of conservation of the resource**

Management is the most difficult aspect of dealing with the native pinewoods. Controversy arises from arguments over how much interference by man is acceptable. It is sometimes overlooked that all plant communities, of which pine forests are one example, are subject to changing patterns; that it is perhaps the rate of change and direction of these patterns that is important; and that this direction should not be towards decay.

If, therefore, we wish to move towards our second objective we must seek to manipulate the paradox to which I referred at the beginning of this paper. We must endeavour to marry together conservation of the resource and maintain the revenue-producing potential of the forest, so that we may be able to build a sound foundation for the continuance of these forests, patterned on the past, but varying as they must have done over the centuries.

In practice, what should this marriage be like? From the conservation point of view, there are, I think, at least three essentials. The use of only local pine seed when natural regeneration is insufficient, the growing of trees to an old age, and the maintenance of a forest and not a plantation structure. In the larger areas of well-grown native pine, I do not see too many problems for the forest manager. Local seed can be gathered for use when natural regeneration requires assistance. Open areas in the forest, where these result from natural bogs or exceptionally poor ground, can be accepted on financial as well as conservation grounds. Long rotations to allow the trees to grow old should be acceptable in a continuous forest, already stocked to a fairly considerable degree. In other words, we require a low input and output management regime. To maintain a forest, rather than a plantation, structure does however require new approaches and new skills on the part of the forester. What kind of management is needed at the thicket stage, whether this results from natural regeneration or planting, or both, so as to gain revenue and not create a long term plantation pattern. Even at a much older stage, the correct pattern of timber extraction is not easy.

The right kind of marking for selective felling requires new skills on the part of the forester, whose natural instinct is to even out the gaps between the stems rather than to recognise the natural clumping and grouping which is part of the forest pattern. Less difficult problems are areas of clear felling which differ little from the results brought about by wind blow, fire, or the York Building Company of the past.

3. **Creation of suitable reserve areas**

My third objective would be to create a network, not too large, of reserve areas. In seeking a dynamic, expanding forest and also the marrying of forest management and conservation, I recognise the need for carefully-selected, fairly small areas where the hand of man should be largely exluded. These would be control areas, for study, and for monitoring change both within the forest and in relation to the outside areas. In short, we require a series of undisturbed, representative samples, Such areas, at least in part, should, however, be subject to fencing where necessary to exclude grazing, which has become unnaturally heavy over the century.

The choice of reserve areas of appropriate and realistic size is something which needs careful thought, both in conservation and financial terms. Such reserve areas could mean loss of revenue through sterilisation, and, where this is the case, the nation should recognise its responsibility if this part of our national heritage is to be safe-guarded and studied. In this context, as I indicated earlier, the public sector has a special responsibility, and it would therefore seem reasonable that they would be able to accept larger reserve areas than would the private sector.

The Way Forward

When I was asked to speak to you tonight, it was suggested that I might attempt to set the scene for this symposium. Based then on the three broad objectives I have tried to outline, I would like those present to turn their thoughts, before the week is over, to action related to the art of the possible.

I believe the Forestry Commission is taking positive steps in their native pinewoods, often, I know, with help from the Nature Conservancy Council. I hope it will feel able to formulate long term plans in such a way that they will not be subject to change based on changing personnel, and that it will consider some special designation suitable, not only for native pine woods, but also for other types of continuous forest which they own. It is the private sector where encouragement is necessary, perhaps even a need to encourage an awareness in some cases, and certainly a need to give guidance quickly when this is required, and to seek practical solutions. The new burdens of capital transfer tax, if they continue, cannot but change drastically the present pattern of land holding and these changes must affect the private woodlands.In the exemption of the new (1975) finance act for areas of outstanding scenic and scientific interest, perhaps, lies a tool for safeguarding native pinewoods in the private sector, but, as yet, criteria have to be worked out. Much still depends on the private sector having faith in the future, and on scientists and others helping them with practical proposals.

The great danger today is not that we take the pine forests for granted, but that, in talking about them, we forget that talk is no substitute for action. Without action, successors to this Group in a 100 years' time may find much of the forest has ceased to exist.

The status of pinewoods in British ecosystems

C.H. Gimingham   Department of Botany, University of Aberdeen.

Not long ago, a conference was held on the theme of "The British Oak — its history and natural history", and its proceedings were published as a "Conference Report" (Morris and Perring, 1974). A recent reviewer, while praising the volume, added significantly that "a collection of papers prepared before the conference does not reflect what the contributors learnt from each other at the conference" (Cousens, 1975b). It seems to me that, in the programme before us on the subject of Scottish pinewoods, we have the opportunity of learning a great deal from each other, and, as an ecologist who has had a general rather than a specialist interest in our native pinewoods, I hope to be one of those who learns most. Unfortunately, being the opening speaker, my paper cannot reflect the rapid education I hope to receive; but I have been asked to look at the ecology of pinewoods rather generally, and perhaps bring to bear on pinewoods some attitudes and ideas derived from the investigation of other types of vegetation in Scotland and the rest of Britain.

It is as well to recognise that it is particularly difficult to examine the topic of the status of pinewoods with a completely open mind, because, to varying degrees, I think most of us approach it with preconceived ideas — which I believe should be carefully identified and examined. In the first place, there are those ideas which arise from the well-documented view that numerous examples of pinewood in Scotland are surviving fragments of native pine forest and do not owe their existence to intentional planting by man. This view has been attested by exhaustive enquiries, notably by Steven and Carlisle (1959). The historical accuracy of this conclusion is not in doubt; however, it has overtones to which I wish to draw attention. There is an aura which attaches to the knowledge that these are lineal descendants of the "old wood of Caledon", and even Steven and Carlisle say "To stand in them is to feel the past." This may be so, and it is pleasant to praise the "quality of the real wilderness of the boreal regions" (Ratcliffe, 1974), but it has led to an easy assumption that these woods are in a natural or near-natural condition. This is an assumption that we must examine. Tansley (1939), who has shaped so many of our ideas about British vegetation, refers to "characteristic examples of old native pine forest", a phrase which creates an impression not easily modified by references elsewhere in the book to British woodlands being "semi-natural".

The other context in which I believe we sometimes suffer from pre-conditioning in our approach to the Scottish native pinewoods is that of the uncritical use of the concept of "the climax". The "old wood of Caledon" was undoubtedly widespread N. and W. of the Highland Boundary Fault, and therefore must be regarded as constituting one of the major regional vegetational complexes of Britain (corresponding to the Mixed Deciduous Wood, and possibly the Sub-Arctic Birch wood of the extreme North: McVean and Ratcliffe, 1962). There

is plenty of evidence to support the view, derived from pollen analysis (Durno, 1957; Birks, 1970), that pine spread into this area after about 5000 B.C. and thereafter continued in place until the forests were decimated by man (Godwin, 1949). It is hardly surprising, therefore, that, whatever the exact connotation we attach to the term "climax", it has been associated with this forest type. Tansley links the native Scottish pinewoods to the coniferous forest formation of northern Europe, or at least to the transitional zone between this and deciduous summer forest. This, however, is a very different matter from saying that the pinewoods as we have them today are climax communities, but this has also become an assumption — again one which I believe should be very carefully examined.

Hence, we have two related assumptions to examine, both derived from the fact that our present-day pinewoods are lineal descendants of a Caledonian pine forest; one, that they are near-natural, and the other, that they have the properties of climax communities.

Modification of the Pinewoods by Man

The first of these assumptions is perhaps the easier to deal with. On reflection, few would disagree that our pinewoods have been more or less profoundly altered, directly or indirectly, by man. The exact consequences are less easy to identify, but among them are the following:

(a) Drastic reduction of the total area occupied by anything approaching native pine forest, and — apart from the splendid exception of the Speyside forests — reduction to small fragments. These processes must have led to substantial reductions in species complement. The phytosociology of the extensive pine forest prior to exploitation is presumably something we can never know in full, but it is clear that even the tree and shrub flora was rather more diverse than it is today. *Betula* sp., *Sorbus aucuparia, Populus tremula, Ilex aquifolium* (especially in the west) and *Juniperus communis* were probably all more abundant than they are now in most of the native pinewoods. In addition, there may have been some admixture of *Quercus* sp., *Ulmus* sp. and *Corylus avellana,* in suitable sites. There can be no doubt that the herbaceous flora was also more varied in the past. For example, several species which are common in Scandinavian forests, such as *Lycopodium annotinum, Vaccinium uliginosum* and *Linnaea borealis,* are absent from, or rare in, the surviving Scottish pinewoods. Climatic differences may be sufficient to explain these absences, but, on the other hand, they might, at least in part, be due to drastic reduction of the area occupied by this vegetation type in Scotland. Inevitably, floristic impoverishment will have occurred, and, in so far as there is some relationship between diversity and stability, we may expect some decline in the latter.

(b) Changes in the relative proportions of major tree

species. Most noticeable here seems to be a decline in the proportion of *Betula* spp. in some at least of the Scottish pinewoods, particularly those in the east of the country. Pollen diagrams lend support to the view that birch played a greater part prior to exploitation, as it still does today in comparable woodlands in Scandinavia.

(c) Changes in the density and age structure of pine stands. These have resulted from selective extraction of timber, and from a variety of influences on regeneration. In some cases, where, for example, increased grazing pressure (either from deer congregating in the greatly reduced areas of woodland, or from domestic animals) has inhibited regeneration, we are left with very open stands of pine-heath; in others, where a fire or other cause has opened up an area to regeneration, a dense, almost even-aged stand has resulted. The observed consequence is a "mosaic of segregated age classes" (McVean, 1964), comprising some stands composed largely of a single age class and others of two generations, but very few of mixed ages.

Pinewoods as "climax" communities

If these are among the effects of exploitation, the question arises as to how far our surviving stands retain the characteristics of "climax" vegetation. The alterations to which they have been subjected may have been such that they can no longer be said to have this status, and this is a matter of great significance in relation to attitudes towards their conservation. One difficulty is that, while the term "climax" still has wide currency, it is not always clear just what is meant by it. For the present purpose, relevant definitions appear in Cousens (1975a)...."if a woodland area has remained substantially unchanged for many centuries", and Mueller-Dombois and Ellenberg (1974)...."a stage of relative stability in species composition". In one sense, it is already clear from what has been said about human intervention that Scottish pinewoods have not remained substantially unchanged, and that stability has possibly been reduced; but it is still possible to consider the hypothesis that there have been only minor departures from what is perhaps best described as a "steady-state ecosystem". In what follows, the extent to which the Scottish pinewoods of today display some of the characteristics of steady state ecosystems will be examined briefly. Unfortunately, however, this is an area in which there are serious gaps in our knowledge of these ecosystems.

For example, it is regarded as characteristic of the steady state that the ratio of ecosystem respiration to gross productivity = 1. As a corollary, annual net primary production above ground is expected to be counterbalanced by litter fall, while litter supply to the soil is counterbalanced by litter decomposition, so that there is relatively little total accumulation of organic matter in the ecosystem. I know of no figures on this for native pinewoods.However, the accumulation of mor humus, or, in the west, of peat may be regarded as incompatible with the concept of the steady state, and the same may be said if it can be shown that increases are occurring in acidity, leaching and iron-pan formation.

It may, of course, be questioned whether a boreal pine forest such as that of N. Scotland was ever in a steady-state in this sense. Such a question is virtually impossible to answer. Slow accumulation of organic matter might well be expected under cold temperate conditions. However, it is relevant to repeat that birch and other broadleaved trees were more frequent, producing more rapidly decomposed litter, and that it is not necessary to postulate a completely mixed, uneven-aged structure. Jones (1945) has argued that this is unlikely in temperate forests, where conditions suitable for regeneration may be relatively infrequent. The result, under natural conditions, would be a forest consisting of a mosaic of patches of varying proportions of different trees, differing age structure, and varying density. In some of these patches, perhaps those which for a time were very open or had a high proportion of birch, humus breakdown would be rapid, even though there was net accumulation elsewhere.

The difference in the pinewoods of today is that (1) dominance is exerted exclusively by pine, and (2) where the pine canopy is open, the community consists normally of a dense *Calluna* stand. This community may well be responsible for increased mor accumulation.

In the absence of firm data on production and decomposition in the pinewood ecosystems of today, perhaps some indication of status can be derived from their structure and composition. It has been suggested in the past that, to qualify as "climax", a community must show a completely uneven-aged structure: "the tree species should be present as seedlings, saplings, subcanopy and canopy trees" (Mueller-Dombois and Ellenberg, 1974). However, at least as far as temperate forests are concerned, the mosaic of patches already referred to appears to fit the evidence better. This results, in the first place, from the operation of factors which interfere with the casual death of individuals, for example windthrow, disease and fire, all of which may clear patches of varying size at one time. The last of these certainly seems to have affected Scottish pinewoods before exploitation by man began (Durno and McVean, 1959). A second cause of mosaic is the operation of factors which interrupt the continuity of regeneration, such as irregularity of good seed years, and climatic variation. The mosaic of patches so produced represents, in effect, the phases of a series of stand cycles.

The fact, therefore, that; in the pinewoods of today, there are areas of various different kinds of age structure does not necessarily mean great departure from the organisation of the former forest. What is important, however, is that conditions for continuation of the stand cycles should remain, if the perpetuation of the community is to be ensured, and this at least must be expected of a "climax" or steady state ecosystem.

This is perhaps where major changes in status of our present-day pinewoods may be evident. First, there tend to be some rather extensive areas of fairly dense, single-age stands resulting from good regeneration in the past, perhaps after extraction and often following burning. But these have a pronounced uniformity of structure and often of ground flora, tending to accumulate organic matter either as mor or peat. Not only is there little or no regeneration in such stands because of shade, but also soil conditions and competition may prove unfavourable even if such stands open up. Hence, particularly in the absence of birch, conditions for maintaining the cycle may be lacking.

At the other extreme are the very open stands caused either by extraction or by grazing, or both. One of the most important factors here is the spread of *Calluna* which has tended to dominate the more open stands of our native pinewoods in extensive even-aged populations. These are far more uniform than was presumably the case in the original forest, where *Calluna* was mixed with *Vaccinium* and many bryophytes in a patchy or hummocky community of considerable variety. Neither birch nor pine will enter readily into even-aged, building-phase *Calluna* ecosystems, and the greatly increased area occupied by these (encouraged by fairly large fires from time to time) may also interrupt the normal stand cycle.

However, neither of these sets of circumstances need interfere with regeneration more than temporarily, so long as grazing is controlled. In the first instance, conditions may become appropriate for some regeneration after a while, once the rather dense canopies have opened up. In the second, in time *Calluna* itself becomes mature or degenerate and gaps appear which may permit the establishment of seedlings. Indeed, it is precisely when this happens amongst old patchy heather, where *Vaccinium myrtillus* has regained a foothold, that regeneration occurs, so long as there are gaps in the tree canopy above.

Nonetheless, the questions remain as to the kind of ecosystem which is being perpetuated, and whether the chances of maintaining viable stand cycles are becoming fewer and fewer. It may be true, as Cousens (1975a) concludes, that "A universal criterion for woodland climax remains elusive and it must be questioned whether the concept is a valuable one today". However, it is clear that numerous patches of our native pinewoods can by no means be described as in steady-state condition, though this may not apply throughout. It is reasonable to suggest that this implies a potential reduction in stability. Departure from the steady-state is indicated by a decline in species diversity, probably an increase in mor or peat accumulation, substantial modifications of age structure, and interference with stand cycles, either because of the development of rather dense even-aged groups from a burst of regeneration after a fire or other disturbance, or else as

a result of the spread of uniform *Calluna* stands amongst rather sparse pine.

Relationships with other vegetation types

This conclusion helps to explain the fact that, floristically, the pinewoods today relate very closely to lowland heath communities. In Scotland, not only have the lowland heaths often been derived from the former extensive forests merely by the exclusion of trees and prevention of tree regeneration, but also many of the features mentioned above apply as well to heathland ecosystems (for example reduced floristic diversity, increasing acidification, leaching and acid litter accumulation, and dominance by uniform even-aged *Calluna* stands). The correspondence is close, in fact closer than that between pinewood and acid oakwood or birchwood, or between Scottish pinewoods and some of their counterparts in Scandinavia, e.g. *Dryopteris* forests, herb-rich forests (Tamm, 1950).

It has been pointed out that, in the drier parts of Scotland, as the pinewoods have retreated, so have the heathlands extended. A similar relationship exists in the wetter, western parts of the country with respect to peat-forming vegetation. As the pinewoods retreated, *Molinia caerulea* or *Trichophorum cespitosum* communities expanded and, in this case, pine stumps preserved in the peat provide direct evidence of tree cover in the past.

It is important to realise that this retreat is to some extent a natural trend, although greatly intensified by man. Pears (1968) has shown how the natural tree limit in the mountains has fluctuated in the past, and was at its highest in the drier late Boreal times and again in the Sub Boreal. Each time it has retreated, and the stumps are there to demonstrate the fact that peat-forming vegetation, especially *Sphagnum* with *Eriophorum* spp., has replaced the woodland. Similarly, we may presume that in the lowland, especially in the most highly oceanic parts of the country, pine would have retreated at the woodland-bog interface. But, from Sub-Atlantic times onwards, woodland suffered the greatest onslaught by man. Decimation and reduction of the woodland has taken place in a relatively oceanic phase of our climate which is not particularly favourable for pinewood to re-occupy lost ground — especially when the mor- or peat-forming processes of the substitute vegetation have been at work. This constraint holds especially for the pinewoods in the extreme west, and emphasises the need for human intervention if the trend of reduction is to be prevented or reversed.

Conclusion

Other papers will deal with conservation, but I would support Mrs. Balfour's plea that in this context we should not be too fearful of human intervention, or management to the end of maintaining or expanding the native pinewoods. Already, as I have argued, they have departed in a number of significant ways from their former ecosystem organisation. It may be that they could struggle on in approximately their present form for a long time, unaided. But there may be no special virtue in that, when we have the chance of returning, at least in part, to an ecosystem which might function properly.

Such an ecosystem would show a greater variety of trees, and my hope would be that we could actively encourage the greater participation of birch. It would show a more intricate mosaic of groups of trees of different age, representing stages in stand cycles. Here I think we must encourage regeneration even by creating gaps in the canopy, departing, as suggested by Mrs. Balfour, from the concept of uniform stem density, and, where possible, by protection from grazing. The forest would also show a greater variety and patchiness in the dwarf shrub and ground flora. This variety would not be easy to recreate where it has been lost, but it would be worth considering the use, under careful control, of some localised prescribed burning, in the knowledge that, in the larger, ancestral forest, lightening strike might have played a comparable role.

In these and other ways, we might move towards an expanding forest, actively directed towards a system which would eventually regain at least some of its ecological independence from human intervention.

References

BIRKS, H.H. (1970). Studies in the vegetational history of Scotland. I. A pollen diagram from Abernethey Forest, Inverness-shire. *J. Ecol.,* **58,** 827-46

COUSENS, J. (1975a). *An introduction to woodland ecology.* Oliver and Boyd.

COUSENS, J. (1975b). Review of Morris, M.G. & Perring, F.H. (1974). *The British Oak: its history and natural history. J. Ecol.,* **63,** 720.

DURNO, S.E. (1957). Certain aspects of vegetational history in North-East Scotland. *Scott. geogr. Mag.,* **73,** 176-84.

DURNO, S.E. & McVEAN, D.N. (1959). Forest history of the Beinn Eighe Nature Reserve. *New Phytol.* **58,** 228-36.

GODWIN, H. (1949). *History of the British flora.* Cambridge Univ. Pr.

JONES, E.W. (1945). The structure and reproduction of the virgin forest in the north temperate zone. *New Phytol.,* **44,** 130-48.

McVEAN, D.N. (1964). Ecology of Scots pine in the Scottish Highlands. *J. Ecol.,* **51,** 671-86.

McVEAN, D.N. & RATCLIFFE, D.A. (1962). *Plant communities of the Scottish Highlands.* H.M.S.O. (Nature Conservancy Monograph no. 1.)

MORRIS, M.G. & PERRING, F.H. (1974). *The British Oak: its history and natural history.* Classey.

MUELLER-DOMBOIS, D. & ELLENBERG, H. (1974). *Aims and methods of vegetation analysis.* Wiley.

PEARS, N.V. (1968). Post-glacial tree-lines of the Cairngorm mountains, Scotland. *Trans. Proc. bot. Soc. Edinb.,* **40,** 361-94.

RATCLIFFE, D.A. (1974). The vegetation. In: *The Cairngorms: their natural history and scenery,* edited by D. Nethersole-Thompson and A. Watson, 42-76. Collins.

STEVEN, H.M. & CARLISLE, A. (1959). *The native pinewoods of Scotland.* Oliver and Boyd.

TAMM, O. (1950). *Northern coniferous forest soils.* (Translated by M.L. Anderson.) Scrivener Pr.

TANSLEY, A.G. (1939). *The British Islands and their vegetation.* Cambridge Univ. Pr.

Scandinavian pine forests and their relationship to the Scottish pinewoods

Egil Ingvar Aune University of Trondheim, The Royal Norwegian Society of Sciences and Letters, The Museum — Department of Botany, N-7000 Trondheim, Norway

About 50 per cent of the land area of Fennoscandia (Norway, Sweden, and Finland) is covered by forest, of which the main tree species are Scots pine, Norway spruce, and birch. Except for the extreme north, western Norway, and the south of Sweden, spruce can be regarded as the climax tree species, and this species is dominant on fairly fertile and well-drained soils. The pine occupies the poorer sites, whether dry or wet, and is therefore regarded as a para-climax tree species. The birch, which is, on the whole, the most important tree species of the sub-alpine region, is also the pioneer species in the low-lands. Table I shows the relative importance of these three forest trees in the Fennoscandian countries.

Since the beginning of this century, Finnish foresters, with A.K. Cajander the most prominent, have described the forest vegetation in terms of forest types. A similar system of forest types was adapted for northern Sweden. However, this system is too detailed to be included in this brief outline of the Scandinavian pine forests, and an alternative classification system was presented in 1973 by a Norwegian forest phytosociologist, Johan Kielland-Lund (Kielland-Lund 1973), as part of the Norwegian IBP programme. Kielland-Lund uses the Central European terminology, in which 'the association' is the basic classification unit. The term association is, however, applied in a wide sense, and this paper deals with only the five Scandinavian pine forest associations. They are:

1. Lichen pine forests *(Cladonio-Pinetum)*
2. Heather pine forest *(Barbilophozio-Pinetum)*
3. *Vaccinium*-rich mixed pine-spruce forest *(Vaccinio-Pinetum)*
4. Pine bog forest *(Vaccinio uliginosi-Pinetum)*
5. Calcicolous pine forest *('Melico-Pinetum')*

The lichen pine forest association is found on shallow soils, on hard rocks, or on coarse and infertile moraines and sediments. The most conspicuous feature of the association is the dominance of lichens of the genus *Cladonia* in the bottom layer. Besides the *Cladonias,* we find drought-resistant mosses such as *Pleurozium schreberi* and several *Dicranum* species. The tree layer consists of almost pure pine stands. On deep soils, the tree canopy is fairly dense, while, on shallow soils, it is more open. The shrub layer is for the most part absent. The field layer is poorly developed and consists of stunted dwarf shrubs, but, in the more open stands, heather *(Calluna vulgaris)* may be fairly prominent. This community is widespread on suitable soils in the lowlands of southern Fennoscandia. Further north, and at higher elevations, it is confined to the drier regions with a continental climate.

The heather pine association is usually found at higher elevations and in regions with a damper climate than the lichen pine forest. The trophic level of these two communities is almost equal. The pine stands of the heather pine forests are in most cases rather open and they normally have an admixture of birch and badly-developed spruce. In the field layer, dwarf shrubs such as *Calluna vulgaris, Empetrum hermaphroditum,* and species of the genus *Vaccinium* (including the moisture-demanding *V. uliginosum)* are to be found. In the bottom layer, lichens play a relatively minor role, but hygrophilous mosses and liverworts are frequent, including *Sphagnum nemoreum* and species of the genera *Barbilophozia* and *Orthocaulis.* The damp and cool climate results in a slow decomposition of the litter, and, consequently, the raw humus layer becomes rather thick. This thick humus layer and the dense cover of the dwarf shrubs together make unfavourable conditions for pine seedlings, and the pine stands become open and consist of trees of varying age.

The lichen pine forest association and the heather pine forest association, from a phytosociological view, both belong to a Nordic group of communities. Closely related communities are found in the sub-alpine birch forests, and among the low-alpine heaths of Scandinavia.

The next association, called the *Vaccinium*-rich mixed pine-spruce forest, is often regarded as a northern outpost of the pine forests of eastern Central Europe. This community is the most typical pine forest type found on sandy plains in the less rainy parts of southern Norway, Sweden and Finland. In the tree layer, pine is usually the dominant species, but the stands near the northern limits of this association may be rich in spruce. The foresters will often have to make a choice between pine and spruce. The pines will be of good quality and may be sold as saw-timber or special logs. The spruce on the other hand, will be of ordinary pulp quality. The field layer is poor in species and dominated by *Vaccinium vitis-idaea* and *V. myrtillus.* Scattered, but characteristic, species are *Goodyera repens, Diphasium complanatum,* and *Pyrola chlorantha.* The bottom layer has a mixture of lichens and mosses, with the latter dominating.

From southern Finland, eastwards and southwards, there is a gradual transition from this community to the drier and steppe-like pine forests of eastern Central Europe. The Central European phytosociologists have called this community *Peucedano-Pinetum.* This association seems to be richer in herbs and xerophilous grasses than its Fennoscandian *Vaccinium*-rich counterpart. Westwards in Central Europe, the *Peucedano-Pinetum* is replaced by another association, called *Leucobryo-Pinetum.* This community has more oceanic species and an admixture of species belonging to the beech and oak domain of western Europe. Among the admixture species are both the Common and the Sessile oak, as well as the beech.

The pine forests so far mentioned are all found on mineral soils with a well-developed podsol profile. The next association, the pine bog forest, is developed on poor peatlands. Usually the peat is of the ombrotrophic type, which receives its water and mineral supply solely from the precipitation. Owing to the low fertility of this acid peat, the pines become very scattered and slow-growing. The field and bottom layers consist of a mixture of the species usually found in the heather pine forests on mineral soils and species from ombrotrophic bog communities, such as *Andromeda polifolia, Eriophorum vaginatum, Rubus chamaemorus, Vaccinium oxycoccus,* and several *Sphagnum* species. Related communities are also present in Central Europe, but most of them lack the boreal species common to the Fennoscandian pine bogs. For instance, dwarf birch *(Betula nana), Rubus chamaemorus,* and *Sphagnum fuscum* are absent or very rare in Central European pine peat-lands.

The last pine forest 'association' included in this short list is the 'calcicolous pine forest'. This name is connected to various kinds of pine forests found on calcareous soils. The soil profile is either an extremely calcium-rich brown soil, or of a type related to what the soil scientists call a rendzina or a pararendzina profile. In these last cases, there is a dark humus layer resting directly on limestone rocks. The tree layer usually consists of open pine stands with spruce intermingled to a greater or lesser degree. In extreme cases, there are pure pine forests, probably due to killing of the spruce seedlings by periodical drought in the upper humus horizon. The field layer is an interesting mixture of calcicolous plants such as *Epipactis atrorubens,* marginal plants such as *Geranium sanguineum,* and the ordinary pine forest species found in the dry and oligotrophic communities.

Before turning to a short comparison of the Scottish and Scandinavian pinewoods, it may be useful to say a few words about the forests of western Norway. Western Norway has an oceanic climate, with high precipitation and mild winters, and the vegetation in this part of Scandinavia is therefore of special interest in comparison with Scottish conditions. It is regrettable, however, that the forest vegetation of western Norway has not yet been satisfactorily examined. Spruce is absent in this part of Norway and it is disputed whether the western distribution limit of the spruce in western Norway is mainly historical or climatological. In the absence of spruce, the pine, together with birch, also occupy the richer sites corresponding to the spruce forests of eastern Scandinavia. Hence, we find various kinds of pine-birch forests with small ferns and/or low herbs etc. On the ordinary poorer pine sites, we have a western race of the heather pine forest *(Bazzanio-Pinetum).* This vicarious western community differs from the eastern heather pine forest in several respects. A shrub layer of juniper is common, and the dwarf shrubs of the field layer attain a more luxuriant growth. Several moisture-demanding herbs, mosses, and liverworts not present in the eastern pine forests are common. In shady, north-faced slopes there is a

sub-type especially rich in *Sphagnum quinquefarium* and other hygrophilous mosses such as *Plagiothecium undulatum.* On shallow soils, there is another sub-type with patches of *Racomitrium lanuginosum* and some species of *Cladonia.*

Turning to the Scottish vegetation, a major difference is at once apparent. While Scandinavia still has large areas with natural or semi-natural forests, most of the original forest cover of Scotland has been destroyed by varying kinds of human activity.

When it comes to the climatic conditions, large areas of northern and eastern Scandinavia have more definite continental climate than anywhere in Scotland. The western districts of Norway, however, have a climate which is very similar to that of much of Scotland. In these most oceanic parts of Norway, we also find deforested areas with secondary heath-land vegetation.

McVean and Ratcliffe (1962) have described two Scottish pinewood associations, namely a pinewood-*Vaccinium*-moss association and a pinewood-*Vaccinium-Calluna* association. The field layer of the former is dominated by *Vaccinium* species, as well as many more or less occasional herbs and grasses. The bottom layer is dominated by *Hylocomium splendens,* with other woodland mosses and a few hepatics intermingled. This association seems to be confined to the less oceanic parts of the country.

The field layer of the latter association has dominating *Calluna,* with co-dominant *Vaccinium.* In the bottom layer, there are, besides *Hylocomium,* many moisture-demanding mosses and liverworts. This association is mainly found in areas with a more highly oceanic climate.

There is, however, a high floristic similarity between the two associations. Both of them contain oceanic species, such as *Erica tetralix, E. cinerea* and *Thuidium tamariscinum,* which are not reported from any Scandinavian pine forests on mineral soils.

The Scandinavian community most closely related to these Scottish associations is without doubt the west-Norwegian heather pine forest. The *Vaccinium-Calluna* association seems to be particularly close to the Norwegian community, both floristically and structurally. Stands with trees of a mixed age, a shrub layer with juniper, leggy heather, and many hummocks on the forest floor are all common characteristics. The main differences seem to be due to the higher oceanity of Scotland, which results in more oceanic species, especially among the mosses and hepatics. The damper Scottish climate also gives rise to a more vigorous podsolisation and a thicker bleached A_2 horizon in the soil profile. McVean and Ratcliffe (1962) report that the A_2 horizon may attain a thickness of over one meter. Bleached horizons of this kind have not been reported in Norwegian forest soils.

The *Vaccinium*-moss association shows relationships to the mixed *Vaccinium*-rich forest of Scandinavia and also to its south-western Central European equivalent, the *Leucobryo-Pinetum.*

The most important floristic differences and similar-

ities of the communities mentioned in this paper are summarised in Table II.

References

AUNE, E.I. (1971). Prosjekt Silva-Vassfaret. Botaniske under-søkelser. In: *IBP i Norge-Arsrapport 1971*, 251-260.

AUNE, E.I. (1973). Forest vegetation in Hemne, Sör-Tröndelag, western Central Norway. *K. norske Vidensk. Selsk. Mus. Miscellanea*, **12**, 1.87.

KIELLAND−LUND, J. (1973). A classification of Scandinavian forest vegetation for mapping purposes. *IBP i Norden* no. **11**, 173-206.

MARKER, E. (1969). A vegetation study of Langöya, Southern Norway. *Nytt Mag. Bot.*, **16**, 15-44.

MATUSZKIEWICZ, W. (1962). Zur Systematik der natürlichen Kiefernwälder des mittel- und osteuropäischen Flachlandes. *Mitt. flor. -soz. ArbGemein.* N.F. **9**, 145-186 + Tab.

McVEAN, D.N. & RATCLIFFE, D.A. (1962). *Plant communities of the Scottish Highlands.* H.M.S.O. (Nature Conservancy Monograph no.1.)

Fig. 1.
Lichen pine forest on shallow soil. Scattered groups of slow-growing pines in patches of *Calluna.* (The trees are labelled for on-going research work). Vassfaret, south Norway.

Table I:

The relative importance of the three main forest trees in the Fennoscandian countries. Volume of wood (under bark) in milliards cubic feet

	Scots pine	Norway spruce	Birches
Norway	1.0	1.9	0.5
Sweden	6.3	6.6	2.1
Finland	7.3	4.5	3.0

Fig. 2.
Lichen pine forest on deep glacifluvial deposits. The canopy is denser and the pines attain a better timber quality than those of Fig. 1. Dominating lichen species in the bottom layer are *Cladonia alpestris, C. arbuscula* and *C. rangiferina.* Vassfaret, south Norway.

8

Fig. 3.
Heather pine forest on a relatively damp north-faced slope. Besides the dominating pines, there are also some badly developed spruces and a few birches. The field layer is dominated by *Calluna vulgaris, Vaccinium uliginosum,* and *V. myrtillus.* Vassfaret, south Norway.

Fig. 4.
Pine bog with scattered pine trees with a sparse foliage, with a few shrubs of birch. This little bog has some supply of minerogenous water, and although they are rather badly developed, these pines have grown faster than the pines usually do on purely ombrotrophic peat. Vassfaret, south Norway.

Fig. 5.
The 'calcicolous' pine forests are found on calcareous soils and have many demanding species not found in the ordinary oligotrophic pine communities. This picture shows a field layer with *Cypripedium calceolus, Polygonatum verticillatum,* and *Rubus saxatilis.* Hattfjelldal, north Norway.

Fig. 6.
An example of the bird life of the pine forests; a heap containing 3,817 pine cones collected by a woodpecker *(Dendrocopus* sp.). The bird has fastened the cones in the tree stump while feeding on the seeds. The forest community is of the *Vaccinium*-rich mixed pine-spruce type. Vassfaret, south Norway.

	Norway				Central Europe		Scotland		Norway	
	Lichen type	Heather type	Western heather type	Vaccinium-rich type	Peucedano-Pinetum	Leucobryo-Pinetum	Moss-Vaccinium type	Vaccinium-Calluna type	Pine bog type	Calcicolous type
Column no.:	1	2	3	4	5	6	7	8	9	10
Species of coniferous forests:										
Vaccinium myrtillus	IV	V	V	V	IV	IV	V	V	V	.
Vaccinium vitis-idaea	V	IV	V	V	V	IV	V	V	V	V
Dicranum scoparium	III	IV	IV	IV	II	II	III	III	II	.
Hylocomium splendens	I	III	V	V	V		III	V	IV	V
Pleurozium schreberi	V	V	V	V	V	V	IV	IV	V	.
Ptilium crista-castrensis		IV	V	V	II		II	V	I	.
Species of pine forests:										
Pinus sylvestris (trees)	V	V	V	V	V	V	V	V	V	V
Calluna vulgaris	V	V	V	III	V	IV	V	V	V	III
Empetrum spp.	IV	V	V	IV		V	IV	III	V	.
Cladonia rangiferina	V	V	II	V	V	IV	.	I	V	.
Cladonia sylvatica coll.	V	V	I	V	IV	IV	.	.	IV	.
Nordic group:										
Vaccinium uliginosum	I	V	V	I	.	.	.	.	V	.
Sphagnum nemoreum	.	II	II	.	.	.	III	IV	II	.
Dicranum fuscescens	V	V	.	IV	.	.	.	.	II	.
Orthocaulis attenuatus	I	IV	I	I	.	.	.	.	I	.
Orthocaulis floerkei	I	II	II	I	.	.	.	II	.	.
Barbilophozia lycopodioides	.	IV	I	II	.	.	.	.	I	.
Cladonia alpestris	V	III	.	II	.	.	.	.	I	.
Cladonia uncialis	V	I	.	I	.	.	.	.	.	.
Central European group:										
Diphasium complanatum	.	.	.	I	III	I	.	.	.	.
Pyrola chlorantha	.	.	.	I	III	III	.	.	.	.
Chimaphila umbellata	.	.	.	.	III	II	.	.	.	.
Luzula pilosa	.	.	I	I	IV	II	I	.	.	.
Goodyera repens	.	.	.	.	I	II	III	.	.	.
South Eastern group:										
Convallaria majalis	.	.	.	.	IV	.	.	.	.	.
Peucedanum oroselinum	.	.	.	.	IV	.	.	.	.	.
Scorzonera humilis	.	.	.	.	IV	I	.	.	.	.
Thymus serpyllum	.	.	.	.	V	.	.	.	.	.
South Western group:										
Quercus robur	.	.	.	.	II	I	.	.	.	.
Quercus petraea	.	.	.	.	.	III	.	.	.	.
Fagus sylvatica	.	.	.	.	.	II	.	.	.	.
Leucobryum glaucum	.	.	.	.	.	III	I	.	.	.
Sub-oceanic group:										
Cornus suecica	.	.	V	.	.	.	.	.	.	.
Blechnum spicant	.	.	III	.	.	.	II	III	.	.
Listera cordata	.	.	III	.	.	I	II	III	.	.
Plagiothecium undulatum	.	.	V	.	.	.	III	V	.	.
Rhytidiadelphus loreus	.	.	II	.	.	.	III	IV	.	.
Sphagnum quinquefarium	.	I	V	.	.	.	.	III	.	.
Scottish group:										
Erica cinerea	.	.	.	.	.	.	II	I	.	.
Erica tetralix	.	.	.	.	.	.	II	III	.	.
Thuidium tamariscinum	.	.	.	.	.	.	I	III	.	.
Bog group:										
Andromeda polifolia	.	I	II	.	.	.	.	.	V	.
Betula nana	.	.	.	.	.	.	.	.	III	.
Eriophorum vaginatum	.	.	.	.	.	.	.	.	V	.
Rubus chamaemorus	.	.	II	.	.	.	.	.	V	.
Sphagnum fuscum	.	.	.	.	.	.	.	.	IV	.
Sphagnum magellanicum	.	.	.	.	.	.	.	.	III	.
Eutrophic group:										
Epipactis atrorubens	.	.	.	.	.	.	.	.	.	II
Geranium sanguineum	.	.	.	.	.	.	.	.	.	III
Hepatica nobilis	.	.	.	.	.	.	.	.	.	V
Melica nutans	.	.	.	.	.	.	.	.	.	V
Trifolium medium	.	.	.	.	.	.	.	.	.	V
Other species:										
Betula pubescens (trees)	.	III	I	III	V	.	I	II	I	.
Picea abies (trees)	I	IV	.	V	III	I	.	.	II	.
Juniperus communis	.	.	V	.	V	II	I	?	.	V
Deschampsia flexuosa	I	IV	V	V	I	V	IV	V	I	.
Rhytidiadelphus triquetrus	.	.	.	.	.	.	I	III	.	V

Table II.

Examples of the pine forest associations presented in this paper. Geographical designations applied to the species groups do not refer to the overall distribution of the species, merely to their occurrences within pine forest communities. Only a limited number of species is included in the table.

Roman numerals refer to 'class of presence, V= present in 81-100% of the stands analysed, IV=61-80%, III=41-60%, II=21-40%, 1=1-20%.

The columns:
1. Vassfaret, South Norway, 10 analyses (Aune 1971).
2. Vassfaret, South Norway, 5 analyses (Aune 1971).
3. Hemne, North Western Norway, 8 analyses (Aune 1973).
4. Vassfaret, South Norway, 10 analyses (Aune 1971).
5. NE Central Europe, 16 analyses (Matuszkiewicz 1962).
6. SW Baltic coast, 31 analyses (Matuszkiewicz 1962)
7. Scotland, 14 analyses (McVean and Ratcliffe 1962).
8. Scotland, 9 analyses (McVean and Ratcliffe 1962).
9. Vassfaret, South Norway, 8 analyses (Aune 1971).
10. Longøya, Southern Norway, 7 analyses (Marken 1969).

The range of variation within the pinewoods

R.G.H. Bunce Institute of Terrestrial Ecology, Merlewood Research Station, Grange-over-Sands.

Introduction

The book by Steven and Carlisle, published in 1959, recognised 35 sites of native pinewoods, determined by criteria relating to historical records, age structure and the relative absence of human interference. Within the book, the range of tree structures, the history of the forests and their vegetation are discussed individually. However, despite such an intensive study of individual sites, there was not a sufficiently standardised overall framework for the development of an integrated conservation strategy for the whole resource. A requirement for such a strategy is that the range of ecological variation contained within the pinewood sites needs to be defined and then divided into relatively uniform types which would provide a basis for the determination of priorities.

The project described in this paper was initiated by the (then) Nature Conservancy at a meeting held in the Department of Forestry at the University of Aberdeen in November 1970, at which the outlines of the proposed survey were described to other interested organisations and individuals. The project was based upon the use of species data as an index to the characteristics of ecosystems comprising complete sites. It is important to emphasize that the data are primarily to be used as an index of the ecosystem rather than in a traditional phytosociological sense, where homogeneous vegetation samples are required. In the present approach, heterogeneity is accepted as an integral feature of vegetation and used to provide an overall assessment of diversity within the habitats making up the ecosystems.

The vegetation within the pinewoods represents a continuous range between extremes. Any division of such a continuum must therefore be arbitrary and no two systems of classification are likely to coincide in such a separation. Although divisions made by numerical analysis are to some extent arbitrary, they are reproduceable. However, no analysis has shown that anything approaching noda (i.e. dense clusters of points within the general scatter) occurs within such data and therefore divisions cannot be other than arbitrary.

Nevertheless, within the data of the present study, there is a strong structure, readily recognisable in the field situation; the paper by Fitzpatrick describes a similar structure in the range of soil types within the pinewoods. Although certain types are shown to have characteristic dominants, information concerning canopy structure was not used in the definitive classification, which was based on species data. By using this procedure, an independent test is available of the strength of the correlations present and, because random sampling was used, objective comparisons between forests are possible.

A framework is required to define variation in vegetation, and, indirectly, in habitats. Accordingly, a procedure has been developed in which different scales are used, which, although to some extent arbitrary, enable complex, overlapping plant ranges to be understood.

The scales used are defined as follows:—

1. Species level: the affinities of the plot and site types, levels (2) and (3) below, depend upon the association between species. These need to be defined with reference to the whole population of plots, in order to produce the lowest level of analysis at which it is convenient to work. These associated species are termed species groups in this paper.
2. Plot level: at a level chosen to relate to continental phytosociological practice (i.e. 200m² in woodlands), the "species groups" defined by level (1) occur in various combinations to make up these plot types.
3. Site level: sites involve complexes of the types defined above in (2), and their relationships may be explained in terms of the plot types present. The underlying structure of these analyses is shown diagrammatically in Fig. 1, together with the methods of analysis employed.

Methods of survey

The survey was mainly carried out from July 17 to August 24, 1971, by four graduates from the Forestry Department at Aberdeen University, after an introductory course held in Abernethy Forest. 26 of the 34 sites given by Steven and Carlisle were included in the survey, being those for which maps of the outlines of the extent of the native pine were given in the book — these sites included all the major forests. Within these outlines, 16 randomised points were marked and then located in the field by compass bearings and pacing from a recognised nearby landmark. Very strict rules were imposed to ensure that there was no avoidable alteration to the predetermined position of the plots. A list of the sites and their location is given in Figure 2.

Using the procedure advocated by Bunce and Shaw (1972) at each of 16 sample points, the following data were recorded:—

1. All vascular plants occurring in five successive quadrat sizes within a 200m² plot were recorded. A sample of the bryophytes growing on the ground surface was collected for later identification. Herbarium specimens were collected, and later used to check the accuracy of the species identification.
2. The diameter at breast height of each tree in the 200m² plot was recorded.
3. Slope and aspect were recorded and a standard list of habitats, including regeneration, was checked and recorded.
4. A description was made of the soil profile at the centre of the plot and a soil sample collected from the top 10cm of this profile.

All procedures were described in a methods handbook given to the surveyors at the start of the survey.

Data analysis

At the outset of the project, it was decided to use the analysis of the species data as the basis on which to determine other correlations and interpretive comparisons. The strategy of the analysis was based upon the scales defined in the introduction and the following analytical techniques were employed: —

1. Species level: the axes' values for the species obtained from (2) below were used in the minimum variance clustering procedure (Pritchard and Anderson (1971). The clustering was allowed to proceed until seven groups of species were obtained.

2. Plot level: two analyses were carried out at this level
   a) reciprocal averaging ordination (Hill (1973)), to provide axes, values for correlation with environmental data and to examine the relationship between the types defined by (b)
   b) indicator species analysis (Hill et al (1975)) was used to classify the data and to provide a dichotomous key to the plot types produced.

3. Site level: indicator species analysis was used to classify the frequency data from the 16 plots from each of the sites and to provide a site classification and key.

The number of types produced by the analysis depends upon convenience — the exact structure being provided by the number of individuals assigned at each division by the retrospective use of the indicator species in the process of the analysis. Studies of the relative homogeneity of the types have been carried out on data from a national survey of semi-natural woodlands (Bunce & Shaw (1972)) and the results suggest that the mathematical procedures in the analysis standardise the variability within the types. The methods of analysis in the present study are identical to those of the national survey and were produced during that study, with M.W. Shaw being instrumental in their development. Various stopping rules have been investigated in order to determine where to terminate the analyses at a given number of types but all have been shown to be arbitrary. The analyses have therefore been terminated at a level where sufficient samples are present in the types to obtain valid ecological comparisons and on the basis of a convenient number for data handling. Fuller descriptions of the background to the procedures adopted are currently in preparation.

Results

National context

Before considering the results in detail, it is useful to compare the range of variation within the native pinewoods with that on a national scale obtained from a national survey of woodlands. As the same survey techniques were applied, the results are directly comparable and may be compared numerically, without needing to provide detailed interpretations of the underlying ecological meanings or derivation of the types involved.

Although virtually all the species recorded in the native pinewoods survey were also present in the national survey, many were at very low frequencies. However, many of the species in the national survey were absent from the pinewoods. Although the species groups were not strictly comparable, of the eleven groups defined in the national survey, the first four groups consisted of species entirely absent from the pinewoods; these comparisons are shown in Figure 3. 32 plot types were produced in the national survey, and, when the plots from the pinewoods were allocated to these types, 98% came into only two types. At the site level, 16 types were defined in the national survey, but 23 of the 26 pinewoods surveyed were allocated to only one of these. These comparisons serve to emphasize the restricted range of variation within the pinewoods when considered at a national level.

The description of the range of variation within the pinewoods therefore expands a narrow part of the national range and examines it in greater detail. The approach adopted in this paper is to examine the structure of the species relationships, before going on to correlate the vegetation with some measure of the environment. The various scales will be discussed separately when considering the floristic aspects of the data, but will be taken together when the environmental correlations are discussed. It is important to emphasize that the species reflect complexities in the habitats that are difficult, if not impossible, to pick up without extremely ·complex environmental measurements — hence the use of vegetation as an index. No simple environmental interpretations are therefore usually possible. The species data are primarily being used to characterise the sites in the most efficient way.

Associate species

The species groups are given in Table 1 — it is the various combinations in which they occur that form heterogeneity within vegetation. Certain of the types are widely occurring — Group A has representatives in all the plot types, whereas Group C is absent from one type and has low frequencies in several of the others. In broad terms, the species from Group A are generally those associated with the denser pine woodlands, with a trend through the groups of diminishing affinity with such dense stands. The majority of species are not associated particularly with pinewoods — indicating that the species composition, as expressed by the most frequent contributors, reflects the open nature of the forests and the frequency of other habitats such as open bog surfaces. The position of the Scottish pine at the extremity of their range is therefore emphasized. Many of the particular species associated with pinewoods e.g. *Goodyera repens,* do not appear in this classification, because they were not of sufficiently common occurrence.

Plot types

Eight plot types were produced and the occurrence of the species groups within them is shown in Figure 4. Both the different frequencies of the plot types and the way in which the different combinations of species groups make up the vegetation are seen in this diagram. Type 1 is the least heterogeneous of the plot types, being dominated by species group A, whereas 4 and 8 both contain a wide range of different groups, reflecting increasing diversity in vegetation and therefore of habitats. The dichotomous key to the plot types is given in Table 2. The use of this table is given by Hill et al (1975). Ten species were used as indicators in order that the classification will generalise more efficiently to data which may be collected in further surveys and which can then be allocated to one of the types described in the present study by using this key. Summaries of the major features of the vegetation for each type are given in Table 3, together with the indicator species pathway, and the various categories are defined below.

Each type description is headed by the Scots pine plot type to which it refers and the number in brackets immediately following is the frequency out of the 416 plots of the survey. Below the frequency is the name given to the type, which is largely a matter of convenience to provide an alternative to numbers. They are derived from the top selective species in the type concerned (explained below) and the species with the highest average cover. The heterogeneity index is defined as being the average number of species groups per plot within the type. The species groups are those with an average occurrence of over 2/plot (c.f. Fig. 4).

Constant species are ground flora species that occur in over 75% of the plots in the type. Plot dominants are species that have an average cover of over 25% in all the plots belonging to the type. The selective species were obtained by comparing the observed frequency within a type with the expected frequency obtained by dividing the total frequency by the number of plots in each type. The departure from expectation was tested by chi-square and only those with over 99.9% probability are listed in order to obtain the species most closely restricted to the types. The figures in brackets are the observed and expected frequencies, with the lists being ranked in order of selectivity. The figures for trees are given as the average basal area per plot (sq. cm) and for saplings, the percentage of plots containing saplings. A further figure is the number of plots in each type with no trees recorded in them.

As has been pointed out above, the native pinewoods cover a narrow part of the national range of variation within woodlands. They are also, in many respects, relatively uniform in the habitats present — in contrast to the western deciduous woodlands in Scotland which are extremely variable. As a result, the data are continuous and there are no discontinuities present and few pronounced contrasts. The classifications therefore produce types which are closely related, with few marked differences between them. Many of the ecological factors show overlapping distributions and emphasize this feature of the pinewoods. A range of numerical procedures was applied to the data and the results were consistent in emphasizing the continuity and relative uniformity within the vegetation.

The species composition of the types reflects both the limited range in terms of their overall composition, and also the few species that form the main ground cover. Even so, the heterogeneity index is widely variable — from 2.9 in Type 1, where there is often a dense pine canopy, to 6.5 in Type 8, where conditions are more open and a wider variety of habitats is present. The relationship between the types needs to be examined in terms of their relative positions on the reciprocal averaging ordination (as has already been discussed by Hill et al (1975)) and is shown in Figure 5, in which the boundaries between the different types have been inserted. In this diagram, the scatter of points forms a triangle with types 1 and 4 at the basal angles and type 5 at the apex. The species composition in terms of the individual members, as well as in groups, reflects these extremes, with, for example, type 1 having species group A mainly present (as defined by Table 3), type 4, AB and E and type 5, AE and G.

The type summaries given in Table 3 show that the tree composition differs between the floristically determined types. For example, Type 1 has an average of 10.6 pine trees/plot, whereas Type 4 has only 1.4 and Type 5, at the apex of the triangle mentioned above, only 1.1. The constant and selective species show similar differences between types as do also the plot dominants with Type 1 having mainly *Calluna* dominant, Type 4 *Pteridium* and Type 5 *Molinia*.

The types also show contrasts in the relative frequency of seedlings and their rate of survival — studies are in progress to investigate these further by studying a range of sites in greater detail.

Site types

The classification of the site data was terminated after 4 types had been produced. The key to the types is provided by Hill et al (1975). The frequency of the plot types that comprise the site types is given in Figure 6 — which have such clear-cut geographical distributions (Figure 7) that they were named the eastern, central, north-western and south-western. Although the composition of the types is continuous, there are marked differences between their composition. For example, the eastern example has plot type 1 predominating whereas the north-western has plot type 5. As with the plot types, therefore, the picture that emerges is of overlapping variation, distinctive, but within a relatively narrow range.

Table 4 summarises some of the ecological characteristics of the four site types. The constant species in the ground flora reflect the different ecological characteristics of the sites. The basal area and number of the major tree species show similar contrasts, paralleled by the records of the seedling and sapling stages. For example, the eastern type has 111 trees recorded per site whereas the south-western has only 12. There are, therefore, contrasting problems in assessing the conservation measures required in the different types, and the classification of sites enables a range of types to be included in any study within the pinewoods. Some of the groups presented by Steven & Carlisle have remained unaltered whereas others have been split up and recombined. The classification produced has demonstrable criteria for its structure, whereas the basis of the original separation into groups was not defined.

Environmental correlations

These need to be examined, partly to test the value of the vegetation analyses as indicators of site characteristics, but also for the inherent interest of the underlying ecological relationships. The relationships between the ecosystems defined by the vegetation and the environment were mainly examined at the plot level, but similar environmental trends underlie the site classification and these will be outlined at the end of the chapter.

The relationships were examined in two main ways, first by calculating the correlation coefficients between environmental variables recorded from the plots and then the axes' values of the same plot as calculated in the reciprocal averaging ordination. The second procedure was to compare the composition of the plot types in terms of the frequencies of the various factors within them. The results of the first analysis are given in Table 5.

Referring again to the triangle of the vegetation scatter diagram (Fig. 5), the lower basal angle of the triangle is primarily occupied with plots that have largely podsolic soils, and the upper basal angle with acid brown earth types, whereas the apex of the triangle is occupied by plots where soils with a deep organic horizon predominate. The isolation of single variables oversimplifies the situation, but the environmental factors measured are strongly correlated and emphasize the close interaction between the vegetation and environment. For the present paper, principal component analysis was not applied to these data as the paper is aimed at a general readership rather than specifically at readers with numerical experience. Also included in Table 5 are the correlations between girth and height of the pine trees, suggesting that these parameters are controlled by similar gradients.

The highest correlation of the first axis' values are shown to be with peat depth or, strictly speaking, with the amount of organic top soil, and, because such soils are usually deep, also with the total soil depth. Other significant correlations are with the depth of parent material, depth of the podsolic horizon, slope, and the depth of the mixed/mineral horizon. The interrelationship between the variation expressed by these correlations indicates that the first axis of the vegetation analysis is therefore primarily associated with the complex of factors leading to the formation of organic material on the soil surface. Such a conclusion is emphasized by the geographical distribution of the site and plot types, especially in the east-west division. The correlation between the first axis' values for individual sites and distance from the west coast (an indirect measure of oceanicity) was found to be 0.845 (P<.001

for 24 d.f.) and many other features of the sites such as size and altitude are associated with this east-west trend. The dominance of such a trend means that it is difficult to separate individual factors of over-riding importance: it is the whole complex of factors which is important.

The second axis' values are most highly correlated with pH, followed by the depth of the mixed mineral horizon and by negative correlations with the podsolic horizons and northern aspect. The latter correlation suggests a tendency for brown-earth type soils to be on south-facing slopes and it has been noted in previous studies that the pinewoods are mainly on north-facing slopes. The second vegetation axis is therefore primarily associated with the base status of the soil, reflecting a series from brown earth types to podsolic types — emphasizing (from the position of type 1 in Fig. 3) that the most dense pine occurs on podsolic soils. The third axis shows the highest correlation with slope followed by total soil depth and peat depth because of residual information not expressed in the correlations with the first axis.

The second approach is shown below by giving summaries of the eight types (Table 6), following a similar format to those given for the vegetation in order to demonstrate the environmental affinities of the sites. The purpose of these summaries is primarily to enable further plots that are surveyed to be compared with the type description for closeness of fit, but they may also be used for comparison of ecological affinities. Also included in the summaries are the frequencies of some of the recorded habitats and the records of animals made on the same sheet. The distributions are defined according to the site type in which they occur most commonly. The figures for altitude, slope and pH are average values for all the plots that make up the site types. The other categories give the percentage occurrence of that particular attribute within the plots making up the type.

The different characteristics of the types reflect the close intercorrelations between the various factors. For example, type 5 has consistently high scores for all the records concerning high water levels and peaty soil, whereas type 1 has drier soils and evidence of podsolisation. It is also a feature of the data that there are many glades in all types — indicating the generally open nature of the forests. The indirect correlations are shown well by the occurrence of boulders, which are low in numbers on the deep organic horizons but which occur commonly in types 4 and 8, where rocky streams are also major habitat features. The main types associated with pine, i.e. 1 and 2, are therefore identified with freely drained podsolic soils whereas with type 6, also containing pine, the soils have deeper organic layers.

It must be emphasized that the correlations established are not necessarily causal and reflect only trends within the data. Further, more detailed investigations on an experimental basis are required before the underlying causal relationship can be determined — the purpose of the present study is to emphasize areas where such work can be most usefully carried out and to provide a framework for selection of sample sites.

The records made in the plots concerning habitats also contained information on the presence of animals, and these may also be correlated with the types by examining their relative frequency of occurrence.

The grazing animals follow parallel patterns of distribution between types, with the sites containing more brown earth type soils carrying far more sheep as opposed to deer. The overall grazing pressure is also different between types, with indications that some types, e.g. 5 and 7, are under much greater pressure than others. If the vegetation descriptions are referred to, it will be found that these are indeed the types where very little regeneration is occurring, as in the case of type 6 with a high grazing pressure. These are also the least suitable for growth of pine, and hence the pressure in such areas is very much against pine. The squirrel records were taken mainly from two types 1 and 3 — emphasizing that the vegetation analysis is likely to have parallels in other groups of organisms.

The site classification may now be examined in terms of the constituent plot types and the descriptions below summarise an interpretation of their environmental relationships. Their geographical distribution is shown in Fig. 5.

Eastern type: Podsolic soils predominate under low rainfall conditions and often at relatively high altitudes. The sites are relatively sheltered, with a few brown earth soils present, and occur often on fluvioglacial terraces.

Central type: although containing some podsolic soils, the higher rainfall conditions encourage more organic matter accumulation and there are more flushed areas, which in some cases lead to brown earth soils. The fluvioglacial systems are more limited and are in smaller valleys than those in the east.

North-western type: under high rainfall conditions favouring peat accumulation, many of the sites have predominantly organic soils, with few fluvioglacial features. Areas of brown earth soils are patchily distributed and many of the sites are very exposed.

South-western type: under high rainfall conditions, this type contains some of the wettest areas in the pinewood series, as well as many of the higher base-status brown earth soils. The sites are often mosaics with varying conditions always under heavy grazing pressure.

Discussion

Although the study described in this paper mainly deals with the vegetation, the discussion in the last section demonstrates that many other ecological factors are involved in the principal directions of ecological variation defined by the analysis. A general survey of this type can only provide a framework for further detailed study and solves no problems of the dynamics of the sites themselves. Furthermore, much more detailed information is required on other groups, such as the insects, in order to complete the assessment of the ecological content of the site. Nevertheless, a framework is now available within which to carry out more detailed studies of the various aspects of scientific interest centred on the pinewoods.

An important final stage is a comparison of the results described in the present paper with previously described types. As mentioned in the introduction, different phytosociological systems are unlikely to overlap in detail — particularly in the case of the present study, where the vegetation is primarily being used to characterise areas as a basis for comparison.

The descriptions already published, e.g. Tansley (1949), Steven and Carlisle (1959), McVean and Ratcliffe (1962) and Burnett (1964) all differ widely, but the present system, although different again, enables a standardised approach to be used and provides observers with access to the reference framework through the use of the dichotomous key provided. There are no final criteria for the "best" solution that can be produced, as different studies require different objectives to be satisfied. The classification may be used to select sites for detailed studies of an experimental nature that require a maximum range of site types to be included. Furthermore, the basis behind the site groups, defined by Steven and Carlisle (1959), has now been demonstrated and is already being used as a basis for site selection for conservation priorities.

A generally surprising feature of the data was the scattered nature of the trees, as expressed by the low percentage of plots with trees present (47%) and the widespread occurrence of vegetation within the pinewoods that has no direct relationship with pine, including many of the more boggy habitats. The high frequency of such ground types and the absence of trees upon them suggest that many sites are always likely to have had an open canopy, at least of pine. To create a dense pine canopy by ploughing and planting would therefore be to modify extensively the environmental/ecosystem response.

The pinewoods themselves occupy a relatively narrow, continuous range of variation, but, within that range, there are clear-cut extremes. Many of the species present are known throughout the range of pine, although some other Atlantic species will only occur with pine at this, the western extremity, of its considerable range.

Acknowledgements

The fieldwork for the survey was mainly carried out by K. Wilson, M.J. Bottomly, R. Reid and K. Chorlton but M. Ball, M.W. Shaw and D. Taylor also contributed. Mrs. Carole Helliwell, Mrs. J. Brocklebank, and C. Barr provided help in the laboratory. M.W. Shaw carried out the majority of the computer analysis and provided much helpful discussion at all stages. A.H.F. Brown not only read and criticised the manuscript, but provided much useful discussion throughout. M.O. Hill carried out the reciprocal averaging ordination and indicator species analysis. Finally, thanks are due to the many owners who gave permission for the site visits and to Forestry Commission and Nature Conservancy staff who also provided helpful support.

References

BUNCE, R.G.H. & SHAW, M.W. (1973). A standardized procedure for ecological survey. *J. environ. Manage.,* **1**, 129-158.

BURNETT, J.H., ed. (1964). *The vegetation of Scotland.* Oliver and Boyd.

HILL, M.O. (1973). Reciprocal averaging: an eigenvector method of ordination. *J Ecol.,* **61**, 237-249.

HILL, M.O., BUNCE, R.G.H. & SHAW, M.W. (1975). Indicator species analysis: a divisive polythetic method of classification and its application to a survey of the native pinewoods in Scotland. *J. Ecol.,* **63**, 597-613.

McVEAN, D.N. & RATCLIFFE, D.A. (1962). *Plant communities of the Scottish Highlands.* H.M.S.O. (Nature Conservancy Monograph no.1)

PRITCHARD, M.M. & ANDERSON, A.J.B. (1971). Observations on the use of cluster analysis in botany with an ecological example. *J. Ecol.,* **59**, 727-749.

STEVEN, H.M. & CARLISLE, A. (1959). *The native pinewoods of Scotland.* Oliver and Boyd.

TANSLEY, A.G. (1949). *The British Isles and their vegetation,* Vol. 1. Cambridge Univ. Pr.

Figure 1.
Structure of the sampling programme and its relationship with the three levels of analysis.

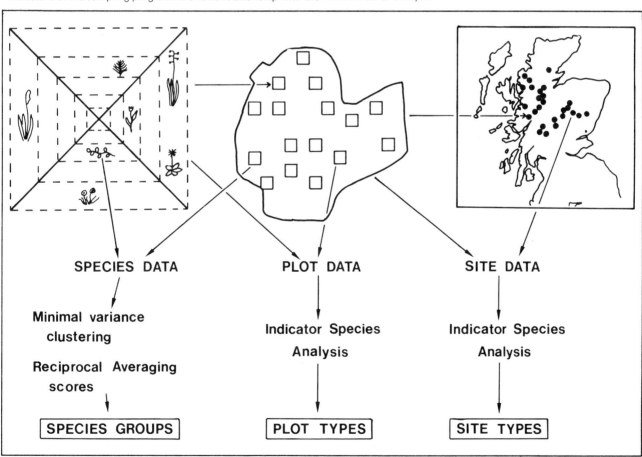

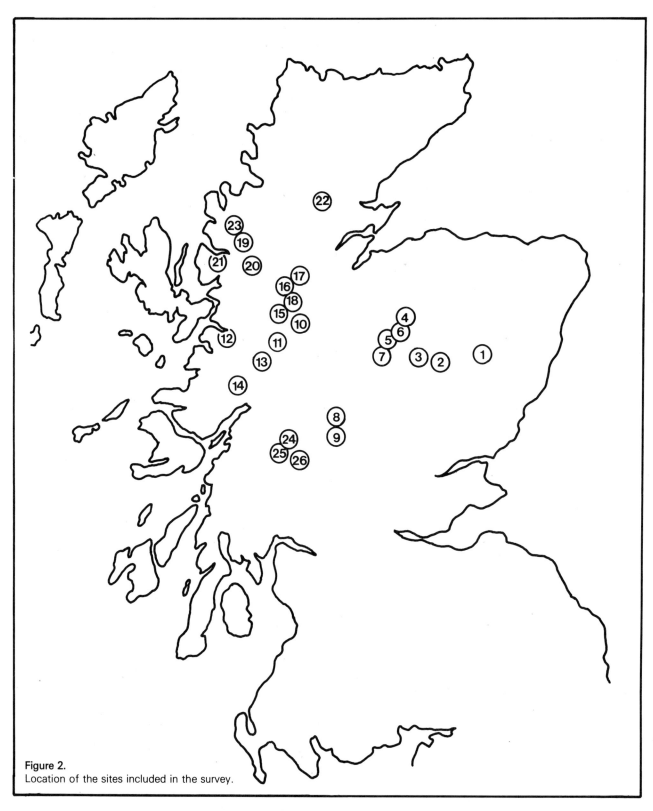

Figure 2.
Location of the sites included in the survey.

1	Glentanar	8	Black Wood of Rannoch	14	Ardgour	21	Shieldaig
2	Ballochbuie	9	Old Wood of Meggernie, Glen Lyon	15	Glen Affric	22	Amat
3	Mar			16	Glen Cannich	23	Loch Maree
4	Abernethy	10	Glen Moriston	17	Glen Strathfarrar	24	Black Mount
5	Rothiemurchus	11	Glengarry	18	Guisachan and Cougie	25	Glen Orchy
6	Glenmore	12	Barrisdale	19	Coulin	26	Tyndrum
7	Glen Feshie	13	Loch Arkaig and Glen Mallie	20	Achnashellach		

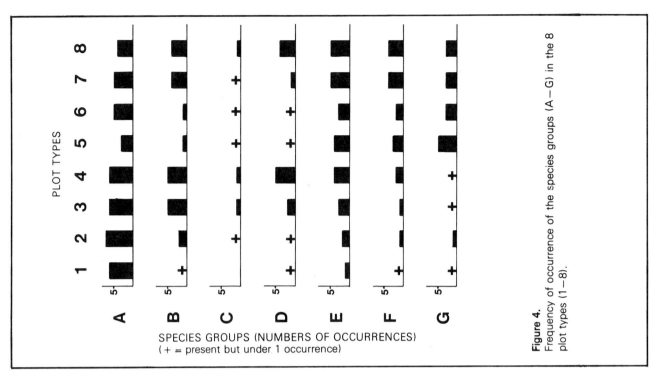

Figure 4.
Frequency of occurrence of the species groups (A–G) in the 8 plot types (1–8).

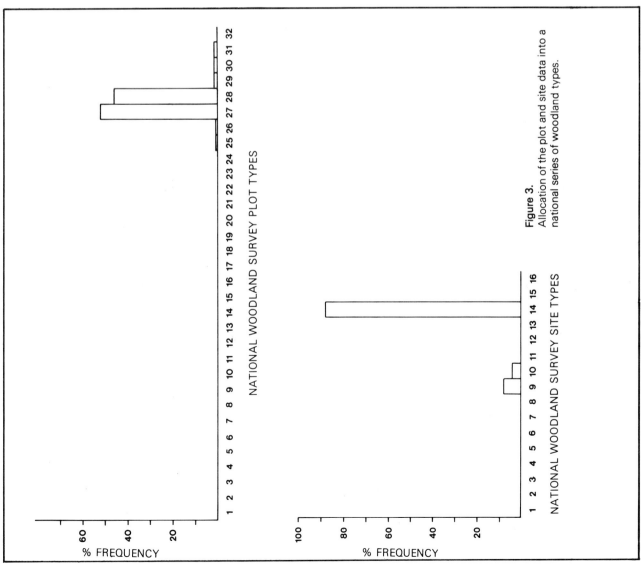

Figure 3.
Allocation of the plot and site data into a national series of woodland types.

18

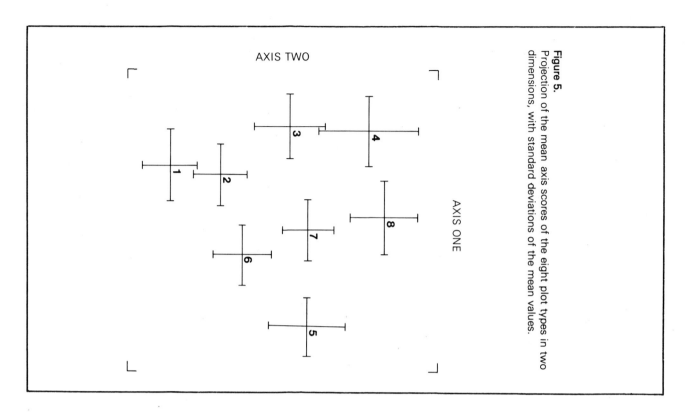

Figure 5.
Projection of the mean axis scores of the eight plot types in two dimensions, with standard deviations of the mean values.

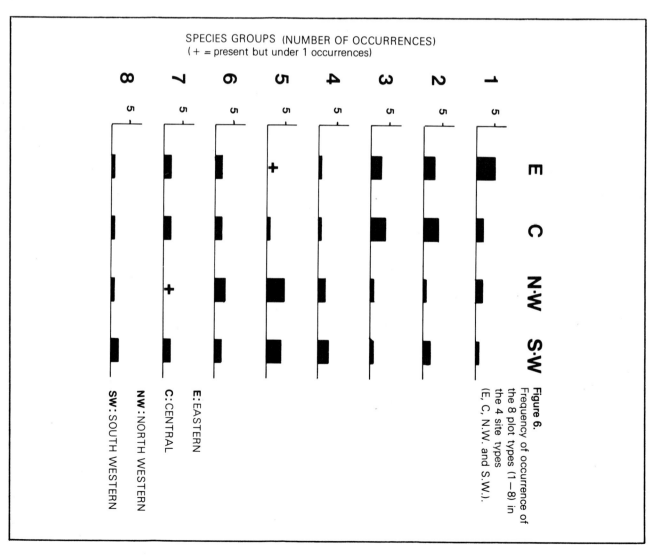

Figure 6.
Frequency of occurrence of the 8 plot types (1–8) in the 4 site types (E, C, N.W. and S.W.).

E: EASTERN
C: CENTRAL
NW: NORTH WESTERN
SW: SOUTH WESTERN

SPECIES GROUPS (NUMBER OF OCCURRENCES)
(+ = present but under 1 occurrences)

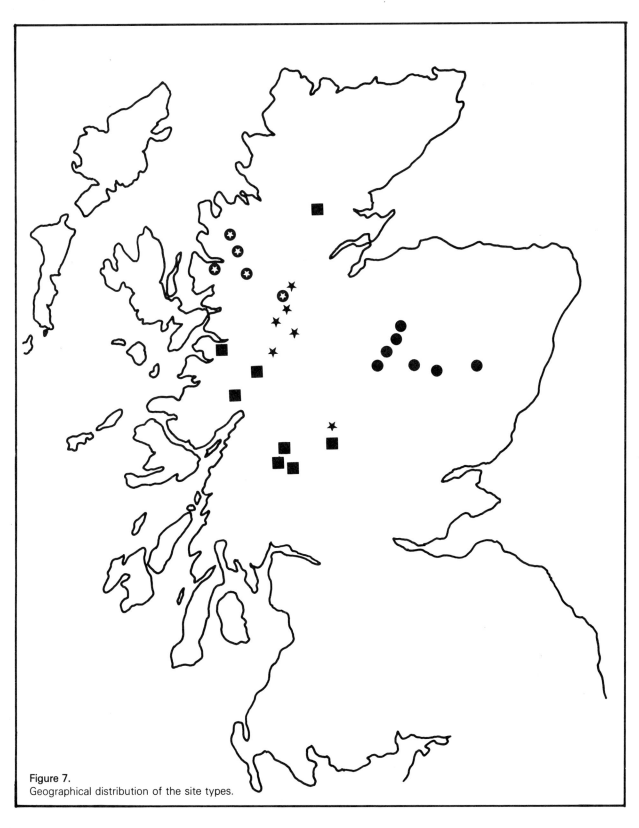

Figure 7.
Geographical distribution of the site types.

● EASTERN

✪ NORTH WESTERN

✷ CENTRAL

■ SOUTH WESTERN

Table 1   Species groups obtained from minimal variance clustering of the reciprocal averaging ordination scores from the 200m data.

A	B	C	D
Listera cordata	Carex demissa	Ajuga reptans	Sieglingia decumbens
Calluna vulgaris	Nardus stricta	Hypericum pulchrum	Euphrasia spp.
Vaccinium vitis-idaea	Luzula multiflora	Cirsium vulgare	Plantago lanceolata
Vaccinium myrtillus	Festuca ovina	Digitalis purpurea	Prunella vulgaris
Empetrum nigrum	Agrostis canina		Dryopteris filix-mas
Melampyrum pratense	Veronica officinalis		Viola riviniana
Luzula pilosa	Festuca vivipara		Ranunculus flammula
Trientalis europaea	Holcus mollis		Holcus lanatus
Pteridium aquilinum	Agrostis tenuis		Ranunculus acris
Blechnum spicant	Oxalis acetosella		Cirsium palustre
	Galium saxatile		Anthoxanthum adoratum

E	F	G
Molinia caerulea	Juncus articulatus/acutiflorus	Trichophorum caespitosum
Potentilla erecta	Juncus bulbosus	Eriophorum angustifolium
Juncus conglomeratus	Carex echinata	Erica tetralix
Juncus effusus	Carex panicea	Narthecium ossifragum
Carex binervis	Dactylorchis maculata	Myrica gale
Polygala spp.	Pinguicula vulgaris	Drosera rotundifolia
Succisa pratensis	Carex pulicaris	Eriophorum vaginatum
Erica cinerea	Carex nigra	
	Juncus squarrosus	

Table 2   Dichotomous key to the plot types produced by Indicator species analysis. The method and use of the key is provided by Hill et al (1975)

	Indicator species	Step 1
Negative	*Positive*	
Deschampsia flexuosa	Carex echinata	
	Drosera rotundifolia	
	Erica tetralix	
	Eriophorum angustifolium	
	Eriophorum vaginatum	
	Molinia caerulea	
	Narthecium ossifragum	
	Sphagnum papillosum	
	Sphagnum rubellum	

Score + 1 or less.. 2
Score + 2 or more... 5

	Indicator species	Step 2
Negative	*Positive*	
Empetrum nigrum	Agrostis canina	
Rhytidiadelphus loreus	Anthoxanthum odoratum	
Vaccinium vitis-idaea	Galium saxatile	
	Hypericum pulchrum	
	Oxalis acetosella	
	Succisa pratensis	
	Viola riviniana	

Score   0 or less.. 3
Score + 1 or more... 4

Continued on page 21

Table 1. Continued from page 20

	Indicator species	Step 3
Negative	*Positive*	
Empetrum nigrum	Agrostis canina	
Rhytidiadelphus loreus	Betula spp.	
	Blechnum spicant	
	Carex echinata	
	Galium saxatile	
	Polytrichum commune	
	Potentilla erecta	
	Trientalis europaea	

        Score 0 or less   Type 1
        Score 1 or more   Type 2

	Indicator species	Step 4
Negative	*Positive*	
Luzula pilosa	Carex binervis	
Trientalis europaea	Carex panicea	
Vaccinium vitis-idaea	Cirsium vulgare	
	Festuca vivipara	
	Prunella vulgaris	
	Ranunculs flammula	
	Succisa pratensis	

        Score 0 or less   Type 3
        Score 1 or more   Type 4

	Indicator species	Step 5
Negative	*Positive*	
Drosera rotundifolia	Agrostis canina	
Rhacomitrium lanuginosum	Anthoxanthum odoratum	
	Galium saxatile	
	Hylocomium splendens	
	Juncus effusus	
	Luzula multiflora	
	Succisa pratensis	
	Viola riviniana	

        Score + 2 or less... 6
        Score + 3 or more.. 7

	Indicator species	Step 6
Negative	*Positive*	
Drosera rotundifolia	Dicranum scoparium	
Erica cinerea	Rhytidiadelphus loreus	
Myrica gale	Vaccinium myrtillus	
Rhacomitrium lanuginosum	Vaccinium vitis-idaea	
Sphagnum spp		
Succisa pratensis		

        Score - 2 or less   Type 5
        Score - 1 or more   Type 6

Sphagna not identifiable with a particular species in the collected specimens

	Indicator species	Step 7
Negative	*Positive*	
Juncus squarrosus	Anthoxanthum odoratum	
Luzula multiflora	Euphrasia spp.	
Polytrichum commune	Ranunculus flammula	
Sphagnum rubellum	Viola riviniana	
Vaccinium myrtillus		
Vaccinium vitis-idaea		

        Score - 2 or less   Type 7
        Score - 1 or more   Type 8

Table 3 Summaries of principal features of the vegetation of the plot types

SPT 1
(60)
Empetrum nigrum/Calluna vulgaris Type

Ground flora

Heterogeneity index	: 2.4	Species groups: A
Constant species	: Callu vul, Vacci vit, Desch fle	
Selective species	: Empet nig (45, 15), Vacci vit (92, 60) Desch fle (95, 64) Melam pra (92, 25)	
Plot dominants	: Callu vul, Vacci vit, Vacci nyr	

Trees	Basal area (sq.m)	No. trees	Large seedlings (%)	Seedlings (%)
Scots pine	0.517	10.6	33	37
Birch	0.013	0.7	13	18
Rowan	0.001	0.3	28	37

No. of plots with no trees: 12%

SPT 2
(66)
Vaccinium vitis-idaea/Calluna vulgaris Type

Ground flora

Heterogeneity index	: 3.9	Species groups: A,E
Constant species	: Callu vul, Vacci myr, Vacci vit, Desch fle	
Selective species	: Vacci vit (92, 59,) Desch fle (93, 63) Melam pra (47, 26) Blech spi (82, 63)	
Plot dominants	: Callu vul, Vacci myr, Pteri aqu, Molin cae	

Trees	Basal area (sq.m)	No. trees	Large seedlings (%)	Seedlings (%)
Scots pine	0.222	3.7	33	38
Birch	0.050	3.0	50	62
Rowan	0.005	1.0	39	52

No. of plots with no trees. 21%

SPT 3
(60)
Oxalis acetosella/Pteridium aquilinum Type

Ground flora

Heterogeneity index	: 5.0	Species groups: A,B,D,E
Constant species	: Poten ere, Vacci myr, Desch fle	
Selective species	: Oxali ace (68, 14), Luzul pil (58, 13), Galiu sax (58, 38) Viola riv (73, 27)	
Plot dominants	: Pteri aqu, Callu vul, Molin cae.	

Trees	Basal area (sq.m)	No. trees	Large seedlings (%)	Seedlings (%)
Scots pine	0.187	4.4	20	22
Birch	0.096	3.4	40	65
Rowan	0.002	0.4	35	65

No. of plots with no trees: 21%

SPT 4
(42)
Cirsium vulgare/Pteridium aquilinum Type

Ground flora

Heterogeneity index	: 5.7	Species groups: A,B,D,E,
Constant species	: Desch fle, Poten ere	
Selective species	: Cirsi vul (40,2), Prune vul (55,6) Anthox odo (74, 18) Ranun acr (50,5)	
Plot dominants	: Pter aqu, Molin cae, Callu vul	

Trees	Basal area (sq.m)	No. trees	Larger seedlings (%)	Seedlings (%)
Scots pine	0.056	1.4	9	14
Birch	0.108	4.2	33	68
Rowan	0.005	0.4	38	45

No. of plots with no trees: 46%

Continued on page 23

Table 3. Continued from page 22

SPT 5
(63)
Drosera rotundifolia/Molinia caerulea Type

Ground flora

Heterogeneity index	:	4.7	Species groups: A,E,G
Constant species	:	Narth oss, Erica tet, Molin cae, Callu vul	
Selective species	:	Drose rot (75,11), Myric gal (67,11), Narth oss (92,32) Erica tet (98,40)	
Plot dominants	:	Molin cae, Callu vul, Eriop vag.	

Trees	Basal area (sq.m)	No. trees	Large seedlings (%)	Seedlings (%)
Scots pine	0.027	1.1	32	41
Birch	0.003	0.1	26	51
Rowan	0	0	17	24

No. of plots with no trees: 69%

SPT 6
(57)
Erica tetralix/Calluna vulgaris Type

Ground flora   Species groups: A,E,G

Heterogeneity index	:	4.4
Constant species	:	Molin cae, Poten ere, Callu vul, Vacci myr
Selective species	:	Eric tet (86,43), Eriop ang (53,22), Narth oss (70,37) Eriop vag (44,17)
Plot dominants	:	Callu vul, Molin cae

Trees	Basal area (sq.m)	No. trees	Large seedlings (%)	Seedlings (%)
Scots pine	0.174	2.9	33	40
Birch	0.010	0.7	51	72
Rowan	0.001	0.1	32	48

No. of plots with no trees: 21%

SPT 7
(37)
Narthecium ossifragum/Molinia caerulea Type

Ground flora

Heterogeneity index	:	5.9	Species groups: A,B,E,F,G,
Constant species	:	Molin cae, Poten ere, Callu vul, Vacci myr	
Selective species	:	Narth oss (84,37), Juncu eff (60,22) Nardu str (30,6) Agros can (89,49)	
Plot dominants	:	Molin cae, Callu vul	

Trees	Basal area (sq.m)	No. trees	Large seedlings (%)	Seedlings (%)
Scots pine	0.059	1.4	11	29
Birch	0.025	1.4	38	70
Rowan	0.001	0.4	22	46

No. of plots with no trees: 46%

SPT 8
(31)
Solidago virgaurea/Molinia caerulea Type

Ground flora

Heterogeneity index	:	6.5	Species groups: A,B,D,E,F,G,
Constant species	:	Narth oss, Molin cae, Poten ere	
Selective species	:	Solid vir (32,2), Ranun fla (42,5) Trich cae (58,10) Euphr spp (42,5)	
Plot dominants	:	Molin cae, Callu vul	

Trees	Basal area (sq.m)	No. trees	Large seedlings (%)	Seedlings (%)
Scots pine	0.049	0.4	7	35
Birch	0.040	1.2	32	68
Rowan	0.001	0.7	13	29

No. of plots with no trees: 46%

Table 4. Ecological characteristics of the four site types — No. of plot types in the average number of plot types/site. Frequent plot types in the three most frequent plot types in the site type; constant species: the five most constant vascular plants, ranked; Basal area: average basal area/site; No. of trees: average number of trees/site; Saplings, larger seedlings and seedlings: frequency out of 16 plots/site.

		Eastern	Central	North western	South western
Ground flora					
No. of plot types:		5.4	6.7	5.8	6.1
Frequent plot types:		1, 2, 3	2, 3, 6	5, 6	4, 5, 8
Constant species:		Callu vul	Callu vul	Callu vul	Molin cae
		Vacci myr	Vacci myr	Molin cae	Poten ere
		Vacc vit	Poten ere	Blech spi	Callu vul
		Desch fle	Molin cae	Eric tet	Vacci myr
		Poten ere	Desch fle	Vacci myr	Blech spi
Trees					
Basal area	(Scots pine)	4.507	3.482	2.383	1.309
	(Birch)	0.260	1.000	0.608	0.680
No. trees	(Scots pine)	111	56	42	12
	(Birch)	6	63	33	21
Saplings (freq)	(Scots pine)	3	4	2	0
	(Birch)	1	4	4	1
Larger seedlings (freq)	(Scots pine)	3	6	6	2
	(Birch)	2	8	7	5
Seedlings (freq)	(Scots pine)	6	5	8	3
	(Birch)	7	13	8	12

Table 5. Plot environmental data. Correlations between diameter, height, environmental variables, and reciprocal averaging ordination scores. For 414 D.F. significance levels of r : P (·001), ≥·162; P (·001 - ·01), ≥·128; P (·01-05), ≥·098.

	1	2	3	4	5	6	7	8	9	10	11	12	13	14	15
2	−.183														
3	−.174	.813													
4	.080	.066	.073												
5	−.124	.189	.130	.106											
6	−.028	.001	−.007	−.030	−.051										
7	−.138	.107	.053	−.005	−.013	.034									
8	−.150	−.055	−.062	−.278	.047	−.019	.068								
9	.173	−.016	−.009	−.008	−.061	.015	.126	−.360							
10	−.195	.022	.059	−.003	.019	.023	−.066	−.146	−.070						
11	.057	−.010	−.031	.063	−.013	.023	−.098	−.286	.039	.086					
12	−.085	−.045	−.069	−.250	.027	−.004	.196	.658	.123	−.027	.366				
13	−.050	−.297	−.377	−.162	.038	−.022	.093	.498	−.134	−.202	−.237	.284			
14	.657	−.309	−.353	−.005	−.128	−.055	−.079	−.058	.221	−.213	.079	.043	.079		
15	.114	.087	.100	.364	.082	−.091	−.060	−.267	−.073	−.012	−.025	−.322	−.006	−.089	
16	−.040	−.063	−.152	−.070	−.230	.095	−.120	−.059	.003	−.035	.037	−.059	.024	−.020	.018

Variables:-

1 pH at centre of plot
2 Diameter of largest tree
3 Height of largest tree
4 Slope between highest and lowest points in plot
5 Aspect (degrees away from N.)
6 Aspect (degrees away from E.)
7 Depth Aoo horizon
8 Depth Ao horizon
9 Depth A1 horizon
10 Depth A2 horizon
11 Depth B horizon
12 Total recorded soil depth
13 Axis 1 ordination scores
14 Axis 2 ordination scores
15 Axis 3 ordination scores
16 Axis 4 ordination scores

Table 6   Summaries of the principal environmental features of the plot types. (Rock categories in cm, Glade categories in m)

SPT 1
(Empetrum nigrum/Calluna vulgaris type)

Geographical dist:	E (C, NW, SW)	Altitude: 296 m	Slope: 13°	pH: 3.9
Soil horizons (%)	Ao: 100	A1: 53	A2: 26	B: 72
Moisture (A1) (%):	V. wet: O	Wet: 32	Damp: 45	Dry: 18
Water habitats:	Streams: 0	Ditches: 0	Small pools: 0	Marsh/bog: 3
Rock/glade habitats:	Rocks 5-50: 30	Boulders>50: 32	Glade 5-12: 45	Glade >12: 47
Animals:	Sheep: 7	Red deer: 40	Other deer: 52	Squirrels: 22

SPT 2
(Vaccinium vitis-ideaea/Calluna vulgaris type)

Geographical dist:	C (E, SW, NW)	Altitude: 269m	Slope: 14°	pH: 4.1
Soil horizons (%):	Ao: 100	A1: 62	A2: 33	B: 72
Moisture (A1) (%):	V. wet: 3	Wet: 33	Damp: 36	Dry: 14
Water habitats:	Streams: 6	Ditches: 12	Small pools: 0	Marsh/bog: 9
Rock/glade habitats:	Rocks 5-50: 58	Boulders>50: 41	Glade 5-12: 35	Glade >12:55
Animals:	Sheep: 18	Red deer: 38	Other deer: 39	Squirrels: 3

SPT 3
(Oxalis acetosella/Pteridium aquilinum type)

Geographical dist:	C (E, NW, SW)	Altitude: 271m	Slope: 12°	pH: 4.5
Soil horizons (%):	Ao: 61	A1: 75	A2: 13	B: 73
Moisture (A1) (%)	V. wet: 5	Wet: 18	Damp: 25	Dry: 10
Water habitats:	Streams: 3	Ditches: 13	Small pools: 0	Marsh/bog: 12
Rock/glade habitats:	Rocks 5-50: 82	Boulders>50: 53	Glade 5-12m: 42	Glade >12: 65
Animals:	Sheep: 25	Red deer: 25	Other deer: 46	Squirrels: 16

SPT 4
(Cirsium vulgare/Pteridium aquilinum type)

Geographical dist:	SW (NW, E, C)	Altitude: 233 m	Slope: 21°	pH: 4.9
Soil horizons (%):	Ao: 52	A1: 76	A2: 9	B: 78
Moisture (A1) (%):	V. wet: 0	Wet: 12	Damp: 36	Dry: 5
Water habitats:	Streams: 38	Ditches: 2	Small pools: 0	Marsh/bog: 14
Rock/glade habitats:	Rocks 5-50: 81	Boulders>50: 74	Glade 5-12: 50	Glade >12: 64
Animals:	Sheep: 45	Red deer: 29	Other deer: 38	Squirrels: 0

SPT 5
(Drosera rotundifolia/Molinia caerulea type)

Geographical dist:	NW (SW, C, E)	Altitude: 213m	Slope: 10°	pH: 4.4
Soil horizons (%):	Ao: 100	A1: 34	A2: 1	B: 25
Moisture (A1) (%):	V. wet: 44	Wet: 43	Damp: 8	Dry: 0
Water habitats:	Streams: 19	Ditches: 12	Small pools: 40	Marsh/bog: 59
Rock/glade habitats:	Rocks 5-50: 63	Boulders>50: 41	Glade 5-12: 6	Glade >12: 87
Animals:	Sheep: 36	Red deer: 60	Other deer: 60	Squirrels: 0

SPT 6
(Erica tetralix/Calluna vulgaris type)

Geographical dist:	NW (SW, C, E)	Altitude: 254m	Slope: 10°	pH: 4.0
Soil horizons (%):	Ao: 100	A1: 24	A2: 0	B: 22
Moisture (A1) (%):	V. wet: 21	Wet: 58	Damp: 17	Dry: 2
Water habitats:	Streams: 5	Ditches: 18	Small pools: 2	Marsh/bog: 51
Rock/glade habitats:	Rocks 5-50: 40	Boulders>50:	Glade 5-12: 28	Glade >12: 77
Animals:	Sheep: 16	Red deer: 54	Other deer: 56	Squirrels: 3

SPT 7
(Narthecium ossifragum/Molinia caerulea type)

Geographical Dist:	E, C, SW (NW)	Altitude: 266m	Slope: 8°	pH: 5.1
Soil horizons (%):	Ao: 89	A1: 22	A2: 8	B: 41
Moisture (A1) (%):	V. wet: 35	Wet: 35	Damp: 11	Dry: 0
Water habitats:	Streams: 10	Ditches: 25	Small pools: 7	Marsh/bog: 42
Rock/glade habitats:	Rocks 5-50: 90	Boulders>50: 55	Glade 5-12: 16	Glade >12: 87
Animals:	Sheep: 32	Red deer: 39	Other deer: 39	Squirrels: 0

SPT 8
(Solidago virgaurea/Molinia caerulea type)

Geographical Dist:	SW (E, C, NW)	Altitude: 215m	Slope: 12°	pH: 4.6
Soil horizons (%):	Ao: 100	A1: 52	A2: 0	B; 35
Moisture (A1) (%):	V. wet: 19	Wet: 55	Damp: 3	Dry: 3
Water habitats:	Streams: 30	Ditches: 26	Small pools: 7	Marsh/bog: 52
Rock/glade habitats:	Rocks 5-50: 90	Boulders>50: 55	Glade 5-12: 16	Glade >12: 87
Animals:	Sheep: 32	Red deer: 39	Other deer: 39	Squirrels: 0

Breeding birds of Scottish pinewoods

I. Newton[1] and D. Moss[2]

This paper describes the birds that breed in the pinewoods of northern Scotland, discusses the main factors that determine their variety and density, and also gives results from some censuses made in natural and planted woods in recent years.

Scots pine *(Pinus sylvestris L.)* is the most widely distributed conifer in the world. It is found naturally from Britain, across Eurasia south almost to the Mediterranean area (Carlisle and Brown 1968). In one region or another, Scots pine occurs from sea level to about 2,400 metres and, while it occurs at greatest altitudes in the south of its range, even in Norway it grows at more than 1,000 m above sea level (Steven and Carlisle 1959). Wherever it grows, moreover, it is almost always a forest dominant. In Britain, it occurs as an undoubted native tree only in northern Scotland; it is naturally established on the heaths of southern England, and has been extensively planted elsewhere in State and private forests.

The native pinewoods in northern Scotland have been so modified by centuries of selective felling and of overgrazing that they tend now to be rather open, in places so much so that they are better classed as wooded heaths than woods proper. This openness allows many birds (such as Meadow pipit[3]) that might otherwise be absent to breed there. In general, few other trees grow among the pines, though birches *(Betula spp.)* are fairly commonly found, aspens *(Populus tremula)* and rowans *(Sorbus aucuparia)* occasionally, while alders *(Alnus glutinosa)* are frequent along stream sides. The commonest shrub is juniper *(Juniperus communis),* and two main plant associations form the field layer, namely *Vaccinium*-moss under the trees, and *Vaccinium-Calluna* in more open areas, though there are many local variants (McVean and Ratcliffe 1962). The buds, shoots, flowers and fruits of all the tree species mentioned provide sustenance for birds, as do the insects which live in the foliage, bark and dead wood. Other main foods in the pine forests include the shoots and seeds of *Calluna* and *Vaccinium.*

The Scottish pinewoods support a characteristic bird population that contains several species that are uncommon elsewhere in Britain, such as Scottish crossbill, Crested tit and capercaillie. These and other conifer-dwelling species probably survived the last few thousand years in Britain only in such pinewoods, but several have spread in recent years, as pine and other conifers have been planted elsewhere by man. In the last 100 years, the remote and inaccessible parts of the native pinewoods may also have acted as important refuges where certain predatory birds survived the ravages of gamekeepers.

General considerations

The importance of the dominant tree in influencing the numbers and variety of birds in a forest cannot have escaped the attention of any ornithologist. But the forest may grow on more, or less, productive soil, and may show different structure according to its age and management. All these factors affect birds. The main problems are to find what determines, for any one forest, (a) the number of species, (b) which species they will be, and (c) at what densities they will occur. These problems are best considered together, because the same factors influence them. From studies in various parts of the world, generalisations can be drawn, which apply as much to pine as to any other woods. The examples quoted are taken mainly from Finland, where much census work has been done (Palmgren 1930; Merikallio 1946; Haapanen 1965), and where the position is simplified by the presence of only three forest-forming trees, namely pine, spruce *(Picea abies)* and birch.

(1) Tree species

There is an obvious division between broad-leaved and coniferous species. Most woodland birds in Britain live in both types, but a few species are almost entirely restricted to one or other type, so that the tree species in a wood influence the composition of its bird fauna. The tree species also influence bird density, as shown by extensive results from Finland (Figure 1, from von Haartman 1971). In any one forest type (similar soil and field layer), breeding birds were more abundant in birch than in spruce, and more abundant in spruce than in pine. Among mixed forests, bird densities in spruce/pine were nearer to pine than to spruce, whereas densities in birch/spruce were as high, or higher, than those in birch, and much higher than in spruce. It was not clear why pine was worst, but pine has less foliage per unit area than do the other trees, and hence less habitat for insects. It also offers less good nesting sites for birds than does spruce (von Haartman 1971).

(2) Soil fertility

As an indication of the productivity of the soil in Finland, the vegetation of the forest floor is used (Cajander 1909, 1925). Arranged according to decreasing productivity, the following main types are distinguished: grass-herb (several types), *Oxalis-Myrtillus, Myrtillus, Vaccinium* and *Calluna.* When other factors were constant, birds were 3—6 times more numerous in woods on the most productive than on the least productive soils (Figure 1). In those species that were examined individually, this variation was proved to result from birds taking smaller territories in the good than in the poor areas (von Haartman 1971; Newton 1972). This trend is understandable in terms of organic production, for all types of productivity were better on the better soils, including not only wood and foliage (Ilvessalo 1920), but also various other crops, from flowers and fruits to earthworms (Karppinen 1958).

1 Institute of Terrestrial Ecology, 12 Hope Terrace, Edinburgh, EH9 2AS.
2 Department of Forestry and Natural Resources, University of Edinburgh, King's Buildings, Mayfield Road, Edinburgh, EH9 3JU.
3 Scientific names of all species mentioned are in Table 1.

(3) Area

Despite the relationship between productivity and bird density, another pattern has been found repeatedly: the larger the area of uniform woodland, the lower the overall density of birds (Oelke 1968). This rule is mysterious but widespread; oceanic islands have astonishingly high densities of birds, as do small islands of habitat in mainland situations (MacArthur 1971). It is unlikely that this effect can be explained in terms of productivity. One factor involved in woodland is the well-known "edge effect" (Odum 1959), in which birds are found at much greater density at the boundary between two habitats than within either one of them. This effect is apparent at the junction between different tree communities, but especially so where a wood adjoins an open area. In this last situation, some species (such as crows) nest on the forest edge, but do not penetrate the forest interior. Some species may be obtaining part of their requirements from the neighbouring habitat, as applies especially to the several species which feed outside woodland, but require trees in which to nest.

While the overall density of birds is greater in small than large woods, the number of species in small woods is often less, especially where a wood is so small that it will not accommodate even a single territory of certain species. Comparing various British woods, Moore and Hooper (1975) found that the number of species became fewer with decreasing size of wood and also with increasing distance from other woods. This situation presents another parallel with oceanic islands, where size and extent of isolation influence the numbers of bird-species present.

(4) Structure

As a forest grows, its bird fauna changes from an initial predominance of field dwelling species, through scrub and thicket species, to woodland species proper (Lack 1933). The overall density of birds also often increases, as may be expected from the increase in structural complexity of the habitat. In a well-grown forest, a many layered stand containing trees and shrubs of varying height holds more bird species than a uniform stand in which all the trees are the same height. In such mature forests, the structure is apparently more important than the number of tree species in influencing the number of bird species present (MacArthur and MacArthur 1961; Orians 1969; Recher 1969).

(5) Nest sites

A special aspect of forest structure concerns the availability of nest sites. Especially in managed forests, where dead timber and scrub may be removed, the densities of hole- and shrub-nesting birds may be held low through shortage of nest sites rather than through shortage of food (Haapanen 1965). This effect has been repeatedly shown by experiments in which the addition of nest boxes or bunches of branches (tied and stuck up to look like bushes) in managed woods was followed by a marked increase (up to ten times or more) in the density of hole-nesting and shrub-nesting birds (Pfeifer, 1953, 1963). The main hole-nesting species involved were various tits, Pied flycatchers and redstarts. The increase in breeding density usually followed immediately, but, in some woods, Pied flycatchers invaded only after several years. In some places, the maximum density of this last species corresponded to 2,000 pairs per km² more than the total density of all birds so far found in any forest without nest boxes anywhere in Europe (Udvardy 1957; von Haartman 1971). Moreover, such increases were achieved over comparatively large areas, say 25 ha (Pfeifer, 1963), suggesting that shortage of nest sites was the main factor limiting density.

To summarise, the number of bird species in a wood may be influenced by tree species, forest structure and area; the type of bird species by tree species, forest structure and area; and the bird density by tree species, forest structure, area and soil fertility. Put another way, irregular forests on good soil, with a mixture of hardwoods and conifers, contain significantly more bird species at a higher density than do regular, intensively-managed, uniform stands on poor soil. Thus stated, it is clear that the planting of trees on open ground leads to an increase in the number and diversity of birds, but modern forestry practice, in well-grown woods, acts against high density and variety of birds.

The birds

At least 70 bird species breed regularly in Scottish pinewoods, but 24 depend on openings for feeding or nesting, and 13 others on water, either streams or lochs (Table 1). Of the four corvids, crows are widespread, while magpies and jays are local, but all three would be commoner if they were persecuted less by gamekeepers. Among the six seed-eaters, the chaffinch is common everywhere, the greenfinch is local near farmland, while the bullfinch breeds mainly in areas of juniper. The numbers of crossbills and siskins fluctuate greatly from year to year, according to the size of the local pine crop, and the numbers of redpolls according to the birch crop (Newton 1972). The crossbills of northern Scotland form a distinct race *(L.c. scotica)* feeding almost entirely from pine cones; they are larger, with heavier bills, than the nominate **L.c. curvirostra** of northern Europe, which feed largely on seeds from softer spruce cones, but are similar to eight other races isolated in various mountain pine forests in southern Europe (Newton 1972). Of 26 insectivorous songbirds the commonest are the wren, Willow warbler (a summer visitor), goldcrest and Coal Tit. In general the Coal Tit outnumbers the Crested by 3 or 4 to 1 (Nethersole-Thompson and Watson 1974) and, while the former can nest among stones and logs on the ground, the latter requires soft, rotten tree stumps, and is thus largely absent from newer plantations. In Britain, the Crested tit is found only in northern Scotland, but has a wide distribution in conifer woods abroad. Blue and Great tits are found only near deciduous trees, while Long-tailed tits and dunnocks nest chiefly in juniper bushes. The

Pied flycatcher, which is common in pinewoods in northern Europe, is absent from such habitats in Britain, though a few breeding attempts have occurred.

Two species have colonised Scotland only in recent years. Redwings sometimes occur in native pine forests, but chiefly in association with birch, while wrynecks have been seen regularly since 1950 and several pairs were found breeding in 1969 (Nethersole-Thompson and Watson 1974). The cuckoo is common in openings and lays its eggs mainly in the nests of the two pipit species; the Great spotted woodpecker apparently became extinct during the last century, but has since re-established itself; while the nightjar has declined in the last 100 years, and is now extremely scarce, as it is in many of its former British haunts. Wood pigeons use the forest mainly for nesting, and are commonest close to farmland where they feed.

Broadly speaking, the three game birds occupy different stages of forest succession; the Red grouse occurs in large openings, where heather prevails; the Black grouse is most numerous in partly grown forests and the capercaillie in mature timber. This last species became extinct in Britain by 1770, but, after abortive attempts to reintroduce it from Sweden to Deeside in 1827 and 1829, it was successfully re-established near Taymouth in 1837 and 1838. Twenty-five years later there were thought to be 1,000−2,000 birds in the area (Ritchie 1920). Birds from Taymouth and fresh importations from Sweden were then released in various parts of Scotland, from which birds spread naturally to other areas, but they are still absent from the south and west parts of Scotland. In the Black Wood of Rannoch, Johnston and Zwickel found densities of one bird per 5−6 ha.

The woodcock occurs in damp areas throughout the forest, but other waders depend on open bogs or water, as do Black-headed gulls. Among the predators, the Tawny and Long-eared owls, sparrowhawk, kestrel and buzzard are fairly widespread, but the osprey depends on waters containing large fish. The Golden eagle and merlin breed only near the tree limit, while the kite, Honey buzzard and goshawk were exterminated last century (Nethersole-Thompson and Watson 1974). The goshawk has been suspected of breeding in recent years, however. In Speyside, buzzard pairs are dispersed about 1.5 km apart from one another (Weir and Picozzi, unpublished), and sparrowhawks about 2.4 km (Newton 1972). The remaining birds are dependent on water: mallard, teal, heron and goosander are fairly widespread, but Red-breasted merganser is found mainly near the sea.

At least four of the species mentioned − the Scottish crossbill, siskin, Crested tit and capercaillie − were formerly more or less restricted to northern Scotland, but all have spread to some extent with the planting of conifers by man. The crossbill and Crested tit have spread only within the north, whereas the others have spread further, and the siskin now breeds wherever there are large plantations of conifers in all parts of Britain (Newton 1972).

Previous census work

Methods:

The rest of this paper is concerned with the bird densities found on individual census plots. Caution is needed in comparing the results from different observers, however, because they used different methods, with different biases.

(a) **The mapping method** entails plotting on a map of a specific census plot the position of all birds encountered on each of 8−10 visits over several weeks and, from the grouping of points, estimating how many territories are involved (Enemar 1959; Williamson 1964). This method has least bias, and gives densities of each species, as well as their relative abundance. It was used in Scottish pinewoods by Williamson (1969).

(b) **The area count** entails a line of observers walking through a wood, on a broad front, counting all the birds that fly back through the line. The method is probably biased towards the more conspicuous species and, by missing any birds which fly right away, underestimates densities. It was used in Scottish pinewoods by Watson (1969).

(c) **The transect method** entails walking a set course, and noting all birds encountered and then calculating the relative abundance of different species. The method is biased towards the more conspicuous species, and does not give densities. It was used in Scottish pinewoods by Yapp (1962) and Simms (1971).

The diversities of the breeding communities can be compared by calculating an index from census results: diversity $= \xi p_i \log p_i$, where p_i = proportion of total represented by the ith species, and the sum is taken over all species occurring. The diversity index increases both with total number of species and the evenness of the distribution of the species.

Results:

(a) In a series of censuses in Wester Ross (Table 2), Williamson (1969) found that pine, even when in a "natural" state, supported a much sparser avifauna than birch or oak, both in terms of number of species and total densities. This result was in accord with the Finnish results quoted earlier (von Haartman 1971). The differences in species composition between Williamson's two pine plots reflected the woodland structure (Table 3), with twice as many birds in total and many more Willow warblers in the more open, shrubby plot (1B), but no Coal tits there.

(b) Watson's (1969) area counts showed a striking difference between the two areas censused, one a natural stand in pinewood at Loch Garten, Inverness, and the other part of a large plantation with no under-growth on sand dunes at Culbin, Moray. The results (Table 3) were probably biased towards conspicuous species, such as chaffinch, and against inconspicuous ones, such as goldcrest. However, they show a striking difference in the overall density of birds on the two areas, underlining the difference between a mature natural wood with undergrowth and a plantation with no undergrowth on poor substrate. The over-riding prevalence of the chaffinch on the Loch Garten plot is an interesting feature (although this is subject to the qualification about conspicuousness made earlier), and the total density was probably less under-estimated at Loch Garten than at Culbin as a result. Note also the greatly increased representation of Crested tit on the Moray plot, and the apparent scarcity of goldcrest.

(c) The transect results (Table 3) are quoted from general books on woodland birds by Yapp (1962) and Simms (1971). They were likely to be biased by differences between species in conspicuousness. The greatest difference between their respective results was the prevalence of the Willow warbler in the natural woods examined by Yapp, and its absence from the planted woods included by Simms. When in coniferous woodland, the Willow warbler requires an open structure with low shrubs. Other differences, as in Tree pipit and Coal tit, also reflected habitat preference.

Neither the diversity indices nor the total number of species (Table 3) could be compared when obtained by different methods, because, in each method, the treatment of scarce species is different, yet it is these which affect the diversity measures. The diversity index for Watson's area count at Loch Garten was an underestimate, as the full data were not given. However, the comparisons within methods showed much greater diversity in bird communities in varied natural woods than in uniform plantations, as was to be expected.

Our own census work

In 1973-74, D.M. censused two pine plots, one natural and one planted on Tore Hill and a birch plot, all in the Abernethy Forest, Inverness-shire (Table 4). In 1973, he used both mapping and transect methods, thus making comparison of results possible, but, in 1974, used only the mapping method.

Methods:

(a) The mapping method followed that of the British Trust for Ornithology in its Common Birds Census, using the same field procedure and rules for analysis of the results (Williamson 1964). The only difference was in the interpretation of territories at the edges of the plots, which were estimated to the nearest quarter-territory within the plot. The visits were made in the first five hours after sunrise, when most birds were in full song (Hogstad 1967), and from April—June, when most territorial behaviour occurs. No visits were made in rain, or in strong wind, which reduces the audibility of bird sounds. In the planted plot, birds could not be seen beyond a short distance, and detection relied almost entirely on songs and calls. In all, eight visits were made to each plot in 1973, and ten in 1974.

(b) Three line transects were made on each plot in 1973, following methods of Yapp (1956, 1962). There was no need for a marked plot for transects, but these were restricted within the plots for comparative purposes, crossing and re-crossing the ground by different routes. Each bird was noted the first time it was seen or heard, and this was called a "contact". Transects lasted about 1.5—2 hours, and were made in the early morning, as with the mapping visits. The total number of contacts of each species on the three transects was expressed as a percentage of the total contacts on the plot. No densities could be calculated.

Results:

In both years, the total density of birds was over twice as great in the natural pine plot as in the plantation; the bird community was also more diverse in the native plot, both as represented by the diversity index, and in that six species each formed 10 per cent or more of the population in each year, compared with only three in the planted plot (Tables 5 and 6). The birchwood was more diverse in structure than the planted pine, but less so than the native pine, so we would judge from Table 5 that birch supported around 50 per cent more birds than an equivalently structured pinewood.

Results were broadly consistent between years, apart from an increase in siskin numbers between the years. From virtual absence in 1973, there were four pairs on plot S1, and there was a smaller increase on S2 in 1974. They were probably attracted into the area by a good cone crop (Haapanen 1966; Newton 1972).

A comparison of the transect with mapping results showed a fair agreement in the native pine plot (S1), with the over-representation of the wren on the transects compensated by under-representation of several other species. However, in the planted plot (S2), there was a much greater discrepancy, favouring the chaffinch particularly at the expense of the goldcrest and Coal tit. The 4 per cent of the contacts due to Willow warblers referred to birds heard on transects, but outside the plot itself. These results illustrate the failure of the transect method to take account of the differences in conspicuousness between different species. The mapping method is thought to be more reliable because it is not open to this error, and because results are built up from a series of observations of the same birds over the season, and hence less subject to daily fluctuations in bird activity. It is, however, probably not very effective for large non-passerine species, such as sparrowhawks, which might leave the area unnoticed when disturbed by the observer.

Comparison between studies

Compared with Yapp's transect results from natural pine in Rothiemurchus, our results from Abernethy indicated a greater relative abundance of wren and goldcrest (5 per cent compared with 37 per cent). Both species suffer severe mortality in hard winters; Yapp did not give the date of his field work, but it may have followed cold winters, while ours followed a long period of mild winters, over which wrens and goldcrests have increased in England (Batten and Marchant 1975). Also, Yapp's study area was probably more open with more young trees, since he also found 23 per cent Willow warblers (14 per cent on S1), and 7 per cent Tree pipits (none on S1).

Our S2 transect results in planted pine can be compared with Simms' from similar habitat. In both, chaffinch outnumbered other species by more than 10 per cent, and wrens were relatively scarce. Again, however, goldcrests were less common in Simms' woods, perhaps for the reason given above.

The comparison between our plot S1 and Williamson's (1969) plot 1A affords a comparison between central and western natural pinewoods. The two most numerous species, wren and chaffinch, switched places between the two areas, and the redstart came in with two pairs on plot 1A, none on S1 (although it was present in birch woods in Speyside). Redpolls were numerous only in the west, and siskins in the east, but as both are irruptive, the situation might be reversed in other years. The whinchat and whitethroat occurred in moderate numbers on Williamson's plot, but were absent from ours, while robin and Willow warbler were both more numerous on ours. It is hard to comment constructively on the twofold difference in total density between Williamson's plot 1A and our plot S1, since there was a five-year gap between the censuses, but the greater numbers in Speyside would be expected from comparison of the soil fertilities.

Conclusions

Results obtained by the mapping method are clearly worth much more than those obtained by the transect method, as usually applied. The attraction of transects to many workers is presumably the ease with which they can be done. But only the mapping method gives densities and figures on species composition which are not biased by species differences in conspicuousness. So far, the method has been applied in northern Scotland only in one year in Wester Ross, in two pine, three alder, one oak and one birch plot and in two years in Speyside in two pine and one birch plot, so there is clearly scope for further work.

Results to date have shown (1) that, with other things equal, pine is much poorer in breeding birds than birch and other broad-leaved trees and (2) that, within pinewoods, the density of birds is much greater in multistructured natural woods, than in uniform planted ones. They are thus in agreement with the results of the more extensive census work in Finland and elsewhere, quoted earlier.

Acknowledgements

We are grateful to Hon. D.N. Weir for commenting on our list of pinewood birds, and to Dr. D. Jenkins for criticising the manuscript.

Summary

1. In general, the variety and density of birds is greater in woods (a) of birch and other broad-leaved trees than of pine, (b) on rich than poor soils, (c) which are small rather than large, (d) which have much rather than little undergrowth and (e) which have many rather than few nest holes.

2. At least 70 bird species breed regularly in Scottish pinewoods, but 24 depend on openings and 13 on water, either streams or lochs. The bird fauna is characteristic and contains the Crested tit, the Scottish crossbill and capercaillie, which are scarce elsewhere in Britain. The siskin was also formerly restricted to northern Scotland, but has recently spread over much of Britain, following the widespread planting of conifers.

3. The commonest birds in Scottish pinewoods are the chaffinch and wren, followed by goldcrest, Coal tit and robin in planted woods, with the addition of Willow warbler in native woods.

4. Census work has shown that Scottish pinewoods hold fewer birds of fewer species than do birch and other hardwoods growing nearby, and that, among pinewoods, natural stands of varied structure contain more birds than do planted stands of uniform structure.

References

BATTEN, L.A. & MARCHANT, J.H. (1975). Bird population changes for the years 1972-73. *Bird Study,* **22,** 99-104.

CAJANDER, A.K. (1909). Ueber Waldtypen. *Acta for. fenn.,* **1,** 1-175.

CAJANDER, A.K. (1925). The theory of forest types. *Acta for. fenn.,* **29,** 1-108.

CARLISLE, A. & BROWN, A.J.F. (1968). *Pinus sylvestris* L. *J. Ecol.,* **56,** 269-307.

ENEMAR, A. (1959). On the determination of the size and composition of a passerine bird population during the breeding season *Vår. Fågelvärld,* **18,** Suppl. 2, 1-114.

HAAPANEN, A. (1965, 1966). Bird fauna of the Finnish forests in relation to forest succession. 1 and 2. *Ann. zool. fenn.,* **2,** 153-196, **3,** 176-200.

HOGSTAD, O. (1967). Factors influencing the efficiency of the mapping method in determining breeding bird populations in conifer forests. *Nytt Mag. Zool.,* **14,** 125-141.

ILVESSALO, H. (1920). Tutkimuksia metsätyyppien taksatoorisesta merkityksestä nojautuen etupäässä kotimaiseen kasvutaulujen laatimiseen. *Acta for. fenn.,* **15,** 1-157. (Not seen).

KARPPININ, E. (1958). Lierolajeistamme ja niiden esiintyminen metsämaassa. *Luonnon Tutk.,* **62,** 137-144. (Not seen).

MACARTHUR, R. & MACARTHUR, J.W. (1961). On bird species diversity. *Ecology,* **42,** 594-598.

MACARTHUR, R. (1971). Patterns of terrestrial bird communities. In: *Avian biology,* edited by D.S. Farner and J.R. King, Vol. 1, 189-221. Academic.

McVEAN, D.N. & RATCLIFFE, D.A. (1962). *Plant communities of the Scottish Highlands.* H.M.S.O. (Nature Conservancy Monograph No.1.)

MERIKALLIO, E. (1946). Uber regionale Verbreitung und Anzahl der Landvögel in Süd- und Mittelfinnland, besonders in deren östlichen Teilen, im Lichte von quantitativen Untersuchungen. *Ann. zool. Soc. zool.-bot. fenn.,* **12,** 1-140.

MOORE, N.W. & HOOPER, M.D. (1975). On the number of bird species in British woods. *Biol. Conserv.,* **8**, 239-250.

NETHERSOLE-THOMPSON, D. & WATSON, A. (1974). *The Cairngorms: their natural history and scenery.* Collins.

NEWTON, I. (1972). *Finches.* Collins.

NEWTON, I. (1972). Birds of prey in Scotland: some conservation problems. *Scott. Birds,* **7**, 5-23.

ODUM, E.P. (1959). *Fundamentals of Ecology.* Saunders.

OELKE, H. (1969). Okologisch-siedlungsbiologische Untersuchungen der Vogelwelt einer nordwestdeutschen Kulturlandschaft. *Mitt. flor.-soz. ArbGemein. N.S.,* **13**, 126-171.

ORIANS, G.H. (1969). The number of bird species in some tropical forests. *Ecology,* **50**, 783-801.

PALMGREN, P. (1930). Quantitative Untersuchungen über die Vogelfauna in den Wäldern Sudfinnlands. *Acta zool. fenn.,* **7**, 1-218.

PFEIFER, S. (1953). Vorläufige Bericht über Versuche zur Steigerung der Siedlungsdichte höhlen- und buschbrutender Vogelarten auf forstlicher Kleinflache. *Biol. Abh.,* **6**, 1-20.

PFEIFER, S. (1963). Dichte und Dynamik von Brutpopulationen zweier deutscher Waldgebiete 1949-61. *Proc. Int. orn. Congr.,* **13**, 754-763.

RECHER, H. (1969). Bird species diversity and habitat diversity in Australia and North America. *Am. Nat.,* **103**, 75-80.

RITCHIE, J. (1920). *The influence of man on animal life in Scotland.* Cambridge Univ. Pr.

SIMMS, E. (1971). *Woodland birds.* Collins.

STEVEN, H.M. & CARLISLE, A. (1959). *The native pinewoods of Scotland.* Oliver and Boyd.

UVARDY, N. (1957). An evaluation of quantitative studies of birds. *Cold Spring Harb. Symp. quant. Biol.,* **22**, 301-311.

VON HAARTMAN, L. (1971). Population dynamics. In: *Avian biology,* edited by D.S. Farner and J.R. King, Vol. 1, 391-459. Academic Pr.

WATSON, A. (1969). Preliminary counts of birds in central Highland pinewoods. *Bird Study,* **16**, 158-163.

WILLIAMSON, K. (1964). Bird census work in woodlands. *Bird Study,* **11**, 1-22.

WILLIAMSON, K. (1969). Bird communities in woodland habitats in Wester Ross, Scotland. *Q. Jl. For.,* **63**, 305-328.

YAPP, W.B. (1956). The theory of line transects. *Bird Study,* **3**, 93-104.

YAPP, W.B. (1962). *Birds and woods.* Oxford Univ. Pr.

Fig. 1 Densities of breeding birds in Finnish forests in relation to forest type and dominant tree species. GH-grass-herb; OMT-*Oxalis-Myrtillus;* MT-*Myrtillus;* VT-*Vaccinium;* CT-*Calluna.* Modified from von Haartman 1971.

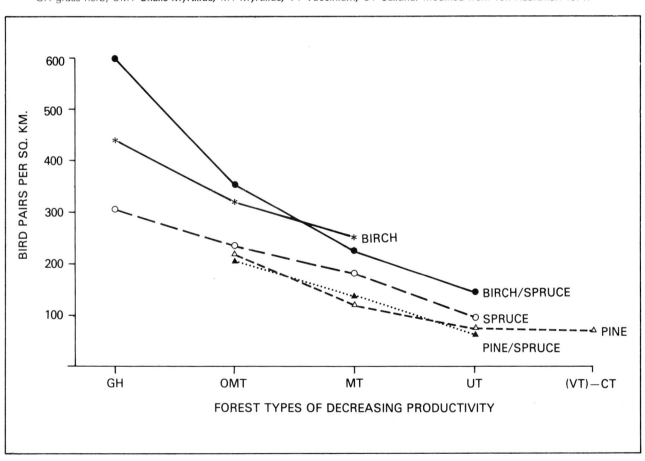

Table 1: Breeding Birds of Scottish Pinewoods:

O — Dependent on openings, B — dependent on broadleaved trees, W — dependent on water.

Corvids (4):
Raven *Corvus corax* (O), Carrion/Hooded crow *Corvus corone* (O), Magpie *Pica pica* (O), Jay *Garrulus glandarius.*

Seed-eating passerines (6):
Crossbill *Loxia curvirostra scotica,* Greenfinch *Carduelis chloris* (O), Siskin *Carduelis spinus,* Redpoll *Acanthis flammea,* Bullfinch *Pyrrhula pyrrhula,* Chaffinch *Fringilla coelebs.*

Insect-eating passerines (29):
Reedbunting *Emberiza schoeniclus* (W), Skylark *Alauda arvensis* (O), Grey Wagtail *Motacilla cinerea* (W), Pied wagtail *M. alba* (W), Tree pipit *Anthus trivialis* (O), Meadow pipit *Anthus pratensis* (O), Tree creeper *Certhia familiaris,* Wren *Troglodytes troglodytes,* Dipper *Cinclus cinclus* (W), Mistle thrush *Turdus viscivorus,* Song thrush *T. philomelos,* Redwing *T. iliacus* (B), Blackbird *T. merula,* Wheatear *Oenanthe oenanthe* (O), Stonechat *Saxicola torquata* (O), Whinchat *S. rubetra* (O), Redstart *Phoenicurus phoenicurus,* Robin *Erithacus rubecula,* Gold-crest *Regulus regulus,* Willow warbler *Phylloscopus trochilus,* Dunnock *Prunella modularis,* Starling *Sturnus vulgaris* (O), Long-tailed tit *Aeigithalos caudatus,* Willow tit *Parus atricapillus* (B), Coal tit *Parus ater,* Blue tit *P. caeruleus* (B), Great tit *P. major* (B), Crested tit *P. cristatus,* Spotted flycatcher *Muscicapa striata.*

Near Passerines (4):
Great-spotted woodpecker *Dendrocopus major,* Wryneck *Jynx torquilla* (O), Nightjar *Caprimulgus europaeus* (O), Cuckoo *Cuculus canorus.*

Pigeons/ Game Birds (4):
Wood-pigeon *Columba palumbus* (O), Red grouse *Lagopus lagopus scoticus* (O), Black grouse *Lyrurus tetrix* (O), Capercaillie *Tetrao urogallus.*

Gulls/Waders (7):
Black-headed gull *Larus ridibundus* (W), Woodcock *Scolopax rusticola,* Snipe *Gallinago gallinago* (O), Oyster catcher *Haematopus ostralegus* (W), Common sandpiper *Tring hypoleucos* (W), Greenshank *T. nebularia* (O), Lapwing *Vanellus vanellus* (O).

Owls/ Raptors (11):
Long-eared owl *Asio otus* (P), Tawny owl *Strix aluco,* Golden eagle *Aquila chrysaetus* (O), Sparrowhawk *Accipiter nisus,* Goshawk *A. gentilis**, Buzzard *Buteo buteo,* Honey buzzard *Pernis apivorus**, Kite *Milvus milvus* (O) *, Kestrel *Falco tinnunculus* (O), Merlin *F. columbarius* (O), Osprey *Pandion haliaetus* (W).

Ducks/Herons (5):
Mallard *Anas platyrhynchos* (W), Teal *A. crecca* (W), Red-breasted merganser *Mergus serrator* (W), Goosander *M. merganser* (W), Heron *Ardea cinerea* (W).

*Exterminated by human persecution.

Table 2: Total bird densities and commonest species in seven plots in Wester Ross censused by Williamson (1969).

Main tree species (area of plot in ha)	Pairs/km	No. of bird species in plot	Prevalent species (% of total birds)
Pine 1A (10ha)	217	11	Wren (23), Coal tit (14)ı
Pine 1B (7.5ha)	444	12	Willow warbler (23), Wren (14)
Birch (10.5ha)	1,100	20	Willow warbler (39), Chaffinch (16), Wren (14)
Oak (8.8ha)	1,320	20	Chaffinch (25), Willow warbler (19)
Alder (5ha)	358	9	Chaffinch (30), Willow warbler (17)
Alder (6.3ha)	543	14	Willow warbler (24), Chaffinch (15)
Alder (4ha)	568	9	Willow warbler (35), Chaffinch (26)

Table 3: Previous census work in Scottish Pinewoods. The results are expressed as percentages of the total; total densities or numbers of contacts are given where available.

Author	Williamson 1969	Williamson 1969	Watson 1969	Watson 1969	Yapp 1962	Simms 1971
Method used	Mapping	Mapping	Area count	Area count	Transect	Transect
Location	Beinn Eighe NNR Plot 1A	Wester Ross Plot-1B	Loch Garten Inverness	Culbin Forest Moray	Rothiemurchus Glenmore, Inverness	12 areas in N. & E. Scotland
Tree species	Scots Pine Mature trees Semi-natural	Scots Pine Scattered matured trees Semi-natural	Scots Pine Mature trees Semi-natural	Scots Pine Planted	Scots Pine Semi-natural	Scots Pine Planted
Understory	Recent regeneration	Broad-leaved shrubs	Juniper (?) Heavy under-growth	None	Juniper?	?
Field layer	*Calluna, Vaccinium*	*Calluna, Vaccinium*	*Calluna, Vaccinium*	None	*Calluna, Vaccinium*	?
Plot area, ha.	10	7.5	4	70	–	–
Pairs/km or contacts	217	444	c850	c55	375	not given
Diversity (no. sp.)	0.977 (11)	1.054(12)	0.667(21)	0.945(13)	0.886	0.823(10)
Species compositions:						
Goldcrest	9	11	21	1	3	8
Chaffinch	11	11	49	22	24	28
Wren	23	14	2	3	2	6
Coal tit	14	–	12	19	7	17
Robin	4.5	11	3	12	2	3
Willow warbler	4.5	23	9	5	23	–
Crested tit	–	–	3	15	2	–
Blackbird	4.5	–	–	1	–	–
Redstart	9	–	–	3	4	–
Dunnock	4.5	7	–	–	–	–
Tree pipit	–	3.5	–	–	7	–
Siskin	–	3.5	–	–	–	5
Redpoll	9	11	–	–	–	3
Crossbill	–	–	–	–	2	5
Other species	Whinchat 7	Long-tailed tit 3.5 Whinchat 3.5 Whitethroat 7	Blue tit 3	Capercaillie 5 Woodpigeon 4 Tawny owl 4 Bullfinch 4	Cuckoo 3 Crow 2 Tree-creeper 1 Song thrush 3 Meadow pipit 3	Pheasant 4 Woodpigeon 5 Great-spotted woodpecker 2

Diversity index = $\leq p_i \log_{10} p_i$, where p_i = proportion of total for ith species.—

Table 4: Details of census plots used in our own census work in Abernethy Forest, Inverness-shire.

Ref. No.	Area (ha)	Altitude a.s.l. ft.	Tree species	Understory	Field layer
S1	8.7	850-950	Scots pine, natural, relatively open, trees of all ages.	Several clumps of Juniper	Thick cover of *Calluna & Vaccinium*
S2	11.7	800-950	Scots pine and Lodgepole pine, planted 1932 canopy almost closed.	Few scattered Junipers	Sparse *Calluna & Vaccinium*
S3	8.8	750	Birch, varying in height and density at different parts of plot.	Few Juniper clumps, birch scrub some Bird cherry *(Prunus padus)*	Grasses; *Calluna* grazed by sheep.

Table 5: Total densities of birds (pairs/km) found by mapping method in three areas in Abernethy Forest, Inverness-shire

	Natural pine, S1	Planted pine, S2	Birch, S3	Prevalent species on S3 (% of total birds)
1973	385	155	418	Chaffinch (27) Willow warbler (22) Wren (11) Blue tit (10)
1974	471	215	455	Chaffinch (35) Willow warbler (25) Wren (11) Blue tit (9)

Table 6: Densities and species compositions of bird populations in semi-natural and planted pine areas, with heavy and sparse undergrowth respectively, at Abernethy Forest, as found by two methods. Composition expressed as percentages:

For details of plots, see Table 4.

Plot	S1: natural pine with heavy undergrowth			S2: Planted pine with sparse undergrowth		
Method	Mapping	Mapping	Transect	Mapping	Mapping	Transect
Year	1973	1974	1973	1973	1974	1973
Pairs/km or contacts	385	471	307	155	215	286
Diversity index	.960	.916	.989	.709	.763	.786
Species compositions:						
Goldcrest	15	18	13	37	28	22
Chaffinch	17	20	18	28	31	35
Wren	15	13	24	3	4	9
Coal tit	12	11	8	17	20	12
Robin	13	9	5	6	2	8
Willow warbler	12	12	14	—	—	4
Crested tit	4	2	4	3	2	—
Tree creeper	4	2	2	6	2	2
Dunnock	2	—	1	—	—	—
Siskin	2	10	1	—	8	—
Crossbill	3	—	2	—	—	—
Other species	Song thrush 2	Bullfinch 2	Redstart 1 Bullfinch 1	Song thrush 3	Mistle thrush 2 Bullfinch 2	
Other Species	Song thrush 1			Woodcock 1 Crow 1 Redstart 1 Bullfinch 1	Woodcock 1 Song thrush 1	Mistle thrush 2 Bullfinch 2

Diversity index $= \sum p_i \log_{10} i$, where $p_i =$ proportion of total for ith species.

Soils of the native pinewoods of Scotland

E.A. FitzPatrick Department of Soil Science, University of Aberdeen

The soils of the native pinewoods are predominantly podzols which are similar in many ways to the podzols that occur under other types of vegetation including plantations of pine. These soils have developed mainly in the very stony, coarse-textured fluvioglacial terraces that occur in many of the valleys, as is well shown in the forests of Rothiemurchus and Nethybridge, in the Spey valley. In some cases, the native pinewoods occur on slopes where the parent materials of the soils are solifluction deposits, and a good example of these soils occurs in Glen Tanar. In a number of isolated pockets, the native pine is found on gley soils or on peat and, somewhat more often, on intergrades to altosols (brown earths), but only the podzols of the pine forest will be discussed in detail in this paper.

Morphology — Fig. 1

The soils have a fairly narrow range of variability in their morphological characteristics, except under extreme conditions when the parent material is highly quartzose or where precipitation is fairly high. At the surface, there is about 1 cm of litter, composed of material derived from the trees themselves, as well as from the ground vegetation. Characteristically, the pine needles demonstrate heavy infestation of fungus *Lophodermium pinastri* as shown by the easily observed black spots and transverse black lines.

Below the litter, there is usually about 5—15 cm of decomposing organic matter which may show two distinct horizons — the fermenton and humifon. The fermenton (F horizon) is the upper, brown, spongy, partially-decomposed organic matter containing recognisable plant fragments and occasional areas of dense growth of fungal mycelium. In thin section, some plant fragments have an overgrowth of fungal mycelium, while other fragments have been invaded and eaten by small arthropods that leave tell-tale evidence in the form of their distinctive ovoid faecal pellets as shown in Figs. 2, 3, and 4.

The lower part of the organic matter, the humifon (H horizon), is a more advanced stage of decomposition with very small amounts of recognisable plant fragments. The whole appears as an amorphous mass in the hand when dry and is plastic when wet. In thin section, the amorphous material is seen to be composed of small irregular granules. There are also sclerotia of fungi which reach a high concentration in the lower part of the organic matter, or in the top part of the adjoining mineral horizon.

Next comes the first mineral horizon, the modon (A1 horizon). It is medium to dark grey, and when wet is massive, but friable; upon drying, it is single grain, but may have a few very weak crumbs. On careful examination, the colour has two components: there are dark areas of black organic material in the interstices between bleached quartz and feldspar grains which sometimes glisten. With depth, there is a change to the paler-coloured bleached horizon, the zolon (E horizon).

This horizon is similar to the modon in many ways, but is much paler in colour as a consequence of having less organic matter.

In many soils of the pinewoods, both native and planted, the modon is very dark in colour. This colour seems to be due to the presence of carbon resulting from forest fires. In some cases, easily recognizable lumps of charcoal can be identified in the horizon.

In thin section, the zolon (Fig. 5) has a distinctive alveolar structure characterised by a continuous soil mass with frequent irregular discrete pores. This structure is in strong contrast to the loose and apparently single-grain structure that is seen in the field. In some zolons, clay coatings line the bottom of the pores, while, elsewhere, there may be thin coatings of silt.

The zolon usually changes sharply into a dark brown sesquon (Bs horizon) or very dark brown husesquon (Bh horizon). Sesquons are common on sloping and undulating sites, while husesquons tend to occur on the flatter fluvio-glacial terraces.

The clay fractions in both sesquons and husesquons contain more iron, aluminium and organic matter than the horizons above or below, husesquons being differentiated by their darker colour and higher content of organic matter. In the field, these horizons are generally friable, with a weak crumb structure and, in thin section (Fig. 6), they have a granular structure which is sometimes extremely well-developed, particularly in the sesquons. In husesquons, the granules tend to form irregularly-shaped clusters. All of the sand grains and rock fragments have a distinct coating of brown isotropic material. In some places, there are fragments of roots which seem to have died *in situ.* In soils that have a husesquon, the horizon is usually followed by a sesquon, otherwise the sesquon forms the principal middle horizon and either grades gradually into the underlying relatively unaltered material or there may be sharp and dramatic change into a very hard ison or indurated layer.

The change to an ison occurs on slopes where it is usually much paler in colour than the overlying sesquon, and, in addition to being hard, it has all the classical features for such a horizon as already described by FitzPatrick (1971), the main properties being its high bulk density, vesicular structure and prominent silt capping on the upper surfaces of the stones and boulders. In thin section, the minerals are seen to be closely packed, while the silt cappings on the upper surfaces of the stones are conspicuous (Figs. 7 & 8). Sometimes, coatings of silt line the bottoms of pores.

Analytical data

The particle size distribution of the < 2 mm fraction is dominated by sand, there being relatively little fine material. The clay fraction seldom exceeds 10 per cent in the modon or zolon, but increases to about 15 per cent in the sesquon or husesquon. This increase is due mainly to the translocation of aluminium and iron hydroxides rather than to the translocation of discrete clay particles.

The organic matter has two maxima, the greater of >70 per cent occurs at the surface and the lesser in the sesquon or husesquon. When there is a husesquon, the second maximum can be over 15 per cent. The C/N ratios have a similar trend, with a maximum of 25–30 in the fermenton; below, in the zolon, the value normally decreases to 10–15 and then increases to 15–25 in the husesquon.

The cation exchange capacity also has two maxima coincident with the distribution of organic matter, which, because of the small amount of clay, is largely responsible. The percentage of exchangeable base cations is low throughout the soil, but the total amount in the surface organic layers is fairly large because they are being released as the plant tissues are decomposed.

The surface organic horizons are acid, with pH values of 3.5 to 4.5 followed by a steady increase with depth up to a maximum of about 5.5 in the underlying ison or fluvioglacial material. These low figures are due to the high degree of leaching, the acid parent material and acid litter.

The relative distribution of silica (SiO_2), alumina (Al_2O_3) and iron oxide (Fe_2O_3) in the $<2\,\mu m$ fraction is the important distinguishing property of podzols. Free Fe_2O_3 shows a maximum of the sesquon or husesquon, and a minimum in the modon or zolon but perhaps the $SiO_2/Al_2O_3 + Fe_2O_2$ ratio of the clay fraction is most characteristic. This ratio shows a marked increase in both iron and, particularly, aluminium in the sesquon and husesquon.

Genesis

The organic layers are undergoing progressive decomposition by organisms, including bacteria, fungi and small arthropods, the evidence being clearly seen in thin section (Figs. 2, 3 & 4). Some of the decomposition products are acids and these dissolve in the percolating rainwater which is charged with CO_2, so that the solution entering the mineral soil is acid and causes profound hydrolysis of the primary silicates and release of various cations.

Most of the base cations released by hydrolysis are washed through the soil, but some are taken up by the plant roots. Some of the iron and aluminium, and most of the silicon released, is also lost in the drainage water, but the greater part of the iron and aluminium is deposited as oxides accompanied by humus to form the sesquon or husesquon, with their characteristic granular structure. There is disagreement about the mode of formation of the granular structure in the sesquon or husesquon. They may be floccular aggregates formed by precipitation, but De Coninck and Laruelle (1961) suggest that they are faecal pellets of organisms.

Variability

The principal variability is in the thickness of the various horizons. The organic horizons vary from 3–30 cm, but are generally about 6–7 cm, with the thicker layers occurring when rainfall is over 800 mm per annum.

The zolon is sometime absent, but is often 4–5 cm thick, and can be up to 1 m, as on the quartzite scree near Loch Maree. The sesquon or husesquon is usually 20–30 cm, but sometimes thicker. When the zolon is absent, the soil is usually an intergrade to an altosol, though such soils are seldom found under native pine.

In some situations, a placon (thin iron pan) is just forming or may be formed within the sesquon or beneath the husesquon, but the pan is thin and brittle and not usually as hard as under heath. These sites occur in open forest or on the higher borders with heath.

Fertility

The fertility of these soils for Scots pine is variable. When the soils are formed on glaciofluvial deposits that contain a small amount of basic material, it would seem that they can continue to support a forest, but there are many areas as in the Spey Valley and the south shores of Loch Maree where the present crop appears to be sustained by the cycling of nutrients, with little release from the highly quartzose material. It is doubtful if, in these situations, a further crop of any quality can be produced, but it might be argued that these soils were always nutrient-deficient and yet have carried pine continuously for a long time, and that there is some justification for thinking that they will carry another crop, providing regeneration can take place. In situations such as these, crop growth is possible only because nutrients are constantly being recycled. The nutrients are taken up by the plant roots, returned to the surface in the litter, which is decomposed to release the nutrients that are again taken up by the roots, hence the reason for finding the greatest number of feeding roots in the organic horizons. In some planted pine forests, fertilizer experiments have shown that nitrogen is the main limiting nutrient, yet there is usually a large amount of nitrogen in the organic matter but it is released only very slowly by microbial decomposition.

References

FITZPATRICK, E.A. (1971). *Pedology - A systematic approach to soil science.* Oliver and Boyd.

DECONINCK, F. & LARUELLE, J. (1964). Soil development in sand materials of the Belgian Campine. In: *Soil micromorphology*, edited by A. Jongerius, 169-188. Elsevier.

Fig. 1 Somewhat generalised data for the podsols of the native pinewoods

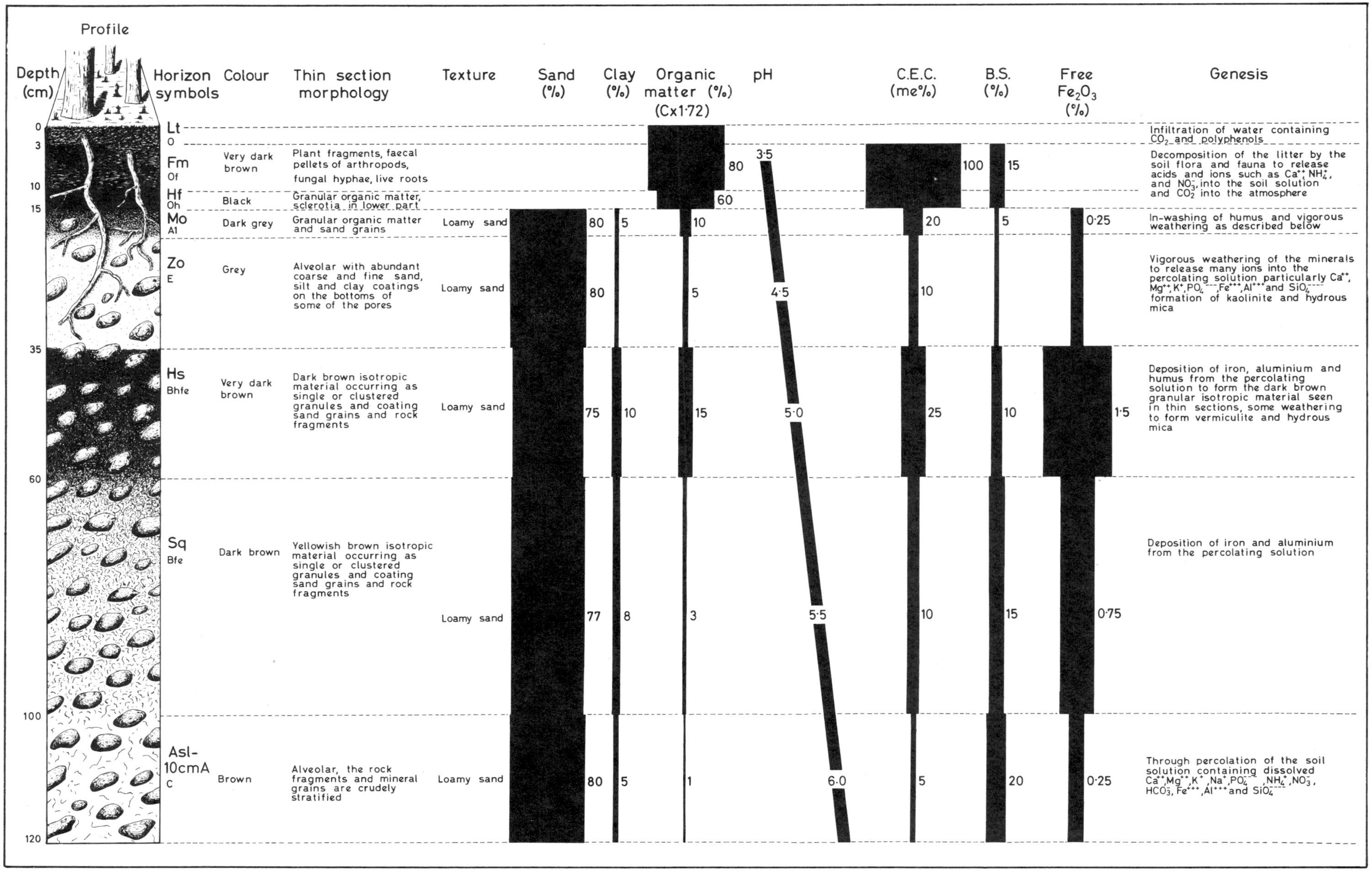

Fig. 2 Faecal pellets of an arthropod replacing the central part of a decomposing twig in the fermenton — F horizon

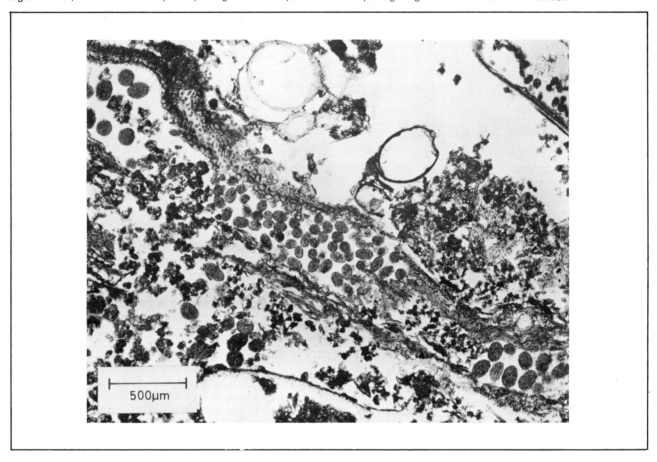

500μm

Fig. 3 Granular and amorphous partially decomposed organic matter and numerous live roots in the fermenton — F horizon

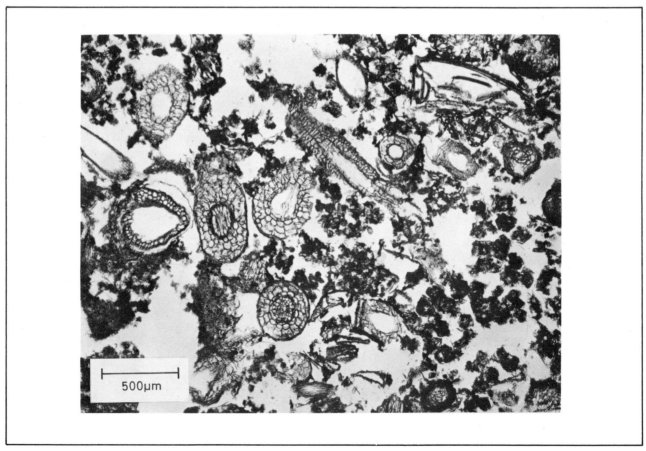

500μm

Fig. 4 Fungal hyphae decomposing the organic matter in the fermenton — F horizon

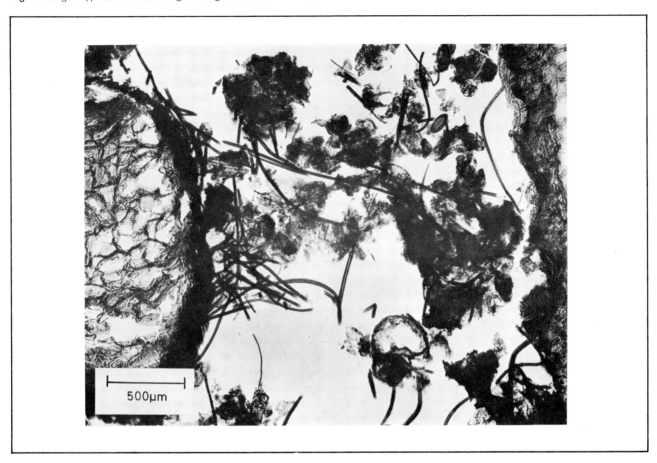

Fig. 5 The characteristic alveolar structure in the zolon — E horizon. There are also many fragments of charcoal with the occasional silt and clay coating on the bottoms of the pores

Fig.6 The distinctive small granular structure in the sesquon — Bs horizon

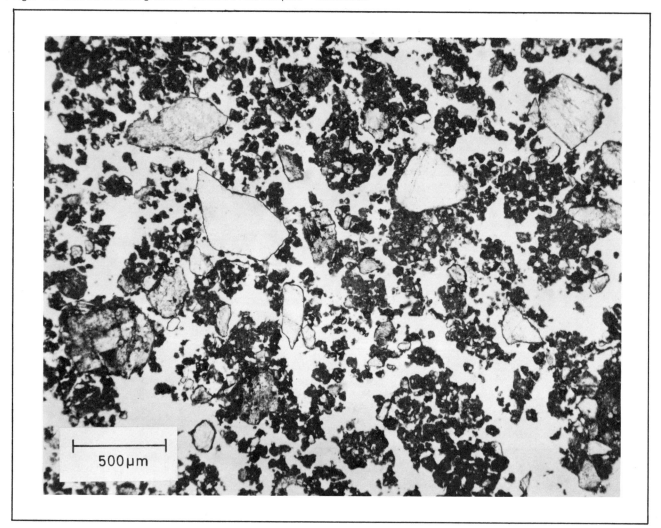

500μm

41

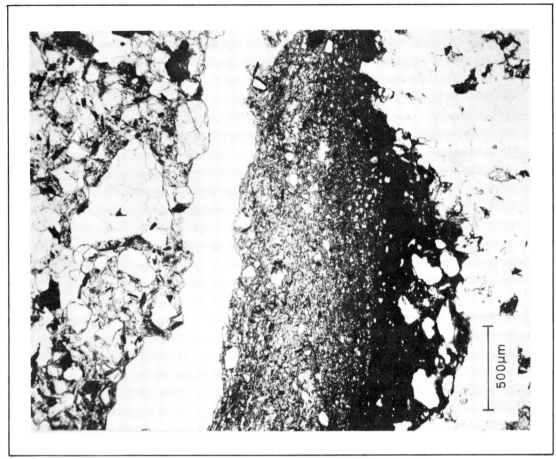

Fig. 8 Enlarged portion of Fig. 6.

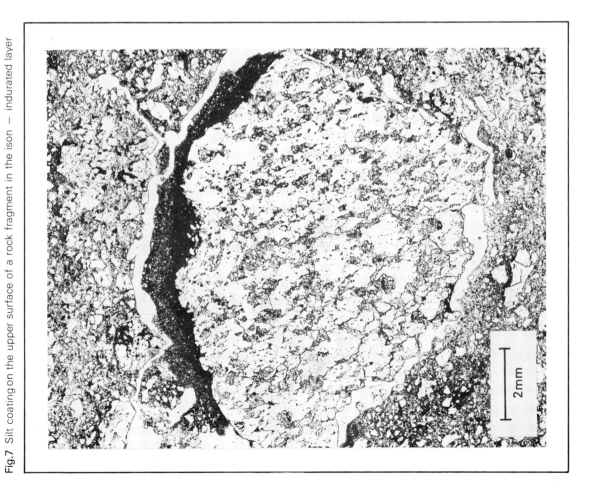

Fig.7 Silt coating on the upper surface of a rock fragment in the ison — indurated layer

Ecology of Pinewood beetles

F.A. Hunter Ministry of Agriculture, Fisheries and Food, Leeds

Introduction

In introducing his assessment of oak as a habitat for insect life, Morris (1974) contended that "All naturalists know that in Britain more species of insects are associated with oak than with any other tree, or indeed with any other plant". He also pointed out that this knowledge, acquired by naturalists through experience, had been corroborated by data brought together by Southwood (1961). Southwood compared the numbers of species of insect associated with various trees and whilst, for Britain, oak had 284 species dependent on it, pine came seventh in his list with only 91 species recorded as dependent. Southwood's data were compiled by adding together other authors' figures for various orders of insects, but his conclusions are as applicable to beetles in particular as to insects in general. Clearly, these figures justify the common belief that oak woodland, particularly ancient oak woodland containing over-mature trees — where the widest variety of insect species is to be found — deserves conservation in Britain. On the other hand, any judgement of the value of pinewoods based solely on such figures would be underestimated. Many of the species of beetles that feed on oak occur frequently on other species of broadleaved trees such as Sweet chestnut, beech, hazel, willow, elm, or birch, and it could be argued that, provided these alternative host trees were present in sufficient numbers, including enough ancient individuals, the removal of oaks from mixed woodland would impoverish the beetle fauna to only a limited extent. The beetles associated with the relict Caledonian pinewoods are, by contrast, more vulnerable because many of the species that feed on pine cannot transfer to broadleaved trees, and, of these, many have not even been recorded in Britain from other species of conifer. In any case, over-mature coniferous trees of other species are almost totally absent from the Scottish highland areas where relict Caledonian pinewoods occur, so that, for many beetle species, the removal of pines from such woodland would result in their local extinction.

It is probable that at least some pine trees are growing in every county of mainland England, Wales and Scotland and it is certain that wherever they occur some beetles will also be present in association. However, there are no areas of Wales where pinewoods have occurred sufficiently continuously for development of a comprehensive pinewood beetle fauna. In England, it is evident that pinewoods have occurred sufficiently continuously for a fairly rich beetle fauna to be present (whether by colonisation or as a relict) on the Hampshire/Surrey border and in east Norfolk, particularly the latter. However, within Britain, it is only in the relict Caledonian pinewoods that a rich, stable and well-established beetle fauna associated with pine trees is to be found. Although this paper is concerned mainly with the beetle fauna of relict Caledonian pinewoods, sufficient reference to the occurrence of pine-feeding beetles in England and Wales has been included to set this fauna in context.

One of the objectives of this paper is to provide an assessment of the ecological importance of the pine within England, Wales and Scotland, as measured by the number of beetle species rarely found on other trees, and, in particular, to demonstrate, by the use of this criterion, that the relict Caledonian pinewoods are especially important and deserve a high priority for conservation.

The beetle habitats in a tree

Elton and Miller (1954) suggested, and Elton (1966) refined and amplified the idea, that woodland could be divided, for the purpose of ecological description, into seven "vertical layers". They visualised these layers as lying above each other to form a series of horizontal strata which they termed: sub-soil and rock, topsoil, ground zone, field layer, low canopy, high canopy, and the air above the vegetation. This sytem is simple and works well for vegetation and also for some animals, notably birds, as had already been shown by Colquhoun and Morley (1943). These authors proposed a system of "vertical zonation" divided into three communities: upper canopy, tree/shrub layer, and ground zone and showed a pattern of time division for the bird species between the zones that was different and characteristic for each species, and explained this pattern by availability of food in different zones. Hartley (1953) showed that five species of titmice living in an English woodland each had a characteristic height distribution of foraging activities and, in addition, that each showed a preference for particular parts of trees. Paviour-Smith (1964) has demonstrated that there is at least one beetle, *Tetratoma fungorum* F., which has a preferred height range on a tree, being found more commonly in birch-bracket fungi (its larval food) situated between 3 and 15 feet above the ground than in those at other heights. She concluded that predation has a limiting effect nearer the ground and that fungus fruiting-bodies could be made unsuitable for the beetle by the drying winds which occur above the shrub layer. However, this conclusion, although interesting in relation to this species, provides information about only one aspect of the beetle's ecology and this is an aspect that is far from universally relevant to beetles generally.

Whilst Elton and Miller's system provides a useful tool for the description or investigation of the ecology of the total woodland, its application to the study of individual animal species is often of limited value, for instance to most beetles it is the existence of suitable habitat that is important and not the height of the habitat above the ground. Indeed, the habitat for beetles may occur within a wide range of height with some exceptions, e.g. roots.

Some continental authors, especially Palm (1951, 1959) and Saalas (1917, 1923), have devised systems of recording the exact habitats of beetles. In recent years coleopterists working in Britain have published increasingly detailed and precise accounts, so that there has been a welcome evolutionary convergence in the publications of coleopterists on the one hand, and of ecologists on the other. Even so, only one general publication on beetles (Dibb, 1948) can be cited in which an attempt was made to combine the information required by coleopterists with an ecological approach, and precise information may still be assembled only by consulting the many papers published on individual taxa of beetles.

It is obviously desirable, though perhaps not always possible, to design ecological niches by which to classify our records of the occurrence of species in such a way that they are mutually exclusive. Many beetle larvae develop in habitats that are capable of precise description and a detailed account of the ecology of beetles in woodland should use a zonation system that is as sophisticated as is necessary. Morris (1974) separated the oak tree into eleven "habitat components", each of which he regarded as supporting a different and characteristic community of insects. He also pointed out that an insect may feed on oak leaves, pupate in the soil and overwinter as an adult among soil litter so that its total habitat (biotope) comprised foliage plus soil plus litter. According to Paviour-Smith (1960), Elton "informally suggested" the concept of a "headquarters" indicating the "main centre or centres of biological activity of the species".

In a system of classification of the habitat components of a tree which is, in effect, an extension of that used by Morris, 24 distinct components have been distinguished, as in Fig. 1, some of which are divided into sub-components. For instance, beetles living in the trunk, stump, roots, branches or twigs of a tree (whether standing or fallen) may feed in the cambial tissue (A), in the sapwood (B), or in the heartwood (C). The communities of beetles occurring in nests in trees to some extent differ according to whether the nest belongs to a mammal (A), an insect (B), or a bird (C). Woodroffe (1953) recognised that different communities occur in birds' nests that are dry (usually in buildings, but sometimes in trees) and those that are exposed to rain. Distinct beetle communities, with some species in common, are found in subterranean fungi, fungi growing on the ground, and fungi growing directly on the wood of stumps or trunks and these are regarded as distinct habitat components rather than as sub-components. Beetles feeding in timber are divided into categories according to the stage of decomposition of the wood by the suffixes (I, F, M, O and VO) and the suffix P is used to denote that a species is predatory.

In Tables 1—4, this system of classification of habitat components and sub-components, with qualifying suffixes where appropriate, is used to signify the "headquarters" of each species — in most cases the habitat in which the larva feeds. The symbols used in the tables to denote the habitat components, sub-components and suffixes are explained in the legend to Fig. 1.

Published ecological information is incomplete for some species, and shortcomings are signified by question-marks in Tables 1—4.

The beetles found mainly or exclusively in association with pine trees (*Pinus* spp.) in England/Wales, or Scotland.

Many species of beetles, e.g. *Rhagium bifasciatum F.* and *Melanotus rufipes* (Herbst), are associated indiscriminately with a wide variety of tree species; this paper is confined to those species which are, in England, Wales or Scotland, more frequently in association with pine than with any other tree. Four groups of species have, however, been added.

Dendrophagus crenatus (Payk.) and *Harminius undulatus* (Deg.) are included because they are characteristic species of relict Caledonian forest areas and do, perhaps, occur rather more often in pine than in alternative host trees such as birch and alder. Some beetle species found mainly in relict forest areas are clearly associated with pine in Scotland but with other tree species, often oak, in England or Wales, and are indicated in Tables 1-4 by asterisks in column 2. There is disagreement on species of gymnospermophagous Scolytids in Britain as to both the range and preferences of host plants, possibly reflecting different host preferences in different geographical areas. For this family, species recorded from pine and other coniferous trees have been included. The two species associated with converted coniferous timber have also been included although they occur in a wide variety of softwood timbers.

Anisotoma castanea (Herbst), *Agathidium rotundatum* Gyll. and *Quedius laevigatus* (Gyll.) have been omitted as they have been found frequently in association with trees other than pine and, in some cases, not in areas of relict Caledonian pinewood. *Phloeonomus pusillus* (Grav.) has also been omitted.

Although all the records from the relict Scottish pinewoods refer to collections made from *Pinus sylvestris* L., beetles collected from other areas have been found on Corsican pine (*Pinus nigra* Arnold), Lodgepole pine (*Pinus contorta* Loudon) or other species, although the species of pine on which they were found has almost never been recorded. It would be difficult to assemble separate British lists of beetles for species of *Pinus* and it is doubtful if such lists would differ. There are relatively few beetle species that are confined to pine throughout their geographical range; where they occur in the coniferous forests of Europe or North America many of the species discussed here are associated with a wide range of coniferous trees.

There are relatively few British lists of the beetles associated with pine, that of Sharp (1871) being an early and notable exception. Walsh (1954) listed a number of species from pine, but some of these are now known to occur equally often on other trees. Munro (1916) did not make the wider survey that the title of his paper implies, but concentrated on the forestry pests in the families Curculionidae (weevils) and Scolytidae (bark beetles). Conversely, the detailed and informative papers of Hanson (1937, 1940), although nominally about the ecology and control of forest pest beetles in the U.K., especially *Myelophilus* spp., do include notes on the other species, especially predators. Many of the older collectors used the terms fir (sometimes even Scotch fir!) and pine indiscriminately, and some interpretation of the meaning of such records has therefore been necessary, but few species have been included in Tables 1-4 on a single authority and these are all modern records, where the identity of the host tree is not in doubt.

Records from England or Wales are placed together in column 1 of Tables 1-4, records from Scotland being recorded in Column 2.

Tables 1-4 comprise a total of 129 species of beetles believed to occur in England/Wales and/or Scotland mainly, or exclusively, in association with pines. Of these, 95 have been recorded from England and/or Wales (of which three occurred only adventively) and 106 have been recorded from Scotland (of which one occurred only adventively). The Scottish records are distinguished in Tables 1-4 as those for species whose geographical ranges lie — or once did — mainly within the relict Caledonian forests (R) and those occurring more generally (r). There are 44 species restricted mainly to Scottish relict pinewoods and, of these, only 18 have found their way to England and/or Wales, and two of these have occurred only adventively south of the Scottish border.

It is of interest to note that at least five of the specialist Caledonian relict species occur in east Norfolk, which is, in addition, the main centre in the U.K. for *Leptura rubra* (L.). It is possible that this group of species represents a relict pine fauna that has survived in an area where there may have been sufficient continuity and abundance of pine, although there are now no relict pinewoods in Norfolk.

In Tables 1-4, the beetles are listed according to the sequence of families given by Crowson (1956), the sequence of genera and species and the names of species following Kloet and Hincks (1945), with a few minor exceptions resulting from more recent taxonomic studies.

Beetle communities characteristic of the habitat components on and near pine trees

Some of the habitat components or sub-components found on or near trees, such as carrion, dung, field layer vegetation, galls, rot-holes containing water, lichen, moss or other epiphytes, and fungi growing from the ground, are not known to support beetles specific to pinewoods. Although cobwebs containing dead insects are often found under pine bark, the most characteristic beetle of this habitat, *Ctesias serra* (F.), is usually found on oak, having been recorded from Dalkeith and Hamilton by Crowson (1962).

Soil (1), litter (2) and subterranean fungi (23)

The larvae of species of *Leiodes* feed in underground fungi (some, e.g. L. *cinnamomea* Panz., in fungi asso-

ciated with broadleaf woodland), and it is presumed that the six *Leiodes* species listed, together with *T. maerkelii,* feed in fungi found only in forests of coniferous trees, especially pine. Obviously adults — which are usually captured by sweeping field-layer vegetation under pine trees — also occur in the soil and litter, at least as transients. *A. quadripunctatum* is said to be associated especially with burnt pine needles in the litter. The larva of *C. nigricornis* was found by its sole captor in Britain (Skidmore, 1973) inside the wood of branches within the litter, especially where these were covered by moss or heather. Larvae of the Cerambycid *J. sexmaculata* move through the soil from root to root and often pupate in dry sandy soil; they too therefore occur as transients in this habitat component.

Wood mould (7)

The larva of *O. ferrugineum* feeds in the heartwood and sapwood of pines that have been extensively rotted by the fungus *Phaeolus schweinitzii* (Fr.) Pat., although the adults are also to be found under bark.

Larvae of *Elater nigrinus* (and presumably those of *E. tristis)* also occur in the wood-mould of old trees, especially fallen logs, as well as in the wood of very old logs and trunks. The same is true of *D. aurora* and larvae and adults of this species have sometimes been found in piles of old sawdust at sawmills within the forest.

Insects' nests (8b)

According to Johnson (1967), two specimens of *A. sahlbergi* were collected from wasps' nests in Scotland, but we may anticipate that mould feeders like *Atomaria* would occur in a variety of situations where their food was available.

Fungi (including myxomycetes) growing directly on trees (9)

A. glabra is usually found in association with myxomycetes growing on stumps. *C. dubia* and *E. rugosus* probably have the same association. (The other Lathridiidae listed in Table 3 cannot yet be ascribed to any particular habitat component.) Paviour-Smith (1971) has drawn attention to the fact that myxomycetes do not develop until at least ten years after the death of the wood on which they grow — an important point for the conservationist. The existence in a woodland locality of a number of beetle species dependent on myxomycetes is one indication that woodland is likely to have been continuous in the locality for a long period. Other "indicator species" of this kind are those found in habitat components 7, 9, 10, 11, 12 or 13 O/VO. The larger the number of indicator species found in a woodland locality, the greater the likelihood that woodland has been continuous in the area. Since all other *Mycetophagus* species whose larval habitats are known feed in macrofungus fruiting bodies, it is assumed that *M. fulvicollis* does likewise.

Most records of **B. pulchra** describe its habitat as "fleshy fungi" although, being a Staphylinid, it is presumed to be predatory.

C. punctulatus, A. triguttata and **Z ferruginea** are all associated with fruiting bodies of the fungus *Hirschioporus abietinus* (Dicks. ex Fr.) Donk., although the latter beetle is also often found in the bark or wood under the fruiting bodies of the fungus.

Stumps, trunks (logs), branches and twigs (11, 10, 12, 13)

By far the largest proportion of the beetles associated with pine is found in this group of habitat components, the total number of species being 83 (64 per cent of the total species recorded). Several factors, acting together, have an effect in determining the distribution in time and in space of each of these species.

(a) Moisture content and temperature

Graham (1925), working in the USA, who used standard logs of five species, including three species of pine, to observe the effect of moisture and temperature on the sites chosen by various beetles for oviposition and development, suggested that *Asemum* required high humidity, and that *Asemum, Pissodes, Hylurgops, Rhagium* and *Pytho* were restricted to the cooler portion of the logs. The only heat-resistant genus he recorded was the Buprestid *Chrysobothris* (a genus unrepresented in Britain). Savely (1939), also working in the USA, came to similar conclusions, but found, in addition, that *Callidium antennatum* could survive in warm dry areas with the Buprestids.

Although the species discussed by these authors are from genera represented by different species in Britain from those occurring in the USA, the results throw some light on the selection of certain habitat components rather than others. It is possible to distinguish a community largely restricted to stumps and roots (sometimes also found on the underside of logs lying on the ground), whose presence in these situations is probably largely governed by a need for high relative humidity or to avoid high temperatures. These communities include: *X. laevigata, A. striatum, A. ferus, A. rusticus, L. sanguinolenta, J. sexmaculata, P. pini, P. notatus, H. abietis* and the six listed species of *Hylastes*. On the other hand, only two British species, *M. acuminata* and *C. violaceum*, are restricted to high temperature habitats.

(b) Size of trunk, branch or twig

The diameter of the trunk, branch, or twig used as headquarters by a species is often characteristic of that species, as Tables 1-4 show, possibly because of interspecific competition.

(c) Nutritional requirements

Graham (1925) argued that, since the proteins in timber are concentrated in the cambial region, whereas carbohydrates are abundant in the xylem, these two regions are of different nutritional status. He pointed out that cambial feeders are of two types, those like the Scolytidae (excluding Ambrosia beetles) that spend their whole life, and those like some Cerambycidae that spend only part of their life in the cambial region, later moving into the xylem. The acquisition of protein is a limiting factor for timber-feeding beetles and they overcome it by: 1. restricting their feeding to the cambial tissue, as do most of the xylophagous Curculionidae and Scolytidae discussed in this paper, 2. like the Ambrosia beetles (of which *T. lineatum* is the only one especially associated with pine in this country), by boring into the sapwood and heartwood of the freshly dead tree and feeding on fungi which grow on the walls of their burrows, 3. feeding on cambial tissue while this lasts, later penetrating the sapwood or heartwood, by which time the presence of fungus may have concentrated the available protein into restricted areas (e.g. many Cerambycidae especially Lepturinae), 4. feeding in timber already affected by fungus and obtaining protein by eating large quantities of fungus-infected wood, 5. becoming, like many Elaterid larvae, at least partly predatory.

Leaves (i.e. pine needles) (14)

Morris (1974) — admittedly discussing insects in general rather than beetles only — considered foliage to be the most important source of food which the oak tree provides. However, no leaf-beetles (Chrysomelidae) are associated with pine in England, Wales or Scotland and the only weevil which feeds solely on pine needles is *B. pineti*. (Bakke 1958) gives an account of the effects caused when this species occurred in Norway at an unusually high population density. The only other beetles regularly associated with pine needles are the nine species of ladybirds (Coccinellidae) listed, all of which are predators either on the **Adelges** or on the Aphids that feed on pine.

Cones (15)

P. validirostris larvae do not always develop in pine cones, but the Forestry Commission's leaflet *"Pissodes weevils"* (Anon, 1952a) and Bevan (1971) demonstrate that they may occur in cones.

Buds and flower buds (17 and 18)

E. pini has been bred from pine buds (Johnson (1965)) but the species is rare and it cannot be claimed with confidence that this habitat is typical. The larva of **A. varians** develops in the buds of the male inflorescence of pine (Dieckmann (1968)) and it is likely that larvae of **C. attelaboides** behave similarly.

Sap runs (21)

Larvae and adults of species which occur under fresh sappy bark are often found at sap runs, and these include **E. pusilla** and **E. thoracica**.

Converted timber (24)

H. bajulus (the House longhorn beetle) has been reported from outdoor timber only rarely in this country (Allen, 1955) and **A. tristis** (the Two-toothed longhorn beetle) never. Both species are recorded from a wide variety of coniferous timbers.

The succession of beetle communities in the life of a pine

B. pineti is recorded particularly from young pine trees by Joy (1932), Fowler (1887-91) and Sharp (1871-1880). Young trees are also favoured by adult *H. abietis* for feeding (Anon., 1952b), although this species does not lay eggs in living trees. As the young tree grows, *C. attelaboides* and *A. varians* may arrive to feed on the male flowers, *P. validirostris* to feed in the cones, and the species that are predators of Hemiptera feeding on the needles may also arrive. However, it is only as the tree matures — or is damaged — that the species feeding in dead wood or in fungi associated with dead wood can colonise. If the beetles associated with subterranean fungi are excluded, 96 species (about 74 per cent of all those recorded here) require dead or damaged wood before they can establish themselves in pine.

In the natural pinewood, mature trees die mainly as the result of fungal attack, because of wind-throw or wind-break, when they are washed down by rivers in spate, or when struck by lightning or killed by fire. Branches or larger parts of otherwise living trees may also die or be broken off by wind or weight of snow. Forestry operations increase the amount of dead, sound wood available for exploitation by beetles, sometimes enormously. However, they break the succession of beetles occuring during the life of the tree, adversely affecting species which require over-mature trees. It is now well established that there is a definite succession of beetle communities which exploit dead sound wood. Blackman and Stage (1924) have described the parallel succession of insects living in the bark and wood of dying, dead and decaying hickory (in USA) and various other north American authors including Howden and Vogt (1951), Savely (1939), Morley (1939), and Graham (1925), have discussed the beetle succession in pine. Krogerus (1927) investigated the succession of insects in dead spruce stumps in Finland. Richard (1926) and Wallace (1953) have studied the succession of insects feeding in dead pine stumps in England and the latter author distinguished three age/decay phases of stump. (His category 1 is equivalent to the tabulated habitat sub-components 11 ABC, with suffixes I or F, his category 2 is equivalent to M and his category 3 to 0 and V0 together.) The suffixes given in tables 1—4 for the xylophagous species enable the reader to infer the succession occurring in dead pine in the UK.

The incidence of a similar beetle succession in fire-killed pine to that found in pine killed in other ways has been demonstrated by Gardiner (1957) and by Richmond and Lejeune (1945) — all North American authors. Several species of beetles associated with pine are found mainly on burnt parts of trees. The occurrence of *A. quadripunctatum* in litter consisting of burnt pine needles has already been mentioned, but in addition, *S. ater, S. reyi* and notably *M. acuminata* are all known to be especially associated with burnt trees. These species are distinguished in tables 1—4 by the symbol Ø. Many other species of beetles that feed on pine are attracted, presumably by an olfactory stimulus, to burnt wood, often before the fire is out, and accounts of observations such as those of Tragardh (1929) of assembling by such beetles are frequent in the literature. Gardiner (personal communication) has even made use of this phenomenon in order to attract Cerambycid beetles into his collecting area. It may be that one should distinguish between beetles that are attracted to burnt wood but oviposit both in burnt and unburnt wood and beetles that seem almost always to be found on or in burnt wood. The association is apparently particularly strong with *M. acuminata* and one is tempted to speculate that only fire-killed pine meets the physical or nutritional requirements, or both, of this species. Certainly this species, like many other Buprestidae, favours dry wood and it seems possible that the fire kills the cambial tissue quickly, thus fixing food reserves that could otherwise be used up during the dying process by the tree — a process similar to the fixing of starch in hardwood timber by kiln-sterilization which, although designed to kill any *Lyctus brunneus* Steph. present in the treated timber, ensures that treated wood remains permanently infestable by the species, which feeds only on the starch in the timber (Anon, 1958).

Although Paviour-Smith (1961) has described the insect succession in the birch-bracket fungus (*Piptoporus betulinus* (Bull. ex. Fr.) Karst., the author has seen no reference to beetle succession in any fruiting body growing on pine. Such studies on *Phaeolus schweinitzii* (Fr.) Pat. could be especially interesting.

The geographical distribution of beetles within the relict pinewood areas

Observations and many published records clearly demonstrate that, although some species have extended their ranges into pine plantations, either near to or, in some cases, at a distance from native pinewoods, many of the species of beetles associated with pine apparently have ranges in Scotland which are almost co-extensive with that of the relict pinewoods. However, there are some evident exceptions and, as climate is likely to be the most significant factor in determining the ability of a beetle species to breed in any particular area within the relict pinewoods, an attempt has been made to test the extent to which the geographical distribution of individual species within relict pinewoods can be correlated with climate. If accurate climatological data of the right type were available for the various pinewoods, together with extensive lists of the Coleopterous fauna of each, reliable conclusions would be possible. The comments that follow are based on insufficient appropriate climatological data and inadequate faunal lists and must therefore be regarded as providing little more than an indication. It must also be borne in mind that some of the relict pinewoods, e.g. Rothiemurchus, are so extensive or vary topographically to such an extent that they can provide in themselves a wide variety of climatic conditions.

Anderson and Fairbairn (1955) have examined certain climatological features of most of the Scottish relict pinewoods and have used their data to classify the areas in which these woods occur from the point of view of their usefulness to the silviculturalist. Since their classification is based principally on measurements of rainfall and estimates of the length of the growing season for trees, their results do not, on their own, provide all the climatological information desirable in order to classify the pinewoods from the point of view of beetles. It is known that some beetles require a more continental climate than do others, and it would pehaps be more useful to employ an index of oceanicity as advocated for Scottish mountain vegetation by Poore and McVean (1957). These authors characterised continental climates by their high summer maximum temperatures (these obviously favour beetle flight), low winter minimum temperatures, deeper and more persistent snow cover and by rapid climatic transitions in spring and autumn. They characterised oceanic climates as having higher precipitation, more sustained high humidity, a higher ratio of precipitation to evaporation, lower insolation and prevalence of high winds. Some of these factors can obviously affect beetles directly as well as indirectly through their effects on the rate of decay of dead trees, and the growth of fungi on trees. Poore and McVean obtained figures for various stations in Scotland by the application of a modification of Kotilainen's law of oceanity using the formula:

$$K_{00} = \frac{N_{00} \, dt}{100\triangle}$$

where K_{00} is the modified index, N_{00} is the number of days in the year with measurable precipitation, dt is the number of vernal and autumnal days in the year (days with mean temperature between 0-10°C) and $\triangle$ is the difference between the mean temperatures of the warmest and coldest months. (N in Kotilainen's original law was simply the yearly precipitation in millimetres.)

The lowest index of oceanicity they obtained from Scotland was 118 for Nairn; figures for the upper Dee valley were 199 and 183, for Fort William 330 and for Achnashellach 452, this latter figure being higher than any recorded index obtained from Norway. There may be no detailed data for the relict pinewood areas that would allow this sophisticated index of oceanicity to be calculated. The extremely detailed map produced by Birse (1971) could, perhaps, be used to divide the relict pinewoods into groups according to their oceanicity, and thermal and moisture characteristics, but several of the relict pinewoods occupy more than one of his categories, and any grouping by this method would be more complex than the faunal lists presently available would justify. A crude index of oceanicity — all that is really needed for the present purpose — may be calculated by dividing the yearly precipitation in millimetres by the difference between the mean temperatures for January and July (thus ignoring the contribution of the number of vernal and autumnal days). Table 5 shows how this calculation, taken together with figures for the mean daily duration of bright sunshine in June (the sunniest month in northern Scotland) and mean annual rainfall, results in a division of 27 of the Scottish relict pinewoods into four climatic groups ranging from the most continental to the most oceanic.

Of the species that, in Scotland, are largely restricted to relict pinewoods, the following occur in a sufficiently wide range of these localities to demonstrate that they can adapt to both oceanic and continental climates.

A. glabra, N. lentus, D. crenatus, P. depressus, X. laevigata, Z. ferruginea, R. inquisitor, P. fasciculatus, A. aedilis, E. ater, A. varians, B. pineti, P. notatus, M. phlegmatica, P. lichtensteini.

O. ferrugineum has been recorded only from Mar and Guisachan and must be provisionally regarded as requiring a relatively continental climate. The species recorded only from pinewoods with more continental climates include *D. aurora, A. rusticus, L. sanguinolenta, J. sexmaculata, M. minor* and *C. nigricornis*, although the latter species is known from Glentanar alone. The only pine-feeding species occurring in pinewoods with more oceanic climates is *H. undulatus* but there are other species recorded mainly from the more oceanic pinewood areas (e.g. *Schizotus pectinicornis* (L.), *Bolitophagus reticulatus* (L.) and *Rhizophagus parvulus* Payk. — the latter recorded only from Glen Affric) and these are all associated with birch rather than pine. (*B. reticulatus* larvae feed in the sporophores of *Fomes fomentarius* (L. ex Fr.) Kickx. which usually grows on birch.)

Obviously, these comments throw limited light on the effect of climate on the geographical distribution of beetles within relict pinewood areas, although they certainly suggest that at least some species have ranges weighted towards the extremes of the available climatic range. It would be particularly useful if collecting could be encouraged in areas representing the extremes of the climatic variation available. There are no published records of beetles from Amat (although all the other more continental pinewoods have been investigated, some of them very thoroughly) or from Coulin, Achnashellach, Ardgour or Barisdale; these latter all have climates at the extreme oceanic end of the range.

Dispersal and colonisation of relict pinewood beetle species

Before attempting the conservation of the beetle fauna of the relict Scottish pinewoods, it is important to determine for each species, apart from its habitat requirements, the following information: 1. the extent to which it is successful in finding and exploiting suitable food within its previous breeding area; 2, the extent to which it can colonise plantations of Scots pine; 3, the extent to which it may be able to transfer to host-trees other than pine; and, of course, 4. its numerical rarity. The first of these questions is often very difficult to answer and is related to the climate of the woodland as well as to the intrinsic capabilities of the insect. The limitations imposed by the Scottish climate on the opportunities for flight of beetles have been discussed by Crowson (1962), but there is no doubt that there is much variation between species, some flying, at least within the shade provided by the woodland canopy, much more readily than others which very rarely do so. All naturalists know the frustrating experience of failing to find species in an apparently suitable habitat; under such circumstances one obviously has no method of knowing whether the habitat is lacking in some subtle, overlooked detail or whether the explanation is simply that the species has failed to discover a completely adequate habitat.

The ability of relict pinewood species to colonise plantations has not yet received sufficient attention, but some coleopterists, including the author, have collected in the Forestry Commission plantations at Culbin. The main tree planting began there in 1921, on what had previously been agricultural land inundated in the late seventeenth century by shifting sand, although some earlier planting had been done, so that, although there are still no over-mature trees present, a fairly wide range of habitats would have been available for beetles by, say, 1950. Published records by Woodroffe (1951) and Angus (1964) and personal observations by the author have shown that the following species, at least, have already colonized the Culbin plantations: *T. rufipes, A. obliterata, N. oblongoguttata, A. ocellata, E. quadripustulatus, E. nigrinus, E. mollis, P. fasciculatus, C. attelaboides, P. pini, P. notatus, M. phlegmatica, M. piniperda, T. formicarius, A. striatum, R. inquisitor* (6 of these are species especially associated with relict pinewoods). In view of what has already been said about the succession of species to be found on pine, the constitution of this obviously fragmentary list is hardly surprising; however, it would be most interesting to monitor the results of further collecting in the area through the coming decades and in particular to know how long it will be before the macrofungus-fruiting-bodies-feeding species like *A. triguttata, C. punctulatus, Z. ferruginea* or the microfungus-feeding species like *D. crenatus* (Crowson and Ellis, 1968), or even feeders in old rotting wood like *E. tristis* and *D. aurora* colonize the area from the relict pinewoods.

According to Godwin (1956), Norway spruce (*Picea abies* Karsten) was native to Britain before the last glacial phase, but extinct by the post-glacial period. Fir (*Abies* spp.) was also native at the same time, but was evidently less common than spruce. If one accepts Southwood's (1961) generalisation that the commoner a tree species has been and the longer it has been present in an area the more species of insects will be able to feed on it, then spruce is the obvious species to use if we are seeking to find records of alternative host-trees for pine beetles. Saalas (1917, 1923) regards 77 of the species listed in the present paper as being associated with spruce in Finland and 17 of them as being especially closely associated with spruce. A casual search of published British literature (and of the author's collecting records) reveals that, excluding the Scolytidae, the following species, included in the list of pine beetles in this paper, have also been recorded from spruce in Britain: *E. tristis* (Ashe, 1952); (Joy, 1932) *D. crenatus* (Hunter, at Aboyne, unpublished), *A. obliterata* (Angus, 1964), *D. aurora* (Joy, 1932), *R. inquisitor* (Hunter, at Aviemore, unpublished), *B. nebulosus* (Crowson, 1971). No doubt many other species are capable of the same transition.

Duffey (1953a) has reviewed the principle of host-selection in polyphagous, xylophagous insects with special reference to the Cerambycidae and came to the conclusion that by far the most significant factor in host-selection was the condition of the host (i.e. thickness of bark, stage of decay, and moisture content). Other experience agrees with this view, but the condition of the host wood is at least partly dependent upon the species of tree. For instance, *Phymatodes testaceus* (L.) feeds under the bark of fairly dry timber (of broadleaved trees) so that, under natural conditions, trees such as birch which are rapidly affected by fungus after death are rarely in suitable condition for *P. testaceus.* However, when birch is kept dry, as in a timber yard, *P. testaceus* is perfectly capable of feeding successfully (Hunter, 1962b). In general, beetles feeding in the wood of living trees have few hosts; beetles feeding in freshly dead wood have rather more; and those feeding in well-decayed wood often appear almost indifferent to host species. This general rule may be complicated occasionally when a species reaches a particularly high population density in an area, when oviposition frequently takes place on unusual host plants. It has been shown by Craighead (1921, 1923), who also worked with Cerambycidae, that there is a considerable degree of preference on the part of ovipositing females for the host in which they themselves fed as larvae. Mortality of immature stages is enhanced if adults are allowed to lay eggs on only a new host. Craighead also came to the conclusion that continued breeding in any given host intensified the preference for that host. Duffey (1953a) showed that, when a variety of suitable hosts was present, oviposition occurred on whichever host was the more abundant. As there is a limited range of host trees present in the Caledonian forest, where only Scots pine, birch and, to a lesser extent, alder with some aspen, sallow and juniper are at all frequent, and only Scots pine and birch are numerically abundant over large areas, these host-selection principles could have led species into evolutionary blind alleys with some being particularly associated with birch, others with pine. This limitation could be one reason why some species associated with pine occur frequently in a much wider range of trees in Fennoscandia as the records of Palm (1951, 1959) and of Saalas (1917, 1923) show.

On the question of rarity, many of the species listed in tables 1-4 are considered to be rare or very rare, and obviously these could only be conserved by conservation of their habitats.

Conclusions and implications
1. Many species of beetles, a high proportion of them of considerable rarity, are largely confined, in Britain, to the relict pinewoods of Scotland.
2. A high proportion of these species depend on dead wood for their existence, and some of them are absolutely restricted to wood that has been dead for a long time, or to trees that have become so overmature that they are attacked by heartwood-rotting fungi. Normal forestry practice restricts the natural succession of habitats in woodland and therefore the succession of beetles that can live in the pinewood. If the species occurring at the end of the succession are to be conserved, then a sufficient number of large trees must be allowed to survive long past maturity until they decay naturally.
3. It is important to remember that birch, alder, aspen and other trees form part of the relict Caledonian forest. Some beetle species are associated with each of these trees and conservation of the relict pinewood areas means conservation of these other tree species as well as of pine. A small number of species usually associated with pine also develop in birch or alder.
4. At least some of the beetle species associated with relict pinewoods can spread to pine plantations, al-

though some of them may take a very long time to do so. Some can even colonize spruce plantations. The harm done to the beetle fauna by felling relict pinewoods and replacing them with plantations of pine or even spruce, although serious, is not as devastating as the replacement of relict oakwood by conifer plantations.

5. The species most at risk are those with the most specific or rarest-occurring headquarters, those with the poorest powers of dispersal or colonization, those which occur within the most circumscribed geographical areas, and those which are numerically rare. On these counts, *O. ferrugineum* and *C. nigricornis* are the most threatened species.
6. It is to be expected, on the other hand, that species which feed in timber at the stage when it is commercially valuable will continue to move about in trade, both within Britain — as *A. striatum, P. notatus* and other species have done in the past — and also internationally, until they occur wherever suitable habitats occur. Pest species tend to become cosmopolitan and some harmful species, especially *Ips* spp. have reached our shores in this way in the past (Ryle, 1951). It is possible that introduced species could pose an additional threat to our relict pinewoods.
7. It would be useful for research effort to be directed towards the compilation of faunal lists for the pinewoods representing the extremes of climatic variation available in Scotland, and for the development of the beetle fauna in a number of new pine plantations within the Caledonian forest area to be monitored.
8. Some of these points have been made before and conservation-minded estate managers would find useful the summary of the value of old trees as insect habitat given by Stubbs (1972).

Acknowledgements
The author is grateful for helpful suggestions made by Dr. C.S. Elton, C. Johnson, Dr. R.A. Crowson and Dr. M.G. Morris.

References
ALLEN, A.A. (1951a). New records of rare Ipinae (Col., Scolytidae) in Hants and Berks. *Entomologist's mon. Mag., 87,* 115.

ALLEN, A.A. (1951b). *Pityogenes trepanatus* Noerdl. (Col., Scolytidae) spreading in England. *Entomologist's mon. Mag., 87,* 115-116.

ALLEN, A.A. (1955). *Procraerus tibialis* Lac. (Col., Elateridae), *Hylotrupes bajulus* L. and *Obrium brunneum* F. (Cerambycidae) etc. in Hants. *Entomologist's mon. Mag., 91,* 140.

ALLEN, A.A. (1963a). *Nudobius lentus* Grav. (Col., Staphylinidae) in a second Surrey locality. *Entomologist's mon. Mag., 99,* 214.

ALLEN, A.A. (1963b). *Hypophloeus fraxini* Kug. (Col., Tenebrionidae) in Surrey. *Entomologist's mon. Mag., 99,* 167.

ALLEN, A.A. (1964). The status of *Aulonium ruficorne* Ol. (Col., Colydiidae) and *Platysoma oblongum* F. (Col., Histeridae) in Britain, with a few suggestions as to the treatment of imported species in faunal lists. *Entomologist's mon. Mag., 100,* 278.

ALLEN, A.A. (1965). *Cryphalus piceae* Ratz. (Col., Scolytidae); a correction, and notes on its separation from *C. abietis* Ratz.

Enntomologist's mon. Mag., 101, 47-48.

ALLEN, A.A. (1968). *Plegaderus vulneratus* Panz., a Histerid beetle new to Britain. *Entomologist's mon. Mag., 104,* 110-112.

ALLEN, A.A. (1970). A note on *Pissodes validirostris* Gyll. (Col., Curculionidae) and on the British range of *P. pini* L. *Entomologist's mon. Mag., 106,* 204.

ALLEN, A.A. (1972). A second British capture of *Leptura rufa* Brulle (Col., Cerambycidae); and remarks on *L. sanguinolenta* L. in Britain. *Entomologist's mon. Mag., 108,* 92.

ALLEN, A.A. (1973). *Nudobius lentus* Grav. (Col., Staphylinidae): a second British record from beech. *Entomologist's mon. Mag., 109,* 161.

ANDERSON, M.L. & FAIRBAIRN, W.A. (1955). Division of Scotland into climatic sub-regions as an aid to silviculture. *Bull. For. Dep. Univ. Edinb., No.1,*

ANGUS, R.B. (1964). Some northern Scottish coleoptera. *Entomologist's mon. Mag., 100,* 172-182.

ANON. (1946). The black pine beetle *(Hylastes ater)* and other closely allied beetles. *Leafl. For. Commn.,* No. **4,** H.M.S.O.

ANON. (1948). The spruce bark beetle. *Leafl. For. Commn., No.* **26.**

ANON. (1952a). *Pissodes* Weevils. *Leafl. For. Commn.,* No. **29.**

ANON.(1962b).The large pine weevil *(Hylobius abietis). Leafl. For. Commn.*, No. **1.**

ANON. (1952c). *Climatologicial atlas of the British Isles.* H.M.S.O.

ANON. (1958). The kiln sterilisation of *Lyctus*-infested timber. *Leafl. Forest Prod. Res. Lab.*, No. **13.**

ASHE, G.H. (1952). Coleoptera at Nethy Bridge, Inverness-shire. *Entomologist's mon. Mag., 88,* 165-168.

ATTY, D.B. (1964). *Nudobius lentus* Grav. (Col., Staphylinidae) in Gloucestershire. *Entomologist's mon. Mag., 100,* 93.

BAKKE, A. (1958). Mass attack of *Brachonyx pineti* Payd. (Col., Curculionidae) on pine forests in Norway. *Meddr. norske SkogsforsVes., 50,* 125-142.

BEVAN, D. (1971). Notes on *Pissodes validirostris* Gyll. and *P. pini* L. (Col., Curculionidae). *Entomologist's mon. Mag., 107,* 90.

BIRSE, E.L. (1971). *Assessment of climatic conditions in Scotland (3). The bioclimatic sub-regions.* Map and Explanatory Pamphlet. Macaulay Institute for Soil Research, Craigiebuckler, Aberdeen.

BLACKMAN, M.W. & STAGE, H.H. (1924). On the succession of insects living in the bark and wood of dying, dead and decaying hickory. *Tech. Publs. N.Y. St. Coll. For., 24,* (17), 1-269.

BUCK, F.D. (1954). *Handbooks for the identification of British insects, 5,* (9), *Coleoptera (Lagriidae to Meloidae).* R. Ent. Soc. London.

BUCK, F.D. (1957). *Abdera triguttata* (Gyll.) (Col., Melandryidae) in Suffolk *Entomologist's mon. Mag., 93,* 280.

CARLISLE, A. & BROWN, A.J.F. (1968). Biological flora of the British Isles. *Pinus sylvestris* L. *J. Ecol., 56,* 269-307.

COLQUHOUN, M.K. & MORLEY, AVERIL (1943). Vertical zonation in woodland bird communities. *J. Anim. Ecol., 12,* 75-81.

COOMBS, C.W. & WOODROFFE, G.E. (1955). A revision of the British species of *Cryptophagus* (Herbst.) (Col., Cryptophagidae). *Trans. R. ent. Soc., Lond., 106,* 237-282.

CRAIGHEAD, F.C. (1921). Hopkins host-selection principle as related to certain Carambycid beetles. *J. agric. Res., 22,* (4), 189-220.

CRAIGHEAD, F.C. (1923). The host-selection principle as advanced by Walsh. *Can. Ent., 55,* (4), 56-79.

CROOKE, M. & BEVAN, D. (1957). Note on the first British occurrence of *Ips cembrae* Heer (Col. Scolytidae). *Forestry, 30,* 21-28.

CROWSON, R.A. (1956). *Handbooks for the identification of British insects, 4* (1), *Coleoptera, introduction and keys to families.* R. Ent. Soc. London.

CROWSON, R.A. (1962). Observations on Coleoptera in Scottish oak woods. *Glasg. Nat., 18* (4), 177-195.

CROWSON, R.A. (1971). Some records of Curculionidae (Coleoptera) from southern Scotland. *Entomologist's mon. Mag., 107,* 47-52.

CROWSON, R.A. & ELLIS, L. (1968). Observations on *Dandrophagus crenatus* (Payk.) (Cucujidae) and some comparisons with Piestine Staphylinidae (Coleoptera). *Entomologist's mon. Mag., 104,* 161-169.

DE VIEDMA, M.G. (1972). A note on a character to separate *Pissodes notatus* F. and *P. validirostris* Gyll. (Col., Curculionidae). *Entomologist's mon. Mag., 108,* 79.

DIBB, J.R. (1948). *A field book of beetles.* Methuen.

DIEKMANN, L. (1968). Revision der Westpalaarktischen Anthonomyinae. *Beitr. Ent., 18,* 377-564.

DUFFEY, E.A.J. (1953a) *A monograph of the immature stages of British and Imported timber beetles* (Cerambycidae). Brit. Mus. (Nat. Hist.) London.

DUFFEY, E.A.J. (1953b). *Handbooks for the identification of British insects, 5,* (15), *Coleoptera, Scolytidae and Platypodidae.* R. Ent. Soc. London.

ELTON, C.S. (1966). *The pattern of animal communities.* Methuen. (With extensive bibliography.)

ELTON, C.S. (1970). Notes on the fauna of rotting wood in the Spey Valley region, Inverness-shire. *Entomologist's mon. Mag., 106,* 180-185.

ELTON, C.A. & MILLER, R.S. (1954). The ecological survey of animal communities: with a practical system of classifying habitats by structural characters. *J. Ecol., 42,* 460-96.

FERGUSSON, A. (1913-14). Supplements to Dr. Sharp's *"Coleoptera of Scotland".* Scott. Nat. **1913,** 155-160, 178-182, 225-259; **1914,** 34-40, 87-92, 116-117, 139-142.

FOWLER, W.W. (1887-91). *The Coleoptera of the British Islands.* Vols. 1-5. L. Reeve.

FOWLER, W.W. & DONISTHORPE, H. (1913). *The Coleoptera of the British Islands.* 6. L. Reeve.

GARDINER, L.M. (1957). Deterioration of fire-killed pine in Ontario and the causal wood-boring beetles. *Can. Ent., 89,* 241-263.

GODWIN, H. (1956). *The History of the British Flora.* Cambridge Univ. Pr.

GRAHAM, S.A. (1925). The felled tree trunk as an ecological unit. *Ecology, 6,* 397-411.

HALLETT, H.M. (1923). Beetles in imported timber. *Entomologist's mon. Mag., 59,* 13.

HANSON. H.S. (1937). Notes on the ecology and control of pine beetles in Great Britain. *Bull. ent. Res., 28,* 185-236.

HANSON, H.S. (1940). Further notes on the ecology and control of pine beetles in Great Britain. *Bull. ent. Res., 30,* 483-536.

HARTLEY, P.H.T. (1953). An ecological study of the feeding habits of the English titmice. *J. Anim. Ecol., 22,* 261-288.

HOWDEN, H.F. & VOGT, G.B. (1951). Insect communities of standing dead pine *(Pinus virginiana* Mill.). *Ann. ent. Soc. Am., 44,* 581-595.

HUNTER, F.A. (1962a). Notes on *Acanthocinus aedilis* (L.) (Col., Cerambycidae) in some Scottish Pine Forests. *Entomologist's mon. Mag., 98,* 82-84.

HUNTER, F.A. (1962b). A new host plant for *Phymatodes testaceus* (L.) (Col., Cerambycidae). *Entomologist's mon. Mag., 98,* 272.

HUNTER, F.A., JOHNSON, C. & SKIDMORE, P. (in prep.). Notes on the Biology of *Ostoma farrugineum* L. (Col., Trogossitidae) in Scotland.

JOHNSON, C. (1963a). The British species of the genus *Rhizophagus* Herbst (Col., Rhizophagidae). *Proc. Trans. Manch. ent. Soc., 1961-63,* 3-9.

JOHNSON, C. (1963b). *Agonum quadripunctatum* (Deg.) Col., Carabidae) in Scotland. *Entomologist's mon. Mag., 99,* 64.

JOHNSON, c. (1965). Taxonomic Notes on British Coleoptera No.2 - Sharp's species of the genus *Ernobius* (Anobiidae). *Entomologist, 98,* 175-180.

JOHNSON, C. (1966). The Fennoscandian, Danish and British species of the Genus *Enobius* Thomson (Col., Anobiidae). *Opusc. ent., 31,* 81-92.

JOHNSON, C. (1967). Additions and corrections to the British List of *Atomaria s. str.* (Col., Cryptophagidae) including a species new to Science. *Entomologist, 100.*

JOY, N.H. (1932). *A practical handbook of British beetles,* Vol. 1. Witherby.

KAUFMANN, R.R.U. (1948). Notes on the distribution of the British longicorn Coleoptera. *Entomologist's mon. Mag., 84.* 66-85.

KENNEDY, R. & JEFFERIES, M.G. (1975). The two-toothed longhorn *Ambeodontus tristis* (F.) Col., Cerambycidae) breeding in Leicestershire. *B.W.P.A. News Sh.* No. **138,** 1-2.

KEVAN, D.K. (1964). *Leiodes silesiaca* Kr. (Col., Leiodidae) - Second British Record. *Entomologist's mon. Mag., 100,* 116.

KLOET, G.S. & HINCKS, W.D. (1945). *A Check List of British Insects.* The authors, Stockport.

KROGERUS, R. (1927). Beobachtungen uber die Succession einiger Insektenbiocornosen in Fichtenstumpfen. *Notul. ent., 7,* 121-126.

LENNON, W. & DOUGLAS, W.D.R. (1892). Some additions to Scottish Coleoptera, with notes on species new or rare in the "Solway" district. *Ann. Scot. nat. Hist.,* 1 (2), 107-115.

LLOYD, R.W. (1951). *Hypophloeus linearis* F. (Col., Tenebrionidae) in Cheshire. *Entomologist's mon. Mag.,* 87, 231.

LLOYD, R.W. (1953). *Ostoma ferrugineum* L. (Col., Clavicornia, Ostomidae) new to Britain. *Entomologist's mon. Mag.,* 89, 251.

MASSEE, A.M. & GARDNER, A.E. (1962). *Ips cembrae* Heer (Col., Scolytidae) in Britain. *Entomologist's mon. Mag.,* 98, 225-226.

MOORE, B.P. (1957). The British Carabidae (Coleoptera) Part II: the county distribution of the species. *Entomologist's Gaz.,* 8, 171-180.

MORLEY, P.M. (1939). Time of cut as a factor influencing infestation of coniferous logs. *Can. Ent.,* 71, 243-248.

MORRIS, M.G. (1974). Oak as a habitat for insect life. In: *The British Oak,* edited by M.G. Morris and F.H. Perring, 274-297. Classey.

MUNRO, J.W. (1916). Some observations on the Entomology of the Scots Pine. *Trans. R. Scott. arboric. Soc.,* 30, 114-122.

MUNRO, J.W. (1926). British Bark-beetles. *Bull. For. Commn,* 8, H.M.S.O.

MURRAY, A. (1853). *Catalogue of the Coleoptera of Scotland.* Blackwood.

MURRAY, A. (1853). *Catalogue of the Coleoptera of Scotland.* Blackwood.

PALM, R. (1951). Die Holz- und Rindenkafer der nordschwedischen Laubbaume. *Meddn. St. SkogsforskInst.,* 40 (2).

PALM, T. (1959). Die Holz- und Rindenkafer der sud-und mittelschwedischen Laubbaume. *Opusc. ent.* Suppl., 16.

PAVIOUR-SMITH, K. (1960). The fruiting-bodies of macrofungi as habitats for beetles of the family Ciidae (Coleoptera). *Oikos,* 11, 43-71.

PAVIOUR-SMITH, K. (1961). Insect succession in the 'birch bracket fungus', *Polyporus betulinus. Int. Congr. Ent., 11th, Vienna 1960,* 1, 792-96.

PAVIOUR-SMITH, K. (1964). Habitats, headquarters and distribution of *Tetratoma fungorum* F. (Col., Tetratomidae). *Entomologist's mon. Mag.,* 100, 71-80.

PAVIOUR-SMITH, K. (1971). Fungi in Wytham Woods, Berkshire. *Proc. Rep. Ashmol. nat. Hist. Soc. Oxf.,* 1971, 3-13.

POORE, M.E.D. & McVEAN, D.N. (1957). A new approach to Scottish mountain vegetation. *J. Ecol.,* 45, 401-439.

POPE, R.D. (1953). *Handbooks for the identification of British insects,* 5, (7) *Coleoptera, Coccinellidae and Sphindidae.* R. Ent. Soc. London.

POPE, R.D. (1973). The species of *Scymnus (s. str.), Scymnus (Pullus)* and *Nephus* (Col., Coccinellidae) occurring in the British Isles. *Entomologist's mon. Mag.,* 109, 3-39.

RICHARD, O.W. (1926). Studies on the ecology of English heaths III. Animal communities of the felling and burn successions at Oxshott Heath, Surrey. *J. Ecol.,* 14, 244-281.

RICHMOND, H.A. & LEJEUNE, R.R. (1945). The deterioration of fire-killed spruce by wood-boring insects in Northern Saskatchewan. *For. Chron.,* 21, 168-192.

ROBERTSON, A.M. (1954). Coleoptera at Braemar, Aberdeenshire. *Entomologist's mon. Mag.,* 90, 143-144.

RYLE, G.B. (1951). *Ips typographus* L. and *Ips sexdentatus* Boern. (Col., Scolytidae) with a note on *Gastropachea pini* Ochsh. (Lep., Lasiocampidae). *Entomologist's mon. Mag.,* 87, 179.

SAALAS, U. (1917). Die Fichtenkafer Finnlands I. *Ann. Acad. Scient. fenn.* ser A, 8.

SAALAS, U. (1923). Die Fichtenkafer Finnlands II. *Ann. Acad. Scient. fenn.* ser A, 22.

SAVELY, H.E. (1939). Ecological relations of certain animals in dead pine and oak logs. *Ecol. Monogr.,* 9, 321-85.

SHARP, D. (1871a). The Coleoptera of the Scotch Fir. *Scott. Nat.,* 1, 36-42.

SHARP, D. (1871-1880). The Coleoptera of Scotland. *Scott. Nat.,* 1, 202-208, 242-248, 277-280, 2, 44-48, 89-96, 137-144, 185-192, 233-240, 285-288, 329-336, 377-384, 3, 33-40, 133-136, 183-184, 231-232, 277-280, 321-328, 368-376, 4, 35-36, 80-84, 129-132, 176-180, 223-228, 273-276, 362-364, 5, 44-48, 137-144, 188-192, 237-240, 286-288, 371-378.

SKIDMORE, P. (1973). *Chrusanthia nigricornis* Westh. (Col., Oedermidae) in Scotland, a genus and species new to the British list. *Entmologist,* 106, 234-237.

SOUTHWOOD, T.R.E. (1961). The number of species of insect associated with various trees. *J. Anim. Ecol.,* 30, 1-8.

STEVEN, H.M. & CARLISLE, A. (1959). *The native pinewoods of Scotland.* Oliver and Boyd.

STUBBS, A.E. (1972). Wild life conservation and dead wood. *J. Devon Trust Nature Conserv. Suppl.*

THOMPSON, G.H. (1959). *Onthotomicus (Ips) erosus* (Woll.) Col., Scolytidae) in the Forest of Dean. *Entomologist's mon. Mag.,* 95, 95.

TOTTENHAM, C.E. (1954). *Handbooks for the identification of British insects. Coleoptera, Staphylinidae, Piestinae to Euaesthetinae,* 4, (8a). R. Ent. Soc. London.

TOZER, D. (1953). *Pogonochaerus fasciculatus* Deg. (Col., Lamiidae) breeding in England. *Entomologist's mon. Mag.,* 89, 170.

TRAGARDH, I. (1929). Om tallbockens skadegorelse och bekampande. *Meddn. St. SkogsforskInst.,* 25, 171-228. (With English summary.)

TULLY, H. (1950). *Cis punctulatus* Gyll. (Col., Ciidae) in Northumberland. *Entomologist's mon. Mag.,* 86, 273.

WALLACE, H.R. (1953). The ecology of the insect fauna of pine stumps. *J. Anim. Ecol.,* 22, 154-171.

WALSH, G.B. (1950). Further records of *Hylastes ater* (Payk.) and *H. brunneus* Er. (Col., Scolytidae) in Britain. *Entomologist's mon. Mag.,* 80, 43.

WALSH, G.B. (1954). Plants and the beetles associated with them. In: *A Coleopterist's handbook.* The Amateur Entomologist, 11, 83-98.

WATERHOUSE, E.A. (1871). Coleoptera at Rannoch in 1870. *Entomologist's mon. Mag.,* 7, 81.

WOODROFFE, G.E. (1951). Some Hemiptera/Heteroptera and Coleopetera from the eastern Highlands. *Entomologist's mon. Mag.,* 87, 255.

WOODROFFE, G.E. (1953). An ecological study of the insects and mites in the nests of certain birds in Britain. *Bull. ent. Res.,* 44, 739-772.

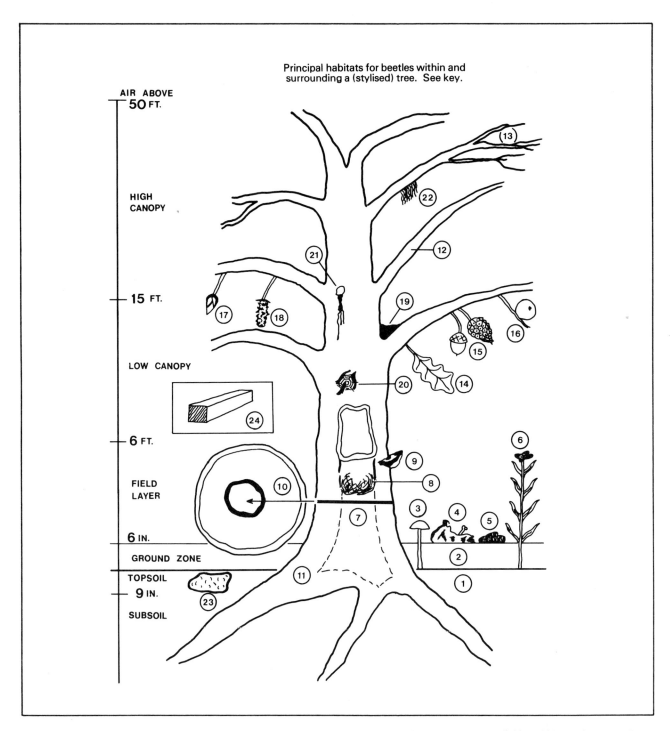

Figure 1. Habitats for beetles, showing the principal habitat components and sub-components available within and surrounding a (stylised) tree. (1) soil; (2) litter; (3) macrofungus fruiting body (MFB) growing from the soil; (4(carrion; (5) dung; (6) field layer vegetation; (7) wood mould caused by the action on the heartwood or sapwood of a wood-rotting fungus (e.g. *Phaeclus schweinitzii* (FR.) Pat.); (8A) mammal nest; (8B) insect next; (8C) bird's nest; (9) MFB growing directly from tunk, stump of branch; (10A) subcortical region (including the bark itself) of a standing or fallen trunk (log); (10B) sapwood of a standing or fallen trunk; (10C) heartwood of a standing or fallen trunk; (11A) subcortical region of a stump or root; (11B) sapwood of a stump or root; (11C) heartwood of a stump or root; (12A) subcortical region of a branch; (12B) branch sapwood; (12C) branch heartwood; (13A) subcortical region of a twig or narrow branch (approx 10-20 mm diameter); (13B) sapwood of twig; (13C) heartwood of twig; (14) leaf (insects feeding on leaves are divided into (a) leaf roller types, (b) leaf miners, (c) leaf chewers feeding externally, (D) sap suckers;) (15) fruit or cone; (16) gall; (17 leaf bud; (18) flower or flower bud; (19) rot-hole containing water; (20) cobwebs containing dead insects in heavily creviced bark or under loose bark; (21) sap run; (22) lichen, moss or other epiphytes; (23) subterranean MFB; (24) seasoned wood or converted timber. The structural divisions of the habitat classification of Elton are included for comparison.

In addition to the use of these numbers and letters to denote principal habitat components and sub-components, suffixes are used in Tables 1−4 as follows:- of beetles from a variety of habitat components, (P) predatory: - of beetles occurring in stumps, trunks, branches or twigs (I) invader of apparently living healthy wood or cambial tissue, whose outer surface usually appears whitish when the bark is stripped; (F) in freshly dead wood (or under its bark) whose outer surface when the bark is removed is usually brown and smells, often strongly of fermenting sap; (M) in timber or under bark, the latter still being largely in place, although often with the cambial layer largely already destroyed and the subcortical space containing much frass resulting from the activities or other species; (0) in wood or bark affected by fungus but still fairly hard, bark may be loose or even absent; (VO) in wood (whose bark is very loose or absent); . . . which is obviously extensively affected by fungus. (N.B. this is not the same as component 7).

Table 1.

Beetles (Carabidae, Histeridae, Ptiliidae, Anisotomidae, Staphylinidae, Buprestidae, Elateridae and Cantharidae) occurring, in England/Wales, or Scotland, mainly or exclusively in association with pine trees (*Pinus spp.*).

Species	England/ Wales	Scotland	Headquarters
Agonum quadripunctatum (Deg.)	r	r	Ø1 and 2 P
Dromius quadrinotatus (Panz.)	r	r	12 AM P
Plegaderus vulneratus Panz.	r	–	10 AM P
Ptiliolum caledonicum (Sharp)	–	R	10 A
Triarthron maerkelii Maerkel	r	r	23
Leiodes silesiaca (Kraatz)	r	R	23
Leiodes lucens (Fairm.)	r	–	23
Leiodes curta (Fairm.)	r	r	23
Leiodes triepkii (Schmidt)	r	r	23
Leiodes macropus (Rye)	r	–	23
Leiodes scita (Er.)	r	r	23
Anisotoma glabra Kug.	r	R	9 ON 11
Agathidium rhinoceros Sharp	–	R	10 A M/O
Phyllodrepa linearis (Zett.)	–	r	? P
Phloeonomus monilicornis (Gyll.)	–	r	10 A P
Phloeonomus lapponicus (Zett.)	r	R	10 A, 11A, P
Nudobius lentus (Grav.)	r	R	10 A P
Placusa pumilio (Grav.)	r	r	10 A P
Bolitochara pulchra (Grav.)	?	R	9 P
Atheta inhabilis (Kraatz)	r	R	10 A P
Melanophila acuminata (Deg.)	r	–	Ø10 AF, 11 AF
Elater tristis L.	–	R	7, 10 ABC O/VO P
Elater nigrinus Herbst	r	r	7, 10 ABC O/VO P
Harminius undulatus (Deg.)	–	R	7, 10 ABC O/VO P
Rhagonycha elongata (Fall.)	–	R	? P
Malthinus frontalis (Marsh.)	r	r	? P

Table 2.

Beetles (Lycidae, Anobiidae, Bostrychidae, Trogossitidae, Cleridae, Nitidulidae, Rhizophagidae, Cucujidae, Cryptophagidae and Coccinellidae) occurring, in England/Wales, or Scotland, mainly or exclusively in association with pine trees (*Pinus spp.*).

Species	England/ Wales	Scotland	Headquarters
Dictyopterus aurora (Herbst)	–	R	7, 10, 11 ABC VO
Ernobius nigrinus (Sturm)	–	R	12A F/M
Ernobius mollis (L.)	r	r	12.10 AF/M
Ernobius pini Sturm	r	–	17 or 18
Ernobius mulsantianus Sharp	r	–	?
Ernobius angusticollis (Ratz.)	r	–	? 15
Stephanopachys substriatus (Payk.)	r	–	10 A
Ostoma ferrugineum L.	r	R	7
Thanasimus formicarius (L.)	r	* r	10.11.12AF/M P
Thanasimus rufipes (Brahm)	r	R	10.11.12AF/M P
Epuraea pusilla (Illig.)	r	r	10 AF and 21
Epuraea thoracica Tournier	r	r	10 AF and 21
Pityophagus ferrugineus (L.)	r	r	10.11. AF P
Rhizophagus depressus (F.)	r	r	10.11. AF P
Rhizophagus ferrugineus (Payk.)	r	r	10.11. AF P
Dendrophagus crenatus (Payk.)	–	R	10.11.12AM
Micrambe abietis (Payk.)	r	r	?
Cryptophagus subdepressus Gyll.	r	r	?
Cryptophagus angustus Gangl.	–	R	10A
Atomaria sahlbergi Sjoberg	–	R	Recorded from 8B
Atomaria bella Reitt.	–	R	10A
Atomaria prolixa Er.	r	* r	?
Atomaria procerula Er.	–	r	?
Atomaria strandi Johnson	r	* r	?
Pullus suturalis (Thun.)	r	r	14 P
Scymnus nigrinus Kug.	r	r	14 P
Aphidecta obliterata (L.)	r	r	14 P
Vibidia duodecimguttata (Poda)	r	r	14 P
Myrrha octodecimguttata (L.)	r	r	14 P
Neomysia oblongoguttata (L.)	r	r	14 P
Anatis ocellata (L.)	r	r	14 P
Chilocorus bipustulatus (L.)	r	r	14 P
Exochomus quadripustulatus (L.)	r	r	14 P

For explanation of symbols see text and Fig. 1.

Table 3.

Beetles (Lathridiidae, Cisidae, Colydiidae, Mycetophagidae, Tenebrionidae, Salpingidae, Pytnidae, Oedemeridae, Melandryidae, Cerambycidae, Nemonychidae and Anthribidae) occurring, in England/Wales, or Scotland, mainly or exclusively in association with pine trees (pinus spp.).

Species	England/Wales	Scotland	Headquarters
Enicmus rugosus (Herbst)	r	R	9 ON 11
Corticaria linearis (Payk.)	r	R	?, 11
Corticaria dubia Dajoz	r	—	9 ON 11
Corticarina similata (Gyll.)	r	r	?
Corticarina latipennis Sahl.	—	R	? 2
Cis punctulatus Gyll.	r	r	9
Aulonium ruficorne (Oliv.)	—	—	10A F/M P
Mycetophagus fulvicollis F.	—	R	? 9
Hypophloeus fraxini Kug.	r	—	10A F/M P
Hypophloeus linearis F.	r	—	10A F/M P
Salpingus castaneus (Panz.)	r	r	12.13.A F/M
Salpingus ater (Gyll.)	r	r	Ø12.13.A. F/M
Salpingus reyi (Abeille)	r	—	Ø12.13.A F/M
Pytho depressus (L.)	—	R	10A M
Chrysanthia nigricornis Westh.	—	R	12 O/VO in 2
Abdera triguttata (Gyll.)	—	R	9
Xylita laevigata (Hellenius)	—	R	10.11.ABC 0
Zilora ferruginea (Payk.)	—	R	9 and 10A 0
Asemum striatum (L.)	r	R	11ABC M/O
Arhopalus ferus (Muls.)	—	R	11ABC M/O
Arhopalus rusticus (L.)	r	R	11ABC M/O
Rhagium inquisitor (L.)	(r)	R	10.11.A F
Leptura rubra (L.)	r	r	10BC 0
Leptura sanguinolenta L.	r	R	10.11.BC 0
Judolia sexmaculata (L.)	—	R	11ABC M/O
Callidium violaceum (L.)	r	(r)	10A F (DRY)
Hylotrupes bajulus (L.)	r	—	24
Ambeodontus tristis (F.)	r	—	24
Pogonocherus fasciculatus (Deg.)	r	R	12.13ABC F
Acanthocinus aedilis (L.)	(r)	R	10.11.A F
Cimberis attelaboides (F.)	r	r	18
Brachytarsus nebulosus (Forst.)	r	r	10.12. M P

Records in parentheses indicate adventive captures due to importation

Table 4.

Beetles (Curculionidae and Scolytidae) occurring, in England/Wales, or Scotland, mainly or exclusively in association with pine trees (*Pinus spp.*).

Species	England/Wales	Scotland	Headquarters
Eremotes ater (L.)	r	R	10ABC O/VO
Anthonomus varians (Payk.)	r	R	18
Brachonyx pineti (Payk.)	r	R	14
Pissodes pini (L.)	r	r	10.A
Pissodes notatus (F.)	r	R	10AF or 13C1
Pissodes validirostris Gyll.	—	R	15 or 13C1
Magdalis phlegmatica (Herbst)	r	R	?12.13.AF
Magdalis duplicata Germ.	—	R	?12.13 AF
Hylobius abietis (L.)	r	r	10.11.AF
Myelophilus minor (Hartig)	r	R	10.12.AF.
Myelophilus piniperda (L.)	r	r	10 A1/F
Hylurgus ligniperda (F.)	?	r	? A ?
Hylurgops palliatus (Gyll.)	r	r	10.11.A F
Hylastes ater (Payk.)	r	r	11.A F
Hylastes cunicularius Er.	r	r	11.A F
Hylastes opacus Er.	r	r	11.A F
Hylastes angustatus (Herbst)	r	r	11.A F
Hylastes attenuatus Er.	r	r	11.A F
Hylastes brunneus Er.	r	r	11.A F
Polygraphus poligraphus (L.)	r	r	10.A F
Crypturgus pusillus (Gyll.)	?	?	? AF
Crypturgus cinereus (Herbst)	(r)	?	10.AF/M
Cryphalus abietis (Ratz.)	r	r	12.13. AF
Dryocoetes autographus (Ratz.)	r	r	10.AF
Pityophthorus lichtensteini (Ratz.)	—	R	10.AF
Pityophthorus pubescens (Marsh.)	r	r	Wind-scorched 13AF
Trypodendron lineatum (Ol.)	r	r	10 BC F
Pityogenes chalcographus (L.)	r	r	10.AF
Pityogenes trepanatus (Noerdlinger)	r	r	10.AF
Pityogenes bidentatus (Herbst)	r	r	10.AF
Pityogenes quadridens (Hartig)	—	r	10.AF
Ips sexdentatus (Boerner)	—	r	10.AF
Ips typographus (L.)	r	r	10.A I/F
Ips acuminatus Gyll.	r	r	10.12.AF
Ips cembrae Heer	—	r	10.A I/F
Onthotomicus erosus (Woll.)	r	—	10.A F
Onthotomicus laricis (F.)	r	r	10.AF
Onthotomicus suturalis (Gyll.)	r	r	10.AF

55

Table 5.
The larger Scottish native pinewoods arranged in groups according to the degree of continentality or oceanicity of their climates.

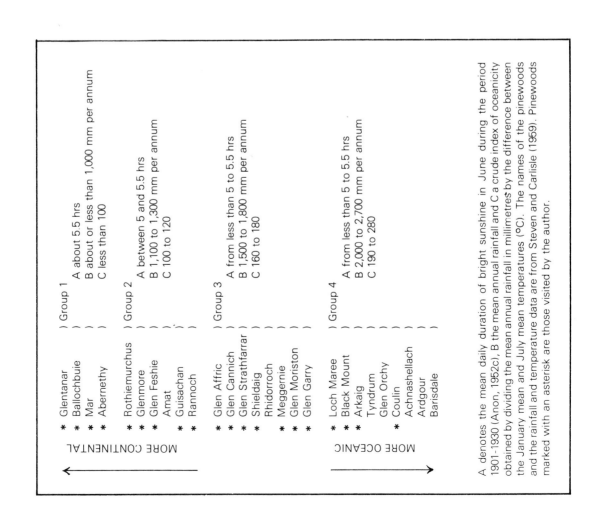

MORE CONTINENTAL ←

* Glentanar   ) Group 1
* Ballochbuie)
* Mar   )   A about 5.5 hrs
* Abernethy   )   B about or less than 1,000 mm per annum
                        C less than 100

* Rothiemurchus) Group 2
* Glenmore   )
* Glen Feshie   )   A between 5 and 5.5 hrs
  Amat   )   B 1,100 to 1,300 mm per annum
* Guisachan   )   C 100 to 120
* Rannoch   )

* Glen Affric   ) Group 3
* Glen Cannich   )
* Glen Strathfarrar)   A from less than 5 to 5.5 hrs
* Shieldaig   )   B 1,500 to 1,800 mm per annum
  Rhidorroch   )   C 160 to 180
  Meggernie   )
* Glen Moriston   )
* Glen Garry   )

* Loch Maree   ) Group 4
* Black Mount   )
* Arkaig   )   A from less than 5 to 5.5 hrs
  Tyndrum   )   B 2,000 to 2,700 mm per annum
  Glen Orchy   )   C 190 to 280
  Coulin   )
* Achnashellach)
  Ardgour   )
  Barisdale   )

MORE OCEANIC →

A denotes the mean daily duration of bright sunshine in June during the period 1901-1930 (Anon, 1952c), B the mean annual rainfall and C a crude index of oceanicity obtained by dividing the mean annual rainfall in millimetres by the difference between the January mean and July mean temperatures (°C). The names of the pinewoods and the rainfall and temperature data are from Steven and Carlisle (1959). Pinewoods marked with an asterisk are those visited by the author.

Some gaps in our knowledge of the Scottish pinewood ecosystem

Colin Millar Forestry Department, Aberdeen University AB9 2UU

That man has affected the Scottish native pinewoods over the centuries is in no doubt. The extermination of the capercaillie and the wolf must be an indication of the extent of man's penetration into even the most remote woods. His exploitation of many of the pinewoods in the nineteenth century is well documented (Anderson, 1967). His appreciation of them has grown over the last century, but only relatively recently have any serious studies of the pinewoods, as an ecosystem, been contemplated.

Brief review of previous work.

The contribution of Steven and Carlisle (1959) is unlikely to be surpassed. It provides a comprehensive description of all the woods and many data which, I am sure, stand up to the severest scrutiny. It sets out to be extensive and non-quantitative and succeeds in providing a framework for further studies.

The Forestry Commission has, over the years, acquired various areas of the native pinewoods and, recognising their uniqueness, has taken steps to study them with a view both to their management and to their conservation. However, many of the studies have been *ad hoc,* and trials rather than experiments were usually employed. The result is that, although much has been achieved, the reasons for success or failure of the trials have often remained obscure (Macdonald, 1952; Herman, 1961).

The Nature Conservancy has also interested itself in the pinewoods, initially in their regeneration, but more recently in their definition and description. The regeneration studies, whilst throwing up many factors which reduce the chances of successful establishment of seedlings, have failed, so far, to come up with any prescription for success. The re-defining and describing of of the pinewoods attempted to be wholly objective, but might be criticised on two main points. The first is that the short survey has under-sampled the pinewoods and the second is that, since relatively inexperienced labour was used, the species lists might be wanting. The intitial survey did, however, largely confirm Steven and Carlisle's subjective division of the pinewoods into several geographically and floristically distinct groups, although some anomalies, such as Amat — a northern wood with affinities to the south western woods — occurred.

Individual workers have concerned themselves more with selected groups of organisms within the ecosystem, with soils or with vegetation history studies. Most animal and plant taxa have been studied in one area of woodland or another, but very few comparisons have been made between sites. The same comment might be made of palynological studies which have mainly been intensive rather than extensive.

Malcolm (1957) paid particular attention to site degradation in the western or moist type of pinewoods and detailed the factors affecting degradation. Whilst not agreeing fully with his conclusion, that artificial mea-sures will be necessary to ensure improvement in the status of the pinewoods, I endorse his approach to the study of the ecosystem and will attempt in this paper to suggest other lines which might be followed profitably.

It seems to me that one *can* point to several more or less obvious gaps in our knowledge of the natural pinewood ecosystem in Scotland despite the work that has been done already. These fall under two broad headings, concerned with the description and the dynamics of the pinewoods respectively.

Description of the pinewoods

The analysis of data collected by Bunce, from a survey of 26 pinewoods, defined four main types covering a wide range of variation. The types showed a pronounced regional distribution correlated strongly with environmental factors. However, in the project plan, it was stated clearly that the survey was designed to provide only minimal data to develop a valid classification and to provide a baseline for regeneration studies. The survey results so far have mainly quantified what we thought we already knew. We should now make fuller use of the data, but not assume that they will go far to filling the gaps in our knowledge.

There should be a further examination of the data by vegetation strata to compare the composition of similar strata in different pinewoods. We know, for example, that the western woods are richer in birch and poorer in pine than the eastern group. Do similar differences occur in the dwarf shrub, herb or bryophyte layers, or are some strata much more constant than others? Which species, if any, actually define the pinewood association, assuming that pine does not need to be a constant?

The division of the pinewoods, by Bunce, into four major site types on the basis of the macroflora should be justified by a similar examination of the fauna, meiofauna and microflora. Comparative data from these these groups is sadly lacking.

There have been several studies of mammals and birds in the native pinewoods, particularly in relation to regeneration surveys and experiments. However, the ecosystem approach has rarely been adopted and, as Lowe states on page 103, the relatively small areas of pinewood which we have in Scotland are not adequate for studies of the relation between mammals and the pinewoods, since the coniferous forest is only part of the habitat in which most mammals occur.

It would be of interest to have complete animal species lists for a range of natural pinewoods, to supplement the information given by Steven and Carlisle, and to relate these lists to the macro-vegetation data. Similarly, additional information on the meiofauna and microflora could usefully supplement that obtained from Rannoch by Usher (1970, 1971) and Hayes (1965) respectively. There is a dearth of such information which is vital to our understanding of the decomposition process in the pinewood ecosystem, a process which has an important bearing on the combustibility of the ground vegetation and the nature of the seedbed in relation to regeneration.

The macrofungi of the pinewoods have not been described systematically. Steven and Carlisle perhaps underestimated the incidence of two important fungi, *Trametes pini* and *Peridermium pini* in the native pinewoods. The latter is certainly prevalent in the Eastern woods and may be the main cause of death of individual trees. Bunce estimated that 6% of the basal area of standing trees was dead and this figure corresponds well with the figure of about 4% for the incidence of *P. pini* found by Murray, *et al.* (1969). Further information on this and other parasitic fungi would extend our knowledge of the ecosystem since it is these debilitated trees which are the home of many insect larvae and which form an important link in many food chains. Such information on dying trees would also help our understanding of the pinewood dynamics.

Non-parasitic macrofungi are often mycorrhizal. Our knowledge of these is scant and could usefully be extended, especially as their role in regeneration is not well understood. Pathogenic microfungi, too, might affect the foliage of seedlings and young trees. It is often stated that seedlings turned brown during regeneration studies, but rarely has disease been considered to be implicated.

Fitzpatrick, in talking about the soils associated with the pinewoods, has indicated that in those that have been investigated there is a tendency not only to podsolization but also to iron pan formation, leading to a deterioration in drainage conditions (page 35). However the soil survey has covered few of the pinewoods and relatively little is known about the nutrient status of the soils. There is scope here for a detailed analysis of soils from selected, well-documented, pinewoods and for the results to be related to those from the vegetation survey. The thin section technique, described by Fitzpatrick, could be used in conjunction with litter decomposition studies to provide much detailed information on this little-explored part of the ecosystem.

Two main points concerning the description of the pinewood ecosystem remain. The first is their definition and extent. The definition given by Steven and Carlisle as 'woods descended from one generation to another by *natural* means' has been accepted as a working definition, with a general recognition that planting may have occurred in most woods over the last four centuries. Most people would accept also that the pinewoods are a mosaic of dense stands, open stands, mixed and pure stands, and include considerable stretches of open ground. Bunce, on the results of his survey, claims that the extent of the pinewoods is exaggerated by the boundaries given by Steven and Carlisle. I do not think that his sample plot density permits such a conclusion and await with in-

terest the results of the analysis of aerial photographs by the Nature Conservancy Council. The survey claims also to have obtained a measure of the rate at which the pinewoods are diminishing (15% over the last 20 years). This I accept with reservation, but include here because it is a matter of description, rather than dynamics, since it relates to clear felling and the planting of exotics. As we shall see, we have very little information on the natural change in extent of the pinewoods over such a short term.

The final point concerned with description is the nature of the trees themselves. Faulkner has presented his ideas on the gene pool of the Caledonian pine (see page 96). It has often been stated that the natural woods might be recognised by the great range of variation among the individuals in a stand as compared with a plantation. I would like to see if this holds true for some of the less accessible woods and especially those at high altitudes, where environmental selection pressures might have reduced variation.

Dynamics of the pinewoods
The project plan for the recent pinewood survey stated that the survey would be used as a method of generating hypotheses about dynamics and regeneration which could then be examined in more detail using the classification as a basic framework. Whether such a survey was necessary to generate hypotheses on such popular topics is debatable.

A consideration of the dynamics of the pinewoods may be divided, for convenience, into historical and contemporary processes. It is clear that the causes of change in the ecosystem, whether by slow death, catastrophe such as windthrow or fire or anthropogenic factors, require further study. Here, further examination of bogwood, charcoal and pollen deposits and contemporary disease, fire and windthrow sites are appropriate. Again, a comparison of the main pinewood types should be attempted, since such an approach might reveal reasons for their existence and might show differences in their histories and longevity.

If we look at the historical processes, we think first of the excellent work that has been done on the analysis of pollen and other deposits. Early and more recent work by Durno, (1967), Birks (1970) and O'Sullivan (1970) relating specifically to pinewoods has shown us the changes in woods, mainly in relation to climate, since the ice ages. Birks and O'Sullivan have worked intensively at a few sites in Abernethy. Unfortunately, most pollen studies have been conducted, for fairly obvious reasons, not in woodlands but in deep peat or in lake sediments. There has been little work on soil pollen deposits in Scotland except for that of O'Sullivan (1973) and, according to Edwards (1974), there has been no substantial work in palynologically-based palaeoclimatology in Scotland, although more precise statements can be expected as our knowledge of plant ecology increases. One of the main criticisms of pollen deposit studies is the inability, through lack of data, to relate pollen densities to tree densities. This situation is slowly being remedied through studies of contemporary pollen rain both by O'Sullivan (1973) and by Birks (1973)

An interesting facet of the history of the pinewoods is the occurrence of buried stumps in peat deposits. Generally, one or two layers are found and these may be referred to the late Boreal and sub-Boreal periods. However, recent radiocarbon datings have emphasised the variation in the dates of these layers and pointed to the need for further studies if we are to understand the factors which led to such burials. Pears has done some very comprehensive work on the history of the tree line in the Cairngorms and his approach could usefully be adapted to other areas (Pears 1968, 1970).

The subject of buried charcoal profiles in pinewood soils has never been tackled systematically. The dating of such layers is an attractive problem, but, unfortunately, radiocarbon dating is still an expensive and slow process. It would help our thinking considerably if we had reliable data on the frequency, and possibly the intensity, of fires in the ecosystem. These then could be related to the subsequent vegetation as indicated by pollen profiles.

We have gained a considerable amount of knowledge from studies of the types outlined above and glibly reiterate the results as if they relate to the whole of Scotland. Non-palynologists should remember that, because of technical difficulties, the data usually refer to only one site and often to a single profile.

If we now turn to the contemporary dynamic processes in the pinewood ecosystem, we should pehaps think first of the soils and the question of site deterioration and amelioration. Fitzpatrick has suggested that the development of an iron pan might militate against the long term survival of pinewood on a particular site. Have we any measure of the degradation of pinewood sites through burning, grazing or felling? Has the balance of species been pushed in the direction of a coniferous dominance and, if so, by what factors? Malcolm (1957) provided some clues to the answers to these questions, but his study was restricted mainly to one site. Far too little is known about the role of hardwood species in our native pinewoods. I like to think of the pinewoods as a mosaic in which the hardwoods had an important role to play. Some regeneration studies such as those by Dimbleby (1953) and McNeil (1955) would seem to support this view. This lack of knowledge of the role of tree species associated with native Scots pine has been mentioned by several colleagues during discussion and would seem to merit attention. Carlisle remembers references to hazel as a component of the ecosystem in historical documents, but did not find it during his survey.

As Gimingham (page 1), has pointed out, there has been no measurement of Scottish pinewood productivity in terms of the biomass concept. Such studies would help us evaluate the pinewoods in relation to other ecosystems. Embodied in such an approach would be a consideration of the litter decomposition process. This aspect, with its important bearing on the seed bed, has been totally neglected. Hayes (1965) has provided an extensive list of microfungi for the Rannoch woods, but his studies told us little of the succession of fungi in decomposition. It would be interesting to know the rate of convergence of the different litters from the various vegetation types to humus. The influence of associated hardwoods on such a process might be substantial.

A most important and controversial question, which seems to dominate our thinking in connection with the natural woodlands, is that of regeneration. Here, I side with those who believe that given time, without undue human interference in the form of introduction of unnatural processes or prevention of natural processes - the pinewoods will regenerate and maintain themselves, provided the climate does not alter drastically in the next century or more.

Most of the work on regeneration has been over relatively short periods and has been inconclusive. Herman (1961) describes the results from the Forestry Commission studies up to that time as a "sad tale". Macdonald (1952) had already concluded that "at best unaided natural regeneration is erratic, undependable and a long drawn out process." McVean (1961) attributed the lack of regeneration in his studies to a variety of factors, including light starvation, frost lift, drips from overhanging branches, drought, waterlogging, moss competition, Brown moth and other insects, slugs, seed-eating birds, mice, voles and Roe deer to name only a few. This situation of having to look for excuses for failed regeneration studies should not be allowed to continue. Experiments should be preceded by a much more comprehensive survey of those sites on which, over the years, regeneration *has* been successful. The history of these sites should be fully explored and every effort made to determine those natural factors which have increased the chance of regeneration.

There seems little evidence that seed is in short supply even at high altitudes or from moribund trees and indeed, though the seeds are small, the germinability is often particularly high. Similarly, most studies would indicate a reasonable germination in the field. The problem seems to be one of establishment and this, as with any introduction into an existing vegetation, must depend largely on a chance combination of favourable circumstances. Such a combination will occur in each area from time to time. Our studies must identify the main factors, so that by management we do not do anything which will militate against such circumstances.

One such factor, on many sites, is almost certainly fire, and in this connection it will be interesting to see the aftermath of the recent fire at Sheildaig. Another is grazing, and here I would agree with Dunlop (1975) who pointed out that total exclusion of grazing animals might actually reduce regeneration. The largest and unsolvable question is the extent to which long-term climatic change is reducing the chances of regeneration. McVean (1961) was of the opinion that the present oceanic climate of Scotland is so favourable to the development of a felted Ao horizon in pine forest soils that it seems unlikely that dense pine forests with a *Vaccinium—Hylocomium* ground layer can regenerate within themselves. A similar view has been expressed very forcibly at meetings of the Pinewood Discussion Group.

In this connection, the concepts of the static, shifting and transient pinewoods should be fully explored, drawing on all historical and contemporary evidence.

Studies of the ecotone area at the perimeter of existing pine woods might be most rewarding (Malcolm, 1957).

In conclusion, I hope that I have shown that I do not subscribe to the view "that we should think of a forest of native Scots pine rather than a native Scots pine forest". I believe that we could usefully re-examine many of the existing data to help us in our understanding of the native pinewood ecosystem, but also that new data must be added in a systematic way.

Concerning the natural regeneration and survival of the pinewoods, I am an optimist; but not so much of an optimist as not to welcome some of the current stopgap measures being taken by various interested parties to ensure the continuation of a forest cover, provided they do not disturb all the sites on which natural regeneration will ultimately occur.

References

ANDERSON, M.L. (1967). *A history of Scottish forestry.* Nelson.

BIRKS, H.H. (1970). Studies in the vegetational history of Scotland. I. A pollen diagram from Abernethy Forest, Inverness-shire. *J. Ecol.,* **58,** 827-846.

BIRKS, H.J.B. (1973). Modern pollen rain studies in some arctic and alpine environments. In: *Quarternary Ecology,* edited by H.J.B. Birks and R.G. West, 143-168. Blackwell. (British Ecological Society Symposium No. 14.)

DIMBLEBY, G.W. (1953). Natural regeneration of pine and birch on the heather moors of North-east Yorkshire. *Forestry, 26,* 41-52.

DUNLOP, B.M.S. (1975). The regeneration of our native pinewoods. *Scott. For., 29,* 111-119.

DURNO,. S.E. (1957). Certain aspects of vegetational history in North-east Scotland. *Scott. geogr. Mag., 74,* 127-135.

DURNO, S.E. (1967). Scottish woodland history since boreal time as revealed by pollen analysis of peat. *Ph.D. Thesis,* University of Aberdeen, Scotland.

EDWARDS, K.J. (1974). A half-century of pollen analytical research in Scotland. *Trans. Bot. Soc. Edinb., 42,* 211-222.

HAYES, A.J. (1965). Some microfungi from Scots pine litter. *Trans. Br. mycol. Soc., 48,* 179-185.

HERMAN, D.W. (1961). Natural regeneration of Scots pine woods in the Highlands. *Scott. For., 15,* 235-242.

MACDONALD, J.A.B. (1952). Natural regeneration of Scots pine woods in the Highlands. *Rep. Forest Res. Lond., 1951,* 26-33.

McNEIL, W.M. (1955). Studies on surface vegetation and natural regeneration in a mature Scots pine wood in Aberdeenshire. *Forestry, 28,* 49-65.

McVEAN, D.N. (1961). Experiments on the direct sowing of Scots pine. *Emp. For. Rev., 40,* 217-227.

McVEAN, D.N. (1963). The ecology of Scots pine in the Scottish Highlands. *J. Ecol., 51,* 671-686.

MALCOLM, D.C. (1957). Site degradation in stands of natural pine in Scotland. *Bull. For. Dep. Univ. Edinb., 4,* 1-38.

MURRAY, J.S., MILLAR, C.S. & VAN DER KAMP, B.J. (1969). Incidence and importance of Peridermium pini (Pers.) Lev. in North-east Scotland. *Forestry, 42,* 165-184.

O'SULLIVAN, P.E. (1970). The ecological history of the forest of Abernethy, Inverness-shire. *D. Phil. Thesis,* New University of Ulster.

O'SULLIVAN, P.E. (1974). Contemporary pollen studies in a native Scots pine ecosystem. *Oikos, 24,* 143-150.

PEARS, N.V. (1968). Post-glacial tree lines of the Cairngorm mountains, Scotland. *Trans. Bot. Soc. Edinb., 40,* 361-394.

PEARS, N.V. (1970). Post-glacial tree lines of the Cairngorm mountains, Scotland. Some modifications based on radiocarbon-dating. *Trans. Bot. Soc. Edinb., 40,* 536-544.

STEVEN, H.M. & CARLISLE, A. (1959). *The native pinewoods of Scotland.* Oliver and Boyd.

USHER, M.B. (1970). Seasonal and vertical distribution of a population of soil arthropods: Collembola. *Pedobiologia, 10,* 224-236.

USHER, M.B. (1971). Seasonal and vertical distribution of a population of soil arthropods: Mesostigmata. *Pedobiologia, 11,* 27-29.

Vegetation history and the native pinewoods

P.E, O'Sullivan School of Environmental Sciences, Plymouth Polytechnic, Plymouth

Introduction

When dealing with the conservation of a community such as the native pinewoods, we are concerned with an ecosystem whose dominant organisms possess a life-span greater than that of man, and consequently we encounter the problem of measuring changes through time. Phenomena such as succession, immigration of new species, the long-term effects of land-use practices, and the periodicity of regeneration, may take place on a time-scale which renders them wholly or partly imperceptible to a single generation of men (Dunlop, 1975). Nevertheless, as Oldfield (1970a) has shown in the case of Blelham Bog National Nature Reserve in the English Lake District, such changes may in fact be of paramount importance in calculations which affect decisions concerning planning and conservation.

Secondly, as has been shown by investigations of their ecology (Steven and Carlisle, 1959; McVean and Ratcliffe, 1962), the native pinewoods consist of several related communities, whose exact status and inter-relationships are imperfectly known, and one approach to this problem would be to investigate the antiquity of the communities concerned, with a view to establishing which have a long vegetational history, and which are fairly recent in origin.

A considerable array of palaeoecological techniques are now at our disposal for use in examining such problems, most of which have been recently described by West (1968, 1971). In the Scottish Highlands, the main approach to vegetational history has been through the joint use of pollen-analysis and radiocarbon-dating of recent organic sediments such as peat, lake muds (Gyttja), and to a lesser extent, Mor humus, and most investigations of this type have been recently listed by Edwards (1974). Other techniques which have been employed are the analysis of the diatom stratigraphy and chemical content of lacustrine sediments (Pennington et al. 1972), and, for more recent periods, documentary records (Murray, 1935; Steven and Carlisle, 1959; Gaffney, 1960; O'Sullivan, 1973c; Carlisle, this volume).

Palaeoecological investigations directly associated with the remaining stands of native pine are in fact rather few in number, being those of Birks (1970) in Abernethy, Durno and McVean (1959) at Beinn Eighe, O'Sullivan (1973b,c, 1974a,b) in Abernethy, O'Sullivan and Brown (1975) in Glenmore, and Pennington et al. (1972) at Loch Clair for the Coulin Pinewood. However, there is a much larger number of investigations indirectly associated, in that they show that the sites examined are in areas which at one time supported dominant pine —, or pine-birch forest, (Birks, 1972b, Durno, 1958c, 1959, Erdtmann, 1928, Johansen in Pennington et al. 1972, Pears, 1968c, 1970, Pennington et al. 1972, and Vasari and Vasari, 1968), and these results are therefore included in this discussion. The vegetation history of north-east Scotland, including some areas of former native pinewood, has been recently summarised by Gunson (1975).[1]

The evidence is perhaps best discussed under three headings, in that it yields information which is plant geographical, palaeoecological, and ecological in its nature.

Former distribution of pine-dominated forests in Scotland

McVean and Ratcliffe (1962), with very much less evidence than now available, attempted a reconstruction of the distribution of post-glacial forest types in Scotland. Later research has proved their ideas to be substantially correct, except perhaps in two respects (Fig. 1).

First of all, there does not seem to have been as much oak or pine in coastal areas of north-east Scotland as they suggest, but rather a coastal forest belt dominated by birch and alder, with some oak and elm (cf. Durno, 1957, Vasari and Vasari, 1968; Gunson, 1975). More important for the purposes of this discussion is the recent work at Loch Sionascaig in Wester Ross by Pennington et al. (1972), which shows that the pine at one time extended much further north along the north-west coast than previously envisaged.

However, apart from these minor adjustments, the distribution map of former pine-birch dominance produced by McVean and Ratcliffe (1962) appears to be one which is more than adequate as a working basis. Thus, it is now clear that the area of pine-birch dominance extended from just south of Crianlarich in the south-west, (Steven and Carlisle, 1959), across Rannoch Moor and the Central Highlands, as far as the upland areas of north-east Scotland (Gunson,1975). Along the west coast, the northern-most limit of pine-dominance so far discovered is the Inverpolly area (Loch Sionascaig), and on the east coast, the limit may have been about the latitude of Helmsdale. The easterly extent of pine-birch forest has been studied by Durno (1967), who concluded that the main boundary was formed by the principal coastal watersheds, and in north-east Scotland, the ecotone between the Highland pine-birch forests and the coastal birch-alder forests presumably lies somewhere between the Loch Kinord and Loch of Park sites of Vasari and Vasari (1968). The northern boundary of pine-birch dominance has been much less investigated so far, although some indications are to be had from the work of Durno (1958c) in eastern Sutherland.

The conclusions by McVean and Ratcliffe (1962) that pine never reached dominance in even the Inner Hebrides has thus been confirmed (Vasari and Vasari, 1968; Birks, 1973), and it also seems correct to suppose that oakwoods did develop in the Great Glen to some extent (Loch Tarff diagram, Pennington et al. 1972), and thus perhaps in other sheltered valleys such as Strathspey. Subsequent research will no doubt add to the accuracy of the distribution of former pine forest given in Fig. 1.

---

1 *Since the time of writing, work by Walker (1975a, b) in the Central Grampians, and H.M. Birks (1975) on pine stump-layers in Scottish blanket peats has also appeared.*

Figure 1. Suggested former distribution of Scots pine dominated pine-birch forests in the Scottish Highlands, with the location of pollen-analytical and other sites mentioned in the text. Based on original map of reconstructed post-glacial forest types by McVean and Ratcliffe (1962).

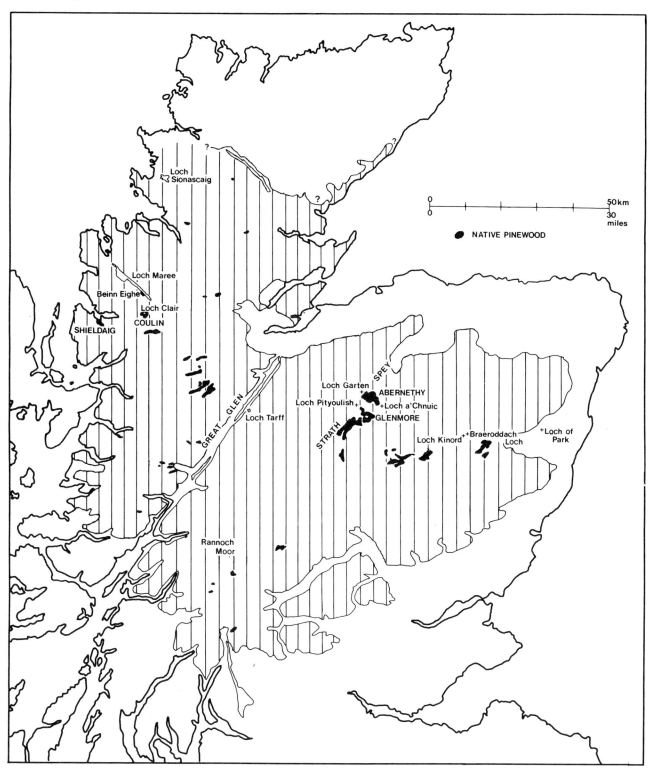

Over a large area of the Scottish Highlands, therefore, there developed a forest dominated not, as in the case of most of Britain and Ireland, by the mixed-oak deciduous forest, but by pine and birch, boreal species, normally thought of in western Europe as pioneers. How and when this forest developed is shown by the palaeoecological results.

Flandrian vegetational history in the Scottish Highlands

Evidence concerning Flandrian vegetational history in the Scottish Highlands is here considered in terms of three time intervals, these being the periods between (a) 10,000 and 6,500 years BP, (b) 6,500 and 5,000 years BP, and (c) the period 5,000 years BP until the present. These dates divide the period into Early,

Middle and Late-Flandrian sub-stages, and, in doing so, I am therefore attempting to follow the method of sub-division of the Flandrian proposed by West (1970), although it has been necessary, for reasons stated below, to define a transition period from 8-6,500 BP (Table 1.)

Table 1. Tentative correlation scheme between radiocarbon-dated pollen diagrams from the Scottish Highlands. (Loch Sionascaig, Loch Clair-Pennington et al. 1972, Loch Maree-Birks, 1972b, Loch Pityoulish, Loch Garten-O'Sullivan, 1974a and 1976).

^{14}C – YEARS BP (x10^3)	LOCH SIONASCAIG	LOCH CLAIR	LOCH MAREE	LOCH PITYOULISH	LOCH GARTEN	SUB-STAGE
1	*Blanket Bog with some human influence*	*Relatively undisturbed Pine–Birch forest with some Blanket Bog*	*Widespread Blanket Bog*	Heathland and Farmland Widespread *Forest clearance* 1014 ± 55 BP	*Pine–Birch forest with Heathland*	LATE FLANDRIAN
2				Pine-Birch forest with Heathland		
3				*Forest clearance* 2990 ± 60 BP		
4	*Widespread blanket bog formation* 4020 ± 100 BP		*Widespread blanket bog formation* 4206 ± 55 BP		*Forest clearance* 3635 ± 205 BP — Pine–Birch forest with Alder	
5	Pine–Birch forest with Alder	*Temporary forest clearance* 5360 ± 110 BP — Pine–Birch forest with Alder	Pine–Birch forest with Alder	Pine – Birch forest with Alder — *Alnus-rise* 5548 ± 50 BP		MIDDLE FLANDRIAN
6	*Empirical Alnus-limit* 6250 ± 140 BP	*Empirical Alnus-limit* 6520 ± 145 BP	*Empirical Alnus-limit* 6513 ± 65 BP	Pine–Birch forest *Empirical Alnus-limit* 6633 ± 57 BP	*Alnus-rise* 5860 ± 100 BP — Pine–Birch forest	
7	Pine–Birch forest — Birch–Pine–Hazel	Birch–Pine–Hazel ---(not dated)----	Pine–Birch forest	Birch–Pine–Hazel	⊕ 7535 ± 335 BP	TRANSITION
8	*Pine-expansion* 7880 ± 160 BP — Birch–Hazel period	Birch–Hazel period	*Pine-expansion* 8250 ± 100 BP — Birch–Hazel period	*Pine-expansion* 7966 ± 60 BP — Birch–Hazel		EARLY FLANDRIAN
9		8910 ± 130 BP	8951 ± 120 BP			

Correlations between sites are made only on the basis of events and pollen-zone boundaries which have been radiocarbon-dated, but, as there are so far very few dates from pollen-analytical sites in the Highlands which can be used, such correlations must remain tentative in their nature, and will no doubt need modification in the light of future studies. All radiocarbon dates, and dates based on them for palaeoecological events, are here expressed in uncorrected radiocarbon years before present (BP). Archaeological, historical or cultural events are expressed in years BC, or as dates AD.

(1) Early Flandrian (10,000-6,500 BP)

The Early Flandrian in the Highlands, as elsewhere, appears to have been a period of succession involving several vegetation types.

At most sites, the pollen record suggests the development of a sequence of communities beginning with park-tundra followed by scrub, then open deciduous woodland in which birch and hazel were among the dominants. Such a sequence is shown at Loch Kinord on Deeside, Loch a'Chnuic on Speyside, and Loch Sionascaig in Wester Ross. However, at Loch Maree, also in Wester Ross, but within the area of the Scottish late-glacial (late-Devensian) ice-cap proposed by Sissons (1974), barren glacial silts are followed by sediments denoting first juniper scrub, and then birch-hazel woodland, without any intervening tundra period.

The first part of the Early Flandrian was thus a period of ecological succession in response to increased temperatures and the availability of new habitats at the end of the last glacial stage of the Pleistocene. The process of woodland establishment appears to have taken about 1,000 years, with birch-hazel woodland present in many areas by about 8,900 BP. The ecological significance of this information is considered below.

Early/Middle Flandrian transition (8,000-6,500 BP)

The pine then appears to have expanded into the open birch-hazel woodlands in the period following 8,000 BP. As pointed out by Dr. Pennington (Pennington et al. 1972), it is difficult to judge accurately from deep-water pollen spectra how much pine is present in the surrounding forest canopy, as pine pollen tends to be concentrated in deep water sediments, but at a number of Highland sites, the beginning of the main Flandrian expansion of *Pinus* frequencies has been dated to the period immediately either side of 8,000 BP, (Table 1). However, the rate of replacement of birch and hazel by pine appears to have varied quite markedly from site to site, with rapid pine expansion at Loch Maree and on Deeside, but slower increases of pine pollen at Loch Sionascaig and Loch Clair, and at Loch Pityoulish in Strath Spey (see below).

(2) Middle Flandrian (6,500-5,000 BP)

The main palaeoecological event of the Middle Flandrian, which has been radiocarbon-dated at several sites, is the arrival of the alder, (Table 1). The first appearance of *Alnus* pollen (empirical limit, Smith and Pilcher, 1973) has been dated at about 6,500 BP and usually coincides with the pine maximum. In the eastern Highlands, the main expansion of *Alnus* frequencies, and therefore presumably its colonisation of its eventual niche, does not occur until later, and on Speyside is dated to the period 5,900-5,600 BP.

An alternative view of the events of this period has, however, been put forward by Birks (1970), who suggested that the arrival of the alder took place almost immediately after that of the pine in the eastern Highlands, around 7,000 BP. The problem of Middle Flandrian pollen zonation in this region is given further consideration in a recent paper by the present writer (O'Sullivan, 1975a).

The Middle Flandrian therefore represents the time in which the pine forests reached a position of dominance over a very large area of the Scottish Highlands (see Fig. 1), and mixed oak-forest seems only ever to have been very limited in its extent. The ecological aspects of this period are dealt with below.

(3) Late-Flandrian (5,000 BP to the present)

The Late-Flandrian sub-stage in Britain is defined by West (1970) as that period of post-glacial time during which the influence of man in determining the composition of plant communities, indeed most ecosystems, has increased to a position of almost total dominance. The opening of the Late-Flandrian in much of Britain is therefore placed at the classical *Ulmus*-decline feature, which has been dated at numerous sites to the period just preceding 5,000 BP (Hibbert, Switsur and West, 1971; Smith and Pilcher, 1973). However, in the Scottish Highlands, it is difficult to detect a distinct elm-decline, both because of the small amounts of this pollen type recorded at Highland sites, and because the timing and impact of prehistoric cultures in the Highlands appear to have been quite different from that experienced further south (Carlisle, page 70). Nowhere does this seem to be more the case than in the blanket bog areas of the far north-west.

However, it has been pointed out by Pennington et al. (1972) that, at some Highland sites, there is a decline of elm pollen which occurs at about 5,000 BP, and which may be due to the decrease of this type in the regional pollen component of the Highlands, following the reduction of elm populations further south in Britain by prehistoric peoples. This feature occurs in the north-west Highlands at Loch Sionascaig, and at Loch Maree, where it has been dated by Birks (1972b) at 5,150 + 65 BP. It can also be detected in Speyside and Deeside pollen diagrams, where its stratigraphic position in relation to dated horizons may allow it to be assigned to the late sixth millenium BP (eg: Loch Garten, Loch Pityoulish, O'Sullivan, 1974a, 1976).

Thus, we can point to a horizon dating from about 5,000 BP or slightly earlier which can be used to define the base of the Late-Flandrian in the Highlands. Within this period, however, the course of vegetational history varies very much from area to area, so that a more empirical approach to the topic is required.

In the north-west Highlands, retrogressive succession of the vegetation is noted in the Loch Sionascaig pollen diagram just before 6,000 BP, and this tendency is accelerated after 5,000 BP, with the beginnings of the formation of blanket peat. About 4,000 BP, regional values of pine pollen are reduced, indicating that, from this time onwards, it was replaced by blanket bog over wide areas. The first undoubted traces of human clearance of forest by fire are recorded about 1,500 BC (Pennington et al. 1972). Similarly at Loch Maree (Birks, 1972b), forests appear to have been replaced by heathland and blanket bog around 4,200 BP.

However, even within this region there is diversity, as at Loch Clair (Pennington et al. 1972), after temporary forest clearance about 5,400 BP, there is no other human or other influence on vegetation recorded, and the pine-birch forest appears to have persisted in a relatively unaltered state until very recent time.

In the eastern Highlands, the general effects of man appear to have been more pronounced. On Speyside, forest clearance around Loch Garten is recorded in 1,700 BC, where it may be linked with movement of Secondary Neolithic peoples into the area (O'Sullivan, 1974b). Later, clearance is also recorded at Loch Pityoulish, in what used to be thought of as Classical Bronze Age times (c. 3,000 BP, O'Sullivan 1976). In the Dark-Age period (AD 500-1,000), it seems likely that much heathland formation, associated with grazing and other activities, took place (O'Sullivan, 1973b). On Deeside, the main forest clearance around Loch Kinord appears to have been delayed until about 1,000 years ago (Vasari, personal communication), although a few kilometres to the east, at Braeroddach Loch in the Howe of Cromar, there is good evidence for a long history of human activity dating back to what appears to be the elm-decline (Edwards, personal communication.). This would, of course, be consistent with the considerable amount of archaeological evidence for prehistoric settlement in that area (Edwards, 1975).

Perhaps a general point that can be made in comparison between the north-west and the eastern Highlands at this time is, therefore, that there are contrasts from east to west. Whereas, in the north-west, the forests were largely replaced by blanket bog (except on steep slopes and in other favourable areas) **before** the large-scale impact of man, in the eastern Highlands it appears that it is largely human activity which has led to the destruction of the forests, and, in this area, heather moor has been the main plagioclimax community. No doubt there are strong climatic and other reasons for this contrast, and there are of course exceptions, eg: the Monadhliath.

Ecological implications of the Palaeoecological evidence

In the Early Flandrian, areas which are now, or were recently, dominated by pine-birch forest supported quite different communities. The pollen-analytical evidence suggests that these were diverse, open vegetation types, dominated at first by heath and scrub taxa, in which species of *Empetrum* were important, and then by shrubs such as juniper and willow. Later came the deciduous pioneer trees such as birch and rowan, and, by analogy with many modern communities, the aspen (McVean, 1963b, 1964), and, finally, the apparently gradual immigration of the pine.

These deciduous pioneers are all members of that category of trees generally known somewhat loosely as "soil improvers", or formers of Mull humus (Handley, 1954), and one might expect therefore that their combined effects on Early Flandrian soil profiles would be to form acid (but brown) soils, with mobile humus, on even the poorest substrates. This property can be demonstrated in several parts of the Highlands at the present day, usually on islands or steep slopes (McVean, 1958, 1959, 1964). However, this very problem of Early Flandrian soil formation has been given particular attention by Pennington et al. (1972) who concluded that early Flandrian plant communities in the North-west Highlands may not have been able to conserve soil status so readily as one might expect.

Chemical analysis of sediments from Loch Sionascaig is interpreted as showing that reducing conditions existed in some parts of the Sionascaig catchments before 9,000 BP, that is, so far as can be ascertained, before the arrival of birch trees. This is deduced from changes in amounts of Fe and Mn deposited in the sediments, as these elements are removed from soils into lakes under reducing conditions. During the following birch-hazel period, the hazel was probably therefore only able to establish itself on those soils which had not yet become heavily leached, and the authors consider that the period of pine expansion, from c.8,000 to c.6,500 BP, coincided with a phase of reduced mobilisation of Fe and Mn, which may indicate a dry interval of climate. However, from 6,250 BP, in the case of the Sionascaig catchment, increased leaching indicates further waterlogging, and from 5,000 BP there is the chemical and pollen-analytical evidence for widespread extension of waterlogged soils and peats referred to above.

It was thus concluded by the authors that the one thousand year delay between the formation of new soils at the end of the last glaciation and the establishment of birch-hazel woodland was crucial in its implications for the subsequent development of vegetation in many parts of the north-west Highlands (Pennington et al. 1972, page 277). Because of the lack of a vegetation cover capable of retaining and recycling nutrients, some soils probably deteriorated to the extent that they were later incapable of supporting even hazel, let alone mixed-oak forest. Consequently, in the succeeding dry period, pine was able to invade areas of already acidified soils, and attain dominance, and, due to continued deterioration, oak was not able to follow, except in very restricted areas of soil, overlying rocks of high base status. Then, when water tables rose and moisture levels increased in the period 5,000 BP onwards, conditions were ripe for blanket bog formation.

According to this theory, the vegetation history of the Early Flandrian, especially the pre-pine period, may therefore be crucial to our understanding of later events, and, to a very great extent, may control their course and nature. It would therefore be interesting to obtain comparable results from other parts of the Highlands, particularly from the lest-oceanic eastern Highlands, where the course of Late-Flandrian vegetation history in particular is somewhat different. In the meantime, the theory goes a long way towards explaining why pine-birch rather than mixed-oak forest developed in the Highlands, and why, subsequently, so many of the forests in the north-west were overtaken by blanket bog. It also serves as a good example of the contribution of palaeoecological studies to problems of conservation, in that it indicates important events not immediately obvious in present-day ecological terms.

In the Middle Flandrian, as shown above, pine-birch

forests became dominant over wide areas of the Highlands after a period of pine .colonisation of varying length according to the site. By comparison of fossil pollen assemblages with modern pollen spectra derived from surface samples, it is possible to suggest that the Middle-Flandrian pine-birch forests were more diverse than many of the present stands. Terrestrial surface pollen samples may not be compared directly with fossil pollen assemblages from lakes as, during transport and sedimentation in water, the pollen spectra are mixed and their composition thus altered (see West, 1971). However, fossil pollen assemblages from peat and Mor humus layers consist largely of windborne pollen, and, given certain reservations about the size of the site of deposition involved, and the scale therefore of the pollen source area (Tauber, 1965; Oldfield, 1970b), they can be compared to, and interpreted using, surface pollen assemblages (O'Sullivan, 1973a) By comparison of contemporary pollen spectra from Abernethy, and pollen diagrams from Mor humus layers and small kettle holes (with no stream inflow) within the forest, it can be shown that the modern and Middle Flandrian pollen spectra differ as follows. The dominant modern taxa are *Betula, Pinus, Calluna* and Gramineae, with some important subsidiary types like *Alnus.* Qualitatively, therefore, the modern assemblages are very similar to the fossil ones, but, quantitatively, they are quite different, in that at the present day there is much more *Calluna,* and much less *Betula* present. Also, in many fossil assemblages, at sites of appropriate size and scale, the pollen of some herbaceous species is more common than at the present day.

The Middle Flandrian pinewoods at Abernethy may therefore have been more diverse than their modern counterparts, and, furthermore, the two principal tree species, pine and birch, may have existed in a more intimate mixture than in modern pinewood communities. This can be deduced from studies of sediments in small kettle-holes in Abernethy, where, from the time of the establishment of pine-birch forest to the beginnings of human influence in the mediaeval period, pollen assemblages denoting mixed pine-birch communities rather than pure pine or pure birch are recorded (O'Sullivan unpublished, Old Forest Lodge diagram).

If so, then here is a second palaeoecological conclusion which has important ecological consequences, again with regard to vegetation-soil relationships, for, presumably, a forest composed of a mixture of birch and pine, and probably rowan and aspen, produces a litter which is less strongly Mor-forming than a pure pine stand, (Tamm, 1950), although this aspect

needs further investigation. There is, however, some indication from the Abernethy evidence that the Ericaceous dwarf-shrubs, today so common in native pinewoods, were also less well-represented in the Middle Flandrian pollen spectra. Thus, it is possible that at least some Middle Flandrian forests were more diverse, less likely to form deep Mor humus, and thus perhaps inherently more stable than their modern counterparts.

On Speyside, there are still patches of more mixed forest which may resemble the type of community envisaged, such as the area at the north-west corner of Loch Garten mentioned by McVean (1963b), and also the mixed pine-birch-rowan wood with holly on the west side of the Pass of Ryvoan.

In the period since 4,000 BP, the pinewoods have been profoundly affected by climatic change, anthropogenic factors, or both. In the north-west, blanket bog had overtaken forest on all but very favourable areas by this time, and it seems that even forests such as Coulin, Shieldaig or Coille na Glas Leitre constitute important relict rather than climax communities. In the case of the Coulin Forest, the Loch Clair pollen diagram of Pennington et al. (1972) shows that, after temporary disturbance by man just before 5,000 BP, this pinewood has remained largely undisturbed until recent times, at least in terms of actual clearance, and historical evidence appears to corroborate this (Steven and Carlisle, 1959). It may therefore be a pinewood in which longterm ecological trends could be most usefully studied.

Similarly, at Beinn Eighe, the results of Durno and McVean (1959) indicate that the Coille na Glas Leitre is a pinewood of considerable antiquity, although, in the absence of radiocarbon-dates, it is difficult to judge its exact age. Of the eight pollen-diagrams described, profile E appears to date from about 6,000 BP, and to be the longest series, and it is interesting that it is a good example of the diversity of the communities recorded in the Beinn Eighe diagrams, with birch mainly dominant rather than pine. Comparison of the Beinn Eighe profiles with the Abernethy surface sample data suggests that, even in the shallow profiles, several generations of forest are represented, and that a mixture of tree species rather than single species stands are recorded. Pine tends to dominate in the shallower, younger (?) profiles.

In the eastern Highlands, the pinewood for which we have the most continuous Late-Flandrian information is Abernethy. Here, a contrast in the pattern of human exploitation within the forest is demonstrable, with prehistoric forest clearance around Loch Garten, close to the Spey Valley, and much later survival of forest around Loch a'Chnuic, five kilometers eastward.

(overleaf)

Figure 2. Flandrian pollen diagram from Loch a'Chnuic, Abernethy Forest, Inverness-shire, (Speyside), showing selected pollen frequencies. Based on a total land pollen sum but excluding *Calluna.* It is like that the rapid rise of the pine curve between Zones LC-3 and LC-4 is a reflection of a period of arrested rate of sediment accumulation.

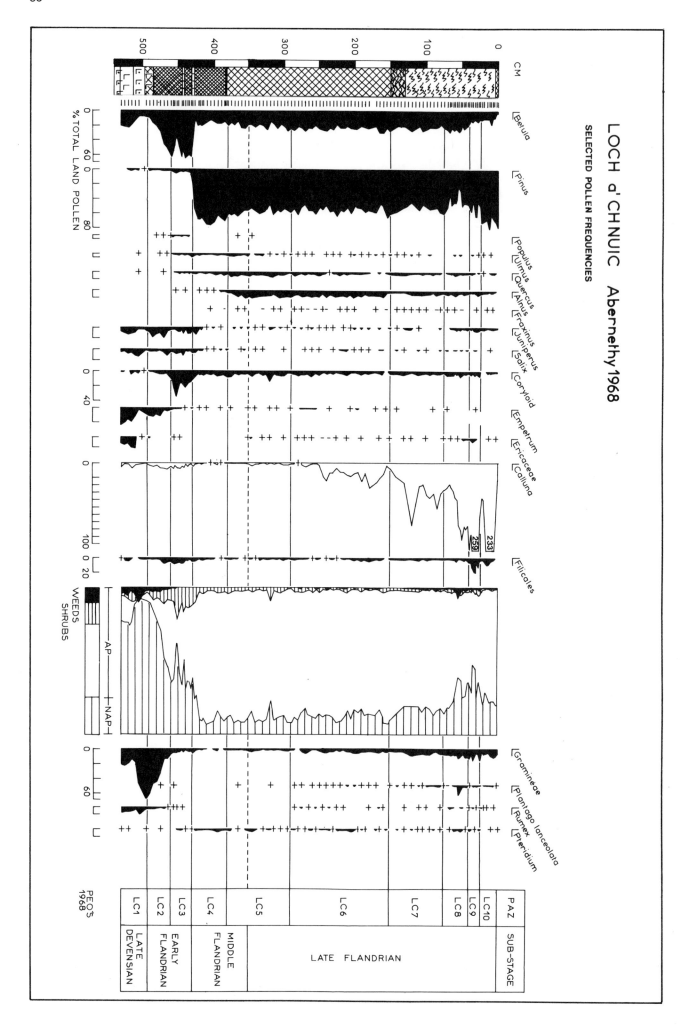

LOCH a'CHNUIC Abernethy 1968

SELECTED POLLEN FREQUENCIES

At the top of the Loch a'Chnuic profile (Fig. 2) are a series of pollen zones which represent recent changes in land-use patterns around the site. In Zone LC-8, declining pine and rapidly expanding *Calluna* values indicate that forest clearance took place. Within this zone are recorded a number of cultural pollen-types, particularly *Plantago lanceolata,* indicating farming, probably mainly pastoral, close by the site. Zone LC-9 records the end of farming, but the persistence of heathland, and Zone LC-10 the regeneration of the forest.

Comparison of this sequence with documentary records for Abernethy (O'Sullivan, 1973c) suggests that these three zones respectively represent a period of farming about 1800 AD, the end of farming in about 1840, and the regeneration of the forest following enclosure in

1869, an event also recorded by Steven and Carlisle (1959). If so, then there is little indication in earlier zones that the forest around Loch a'Chnuic was very much disturbed at all, apart from the steady increase of *Calluna* (Zones LC6-7) which may show the opening of the forest canopy due to grazing.

The pollen assemblages at Loch a'Chnuic thus change from an open forest type to heathland, and back, in the course of some two hundred years. However, the amount of birch pollen recorded declines steadily during the uppermost zones, and there is a complementary increase in *Calluna,* showing that the land-use changes also modified the composition of the forest communities, as well as altering their extent.

Figure 3. Pollen diagram from Mor humus profile near the Faesheallach Burn in the Forest of Abernethy, Inverness-shire (O'Sullivan, 1973b). Pollen percentages are expressed both in terms of total tree pollen and total land pollen. The age of the charcoal layer below the Mor humus shows that the organic matter has accumulated since that time (1505 + 150 BP). During this period, the vegetation surrounding the site has changed from pine-birch heath (Zone FB-2), to *Calluna* moorland (Zone FB-3), and back to pine forest (Zone FB-4). The date of the last vegetation change may be about AD 1860.

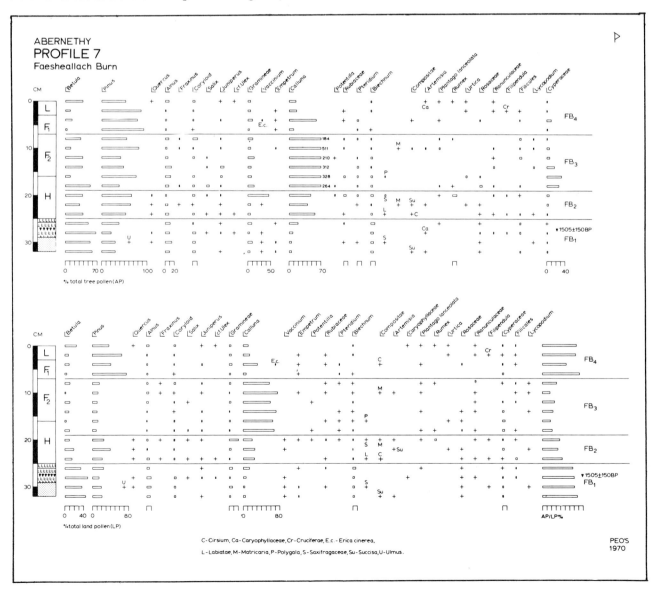

Elsewhere in Abernethy, it has been possible to judge the age of several areas of heathland and forest, by radiocarbon-dating the pollen zone boundaries in a number of Mor humus Layers (Fig.3). These appear to have originated in the Dark Ages, in the period 500-1,000 AD, probably due to clearance for grazing. Their ecological importance is however that Mor humus must form an important sink for what few nutrients are available in Scots pine ecosystems, and the Abernethy evidence suggests that, whilst the deposits are not as old as those described by Iversen (1969) in Draved Forest in Denmark, the effects of persistent Mor humus on nutrient levels in pinewoods can last over many hundreds of years.

Conclusions

The contribution of palaeoecological studies to the problems of Native pinewood conservation can thus perhaps be summarised as follows, under a number of chronological and ecological headings:

(1) Scots pine-dominated forest is a community of considerable antiquity in the Scottish Highlands, dating back to 8,000 years ago with the beginnings of expansion of the pine. By 6,500 years ago, pine-birch forest had become established over a wide area of the Highlands, where it persisted in most cases until about 4,000 BP.

(2) In the west Highlands, some forest may have been destroyed by soil water-logging from 5,000 BP onwards, and a great deal by widespread blanket bog formation from about 4,000 BP. The status of pinewoods as climax forest in this part of the Highlands at the present day must therefore be in some doubt, and it may be more appropriate to regard them, in this region, as important relict communities, in much the same way as many types of Scottish mountain vegetation.

(3) By contrast, in the eastern Highlands, some areas of pine forest may have survived more or less intact until historical times, if unaffected by prehistoric clearance. In this part of the Highlands, heather moor seems to be a plagioclimax community, and therefore it may be possible to regard pine-birch forest as the main climax ecosystem in the area. It is interesting to note that,

rather than being restricted by climatic factors in the east-central Highlands, there is some evidence to suggest that the forests there are capable of extension under existing climatic conditions (Pears, 1967). Ecological considerations (see below) mean, however, that the characteristics of climax ecosystems described by Gimingham (Page 1) may not be fulfilled in the present eastern pinewood context. The events of three periods during the last 10,000 years appear to have had important ecological effects on the development of plant communities in subsequent periods. These are:

(4) In the earliest Flandrian, (10,000-9,000 BP), in the north-west Highlands, leaching of soils proceeded unchecked by the nutrient-conserving effects of woodland vegetation. Soil nutrient content may therefore have declined faster than in areas of Britain further south, and thus affected the ability of other communities to immigrate successfully, particularly the trees of mixed-oak forest.

(5) The period of major pine immigration and expansion, (8,000-6,500 BP), may have been one of rather drier climate in the Highlands than either the preceding or subsequent parts of the Flandrian. This dryness may have aided the pine in its spread over the Highlands to what appears to have been its maximum extent.

(6) After 4,000 BP, the pine forests in the west Highlands were, under the influence of high water-tables and low soil-nutrient levels, unable to survive widespread blanket bog formation. However, in the eastern Highlands the forests were able to withstand Late-Flandrian climatic change to some degree, and here the main factor controlling their subsequent development has been anthropogenic.

(7) There is some evidence to suggest that the undisturbed communities of the Middle Flandrian were more diverse than the modern pinewoods. In this connection, the role of land-use and forest clearance in reducing the diversity of the native pinewood communities appears to have been crucial in terms of the consequent decline in nutrient status due to Mor humus formation. It would thus seem important that conservation policies include provision for the restoration of this diversity.

Acknowledgements

The author is indebted to Professor Yrjo Vasari for discussion of many of the points in this paper, and to Mr Kevin Edwards for permission to refer to his unpublished work on Deeside.

References

BIRKS, H.H. (1970) Studies in the vegetational history of Scotland. I. A pollen diagram from Abernethy Forest, Inverness-shire. *J. Ecol.,* **58,** 827-846.

BIRKS, H.H. (1972b). Studies in the vegetational history of Scotland. III. A pollen diagram from a core from Loch Maree, Ross and Cromarty. *New Phytol.,* **71,** 731-754.

BIRKS, H.H. (1975). Studies in the vegetational history of Scotland. IV. Pine stumps in Scottish blanket peats. *Phil. Trans. R. Soc.,* B., **270,** 182-226.

BIRKS, H.J.B. (1973). *The past and present vegetation of the Isle of Skye.* Cambridge.

CARLISLE, A. (this volume). Man's impact in the pinewoods.

DUNLOP, B.M.S. (1975). Regeneration of our native pinewoods. *Scott. For.,* **29,** 111-119.

DURNO, S.E. (1957). Certain aspects of vegetational history of North-east Scotland. *Scott. geogr. Mag.,* **73,** 176-184.

DURNO,. S.E. (1958c). Pollen analysis of peat deposits from Eastern Suntherland and Caithness. *Scott. geogr. Mag., 74*, 127-135.

DURNO, S.E. (1959). Pollen analysis of peat deposits in the Eastern Grampians. *Scott. geogr. Mag., 75*, 102-111.

DURNO,. S.E. & McVEAN, D.N. (1959). Forest history of the Beinn Eighe nature reserve. *New Phytol., 58*, 228-236.

EDWARDS, K.J. (1974). A half-century of pollen-analytical research in Scotland. *Trans. bot. Soc. Edinb., 42*, 211-222.

EDWARDS, K.H. (1975). Aspects of the prehistoric archaeology of the Howe of Cromar. In: *Quaternary Studies in North-east Scotland,* edited by A.D.M. Gemmell. University of Aberdeen.

ERDTMANN, G.E. (1928). Studies in the post-arctic history of the forests of North-west Europe. I. Investigations in the British Isles. *Geol. För. Stockh. Förh., 50*, 123-192.

GAFFNEY, V. (1960). *The Lordship of Strathavon* - Third Spalding Club of Aberdeen.

GIMINGHAM, C.H. (this volume). The status of pinewoods in British ecosystems.

GODWIN, H. (1956). *The History of the British Flora.* Cambridge Univ. Pr.

GUNSON, A.R. (1975). The vegetation history of North-east Scotland. In: *Quaternary Studies in North-east Scotland,* edited by A.D.M. Gemmell. University of Aberdeen.

HANDLEY, W.R.C. (1954). Mull and Mor in relation to forest soils. *Bull. For. Commn. no. 23.*

HIBBERT, F.A., SWITSUR, V.R. & WEST, R.G. (1971). Radiocarbon-dating of Flandrian pollen zones at Red Moss, Lancashire. *Proc. R. Soc. Lond.* B., *177*, 161-176.

IVERSEN, J. (1969). Retrogressive development of forest ecosystem demonstrated by pollen diagrams from fossil Mor. *Oikos,* suppl. no. *12*, 35-49.

MVEAN, D.N. (1958b). Island vegetation of some West Highland freshwater lochs. *Trans. Bot. Soc. Edinb., 37*, 200-208.

McVEAN, D.N. (1959). The post-glacial history of juniper in Scotland. *Proc. Linn. Soc. Lond., 172*, 52-55.

McVEAN, D.N. (1963). The ecology of Scots pine in the Scottish Highlands. *J. Ecol., 51*, 671-686.

McVEAN, D.N. (1964). Woodland and scrub: pre-history and ecological history. In: *The vegetation of Scotland,* edited by J.H. Burnett. Oliver and Boyd.

McVEAN, D.N. & RATCLIFFE, D.A. (1962). *Plant communities of the Scottish highlands.* H.M.S.O. (Nature Conservancy Monograph no. 1.)

MURRAY, J.M. (1935). An outline of the history of forestry in Scotland, up to the end of the nineteenth century. *Scott. For. J., 49*, 1-19.

OLDFIELD, F. (1970a). The ecological history of Blelham Bog National Nature Reserve. In: *Studies in the vegetation history of the British Isles,* edited by D. Walker and R.G. West. Cambridge Univ. Pr.

OLDFIELD, F. (1970b). Some problems of scale and complexity in pollen analytically-based paleoecology. *Pollen Spores, 12*, 163-171.

O'SULLIVAN, P.E. (1973a). Contemporary pollen studies in a native Scots pine ecosystem. *Oikos, 24*, 143-150.

O'SULLIVAN, P.E. (1973b). Pollen-analysis of Mor humus profiled from a native Scots pine ecosystem, interpreted with surface samples. *Oikos, 24*, 259-272.

O'SULLIVAN, P.E. (1973c). Land-use changes in the Forest of Abernethy, Inverness-shire, AD 1750-1900. *Scott. geogr. Mag., 89*, 95-106.

O'SULLIVAN, P.E. (1974a). Two Flandrian pollen diagrams from the East-central Highlands of Scotland. *Pollen Spores, 16*, 33-57.

O'SULLIVAN, P.E. (1974b). Radiocarbon-dating and prehistoric forest clearance on Speyside (East-central Highlands). *Proc. prehist. Soc., 40*, 206-208.

O'SULLIVAN, P.E. (1975a). Early and middle Flandrian pollen-zonation in the Eastern Highlands of Scotland. *Boreas, 4*, 197-207.

O'SULLIVAN, P.E. (1976). Pollen analysis and radiocarbon-dating of a core from Loch Pityoulish, East-central Highlands of Scotland. *J. Biogeogr., 3*, 293-302.

O'SULLIVAN, P.E. & BROWN, R.H.G. (1975). Loch Morlich. In: *Glen More Forest Park, Cairngorms,* edited by D.A. Woodburn. H.M.S.O. (Forestry Commission Guide).

PEARS, N.V. (1967a). Present tree-lines of the Cairngorm Mountains, Scotland. *J. Ecol., 55*, 815-830.

PEARS, N.V. (1968c). Post-glacial tree-lines of the Cairngorm Mountains, Scotland. *Trans. bot. Soc. Edinb., 40*, 361-394.

PEARS, N.V. (1970). Post-glacial tree-lines of the Cairngorm Mountains, Scotland: some modifications based on radiocarbon-dating. *Trans. bot. Soc. Edinb., 40*, 536-544.

PENNINGTON, W., HAWORTH, E.Y., BONNY, A.P. & LISHMAN, J.P. (1972). Lake sediments in Northern Scotland. *Phil. Trans. R. Soc.* B., *246*, 191-294.

SISSONS, J.B. (1974c). The quaternary in Scotland: a review. *Scott. J. Geol., 10*, 311-357.

SMITH, A.G. & PILCHER, J.R. (1973). Radiocarbon-dating and vegetational history of the British Isles. *New Phytol., 72*, 903-914.

STEVEN, H.M. & CARLISLE, A. (1959). *The native pinewoods of Scotland.* Oliver and Boyd.

TAMM, C.O. (1950). *Northern coniferous forest soils.* Scrivener Pr.

TAUBER, H. (1965). Differential pollen dispersal and the interpretation of pollen diagrams. *Danm. geol. Unders.* II, *89*, 1-69.

VASARI, Y. & VASARI, A. (1968). Late- and post-glacial macrophytic vegetation in the lochs of Northern Scotland. *Acta bot. fenn., 80*.

WALKER, M.J.C. (1975a). Late glacial and early post-glacial environmental history of the Central Grampian Highlands, Scotland. *J. Biogeogr., 2*, 265-284.

WALKER, M.J.C. (1975c). A pollen diagram from the Pass of Drumochter, Central Grampian Highlands, Scotland. *Trans. bot. Soc. Edinb., 42*, 335-343.

WEST, R.G. (1968). *Pleistocene geology and biology.* Longman.

WEST, R.G. (1970). Pollen zones in the pleistocene of Great Britain and their correlation. *New Phytol., 69*, 1179-1183.

WEST, R.G. (1971). *Studying the past by pollen-analysis.* Oxford Univ. Pr.

The impact of Man on the Native pinewoods of Scotland

A. Carlisle Program Manager, Canadian Forestry Service
Petawawa Forest Experiment Station, Chalk River, Ontario.

Abstract

The effects of man on the native pinewoods of Scotland from 500 B.C. to the present day are discussed against a background of climatic changes and natural disturbance. Neolithic man affected many forests and their soils in Britain, but Highland pinewoods were probably little affected until Lowland timber was exhausted in the 16th and 17th centuries. This led to intense exploitation of the pinewoods until the end of the Napoleonic Wars after which activity waned, except for resurgences in the two World Wars.

Felling, burning, grazing, planting etc. have all affected the extent of the pinewoods, age class distributions and regeneration. Regeneration is locally successful though often inhibited by grazing. Scots pine may be a partially fire-dependent species in the natural state, and recent fire control may be the cause of some regeneration problems. Felling is not likely to have greatly affected the Scots pine gene pool in larger forests, but small pine forests have been virtually destroyed and planting of Scots pine of non-local origin has threatened gene pool purity.

Nutrient losses due to logging and fire would be at least partly replaced by rainfall nutrients over the centuries, except for phosphorus. However, although there is not much evidence of nutrient deficiencies in these pines, increment tends to be low, and the soils may have been degraded to some extent.

Changes in climate and man's activities have both been responsible for the extinction of some wildlife species in these forests since Stone Age times. Man still tends to shoot species which interfere with recreation, timber production and agriculture, so that populations of raptors and pine-damaging birds, such as capercaillie and Black grouse, are probably lower than the forest can support.

These forests have been greatly affected by man but still have natural characteristics and a primeval atmosphere. They are well worth preserving.

Introduction

The purpose of this paper is to outline the effects of man on the native pinewoods of Scotland from Stone Age times until the present day, particularly with regard to stand structure, tree regeneration, soil fertility, and wildlife. The question of man's effect on vegetation succession is not considered in great detail as this is the topic of another paper at the same meeting.

Pre-Roman Times

There is evidence that Stone Age man was present in Britain between 20,000 and 10,000 B.C. (Rahtz in Ashe 1971), and there is some indication of his presence in Scotland between the later glaciations (Callendar *et al.* 1927), but his numbers must have been very few. After the glaciations man probably reached Scot-

land at the end of the Boreal period, about 5000 B.C. (Lacaille 1954; Movius 1942), and his food-gathering Stone Age culture persisted in Scotland for much longer than in Central Europe, where Middle East agricultural techniques had been used since the fifth millennium B.C. (Chadwick 1972). Clark (1972) gave a vivid picture of these Palaeolithic and Mesolithic times when he wrote: ''. . . it is doubtful whether more than an occasional wisp of smoke from some camp fire, or maybe a small cluster of huts or shelters by a river bank or old lake bed, would have advertised the presence of man''. It is not likely that these early people greatly affected Scotland's landscape.

About 2500 B.C., however, the Neolithic people reached Britain with a culture based on growing cereal crops and grazing domesticated animals, and from this point onwards man became a threat to the forests. These early farmers practised shifting cultivation, possessed good stone axes, used fire, and utilized wood in house construction. They were also able to cultivate light soils, so it is likely that they had at least a local impact on the forests on the lighter, more fertile soils of the valleys. It is not likely that the pinewoods of Scotland — with their relatively infertile, stoney morainic soils and their inhospitable terrain — would be much affected by cultivation in these times.

The arrival of the Beaker peoples in Britain during the second millennium B.C. greatly increased the importance of cattle as a basis for wealth and prestige (Chadwick 1972). These increased grazing activities, and possibly more land clearance, would again endanger trees locally, but again it does not seem likely that much farming would occur on pinewood soils. The Beaker people mainly used flint and stone implements, but they also imported bronze tools, bringing the Bronze Age to Britain and making possible the cultivation of a wider range of soils. There is good evidence (Dimbleby 1962) that many upland soils in England began to deteriorate in the Bronze Age due to deforestation, burning and grazing, but there is no evidence that the Highland pinewoods were greatly affected. During the Iron Age in Scotland (beginning about 100 B.C. or a little earlier), the better tools made tree felling and timber dressing easier so that much more wood was used in construction; it was estimated by Childe that one of the Gallic forts, which were widely distributed in Scotland at this time, required 100,00 cubic feet (2832 cubic metres) of timber in its construction (Childe 1947; Piggott 1949).

While man's activities and impact changed with time, so did the climate. During the Boreal Period (6800-5000 B.C.), pine forest dominated a large part of Britain, but during Atlantic times (5000-3000 B.C.) the climate became warmer and more humid. The water tables rose, alder spread far inland, and in many places the woodlands were replaced by obrogenous bog. Scotland's forests decreased, particularly those like pine which were adapted to drier sites. In Sub-Boreal times

(3000-500 B.C.), the climate was drier and more continental in Scandinavia, but the situation is less clear for Britain. Godwin (1956) deduced that there was local invasion and spread of pine on the bogs, suggesting that the bogs were drying out, but comparatively few pine remained in the British Isles at this time compared with the Boreal period which was the heyday of pine in Britain. About 500 B.C., as the Sub-Boreal times merged into the Sub-Atlantic, the climate changed to one of lower summer temperatures and greater humidities, typically oceanic as in present times. Pine decreased further, and birch increased in frequency.

The effect of man on the Highland pinewoods in these early times must, therefore, be considered against this background of vegetation changes due to climate. It is safe to say that, although early man affected these forests locally, this effect was small compared to that of climate changes.

The Roman Occupation

A great many people have in their minds a picture of the Romans cutting through the British countryside with fire and sword, destroying the forests and subduing a semi-barbarian people to conform with the Roman concept of civilisation. As far as the Highlands of Scotland are concerned, there is no evidence to support this view. It needs only a glance at the Ordnance Survey Map of Roman Britain (Anon. 1956) to dispel the popular myth that Scotland's pine forests were greatly depleted by the Roman invaders. The map shows that, in the English countryside, there were many Roman and Romano-British settlements, including large coloniae, lesser walled towns, spas, forts, villas, etc., the pattern of a settled country where man's impact must have been considerable. Further north, the pattern was more military, and the Roman installations were mainly forts of various sizes, signal stations and temporary camps, particularly along Hadrian's Wall and the Antonine Wall, and in the land between. North of the Clyde and Firth of Forth, evidence has been found of one legionary fortress near Inchtuthil, eight forts, many signal stations, and a chain of temporary camps, all scattered along the eastern plain from the River Tay to the River Don, with the forts protecting the entrances to the glens and the road from Dunblane to Cardean. It is clear, therefore, that, north of the Clyde, Roman influence was mainly confined to the more fertile lowland soils of the east. It is true that a few Roman artefacts have been found in the Highland glens (e.g. the Great Glen, Speyside, and near Loch Tay) and along the coast, but there is no evidence of much Roman activity in these areas.

All of the remnants of natural pine forest of Scotland lie in the Highland glens. Apart from the pines of Deeside in Aberdeenshire, which could possibly have been threatened by the presence of Roman troops in the lower Deeside camp at Normandykes, it seems likely that few Romans even saw these pinewoods, let alone affected them. A few scouting parties probably penetrated the glens, and some of the pinewoods on the west coast may have been visited by Agricola's ships, but the direct effect of Romans on the Highland pinewoods was probably very small. However, the effect of the Romans on the deciduous forests of the lowland areas to the east and south was probably appreciable, and it is possible that there were pinewoods on the fringes of the Highlands that were destroyed.

In the second century A.D., there is the first mention of the Caledonian Forest as such in the Ptolemy's map of Scotland which was based on scanty information from early Greek travellers who circumnavigated Britain as early as 325 B.C. and from the later Roman invaders (Blaeu 1654; Muller 1883; Rylands 1893). The map is crude and disoriented, but shows a "Caledonia Silva" between Loch Long and Beauly Firth. The Romans knew the forest was there, but this does not mean that they visited it in force or knew much about it.

The Romans were not the only people in Scotland at this time, and the tribes still carried on with their traditional way of life, grazing cattle and raising cereal crops. The Romans may have influenced the Highland forests indirectly, by making life so uncertain and uncomfortable for the indigenous peoples in the eastern and southern lowlands that they fled to the inaccessible glens where, as Strabo (1854) put it, "Forests are their cities", and increased pressures on the forest resource.

The Dark Ages

Early in the fifth century, Rome relinquished all responsibility for maintaining law and order in Britain, leaving behind a Romanized British culture in England, a Celtic culture in Wales partly influenced by Rome, and a turbulent Pictish culture in Scotland. Even before the Romans relinquished power, the northern tribes were on the attack in the Borders, and soon the Saxons, Angles and Jutes were harassing England's south-east and eastern shores. During the same century, the Scots from Northern Ireland invaded western Scotland and the Angles encroached upon southern and eastern Scotland (Wilson 1972; Chadwick 1972; Ashe 1971). Britain was an uncomfortable place in this interregnum between the departure of Roman influence and the final Anglo-Saxon colonization of Britain.

The people of the Dark Ages move as violent, shadowy figures through the mists of conjecture. Most of the surviving written records of this period relate to the church and the state, with little or no information on secular land use, and it is difficult to separate fact from legend and pure fiction.

One of the key sources of information relating to this time is Geoffrey of Monmouth's History of the Kings of Britain (Thorpe 1966). Geoffrey was a creative artist more than a historian who drew upon Welsh monastic records, Breton folklore, poems and legends, and was one of the main instigators of the Arthurian legend

(Ashe 1971). There seems little doubt that Arthur existed, and at this point it is perhaps timely to discuss his connection with the "Caledonian" Forest in the old literature.

During the ninth century, a Bangor (Wales) cleric called Nennius translated a heap of ancient records and Welsh stories into rather clumsy Latin, and the ingredients of the heap are regarded as authentic (Wade-Evans 1938; Ashe 1971). The cleric describes a series of twelve battles which Arthur fought in the fifth century A.D., including one in the Wood of Celidon, a Welsh distortion of the Roman "Caledonia". This could lead to the assumption that this battle was fought in the Highland forests, but Ashe indicates that this Wood of Celidon was located at the headwaters of the Tweed and Clyde, well outside the Highlands. One theory is that all twelve Arthurian battles took place in Central Scotland. Although there are Arthurian associations with Scotland, this theory is not generally accepted since the main foes of the British at this time — the fifth century A.D. — were the Angles and Saxons, and these were not present in force in Central Scotland (Ashe 1971). These events, therefore, are not likely to have affected the pinewoods.

About the same time, the Scots and Picts were fighting in the Highland glens, but we do not know how this affected the forest. Cattle grazing and cultivation of crops doubtless continued, and timber was still being used for building (Graham 1953; Wainwright 1955).

From about the end of the eighth century A.D. until about 1200 A.D., the north and western coasts of Scotland were ravaged by Norsemen as they emigrated to the west and south. Brogger (1929) suggested that the great timber wealth of Scotland attracted the Norsemen, who needed oak for the ships' hulls and pine for the masts. If this was the case, and it is by no means proven, coastal forests could have been affected appreciably over the four centuries of Norse attacks.

Feudal Times

Early in the twelfth century A.D., the feudal system gained momentum in Scotland with the Accession of King David I, who founded a dynasty of feudal monarchs of Celtic and Saxon origins (Skene 1876). All land remained in the hands of the King except for those extensive areas which he granted to monasteries. Fortunately, these monasteries kept records and, if one has the patience to wade through the volumes and deal with difficulties of script and language, they provide a broad picture of forest protection and use, at least for the Lowlands. One of the earliest records of tree conservation dates from these times; in a 13th century grant of forest rights in Eskdale (Anon. 1837, 1868) it was prescribed that trees containing nests of falcons and hawks were not to be felled, with the monks having unrestricted use of other trees. A little later, about the 14th century or a little later, the Forest Laws (*Leges Forestarum*) were enacted by the Scottish Parliament (Anon. 1814-72). These laws prescribed penalties for

cutting oak, encouraged production of acorns for pigs (pannage), restricted grazing, and prohibited the lighting of fires.

We get only a few glimpses of the Highland forests in the 14th century records of travellers such as John of Fordun (Skene 1972), who described vast woods at the foot of the mountains, full of wild animals, these forests providing shelter for both the inhabitants and their cattle when attacked.

Most of the records, however, refer to the Lowlands, where castles, monasteries and churches were being built, with great demands being made upon local forests for timber and grazing.

Feudal times were turbulent, and destruction and reconstruction led to further demands for timber. By the end of the 13th century, shortages of accessible timber were so acute that Baltic timber, including pine, was being imported (Anon. 1878-93).

The Lowland and Border forests were clearly in a state of decline, and legislation was passed in the 15th century (Anon. 1814-72; Murray 1935) to encourage tree planting and prohibit burning trees. However, the depletion continued, and people were transporting timber long distances for building in the lowlands; for example, the oak used in Holyrood came from as far away as Lochaber (Paton 1957). By the 16th century, timber reserves in those parts of Scotland outside the Highlands were virtually exhausted.

The Highland forests at this time were still more or less intact, and it is unlikely that the remote pinewoods were greatly affected by man except for local grazing, accidental fire, and tillage. Man's activities took place against a background of natural fire, flood, wind and grazing wildlife, and it seems likely that these natural agencies affected the pine forests far more than man.

About 1600, the pattern of land use changed due to an increasing population, more building, less available lowland timber, and the development of an iron industry with an insatiable need for charcoal that continued into the 18th century (Anon. 1814-72). The 17th century can be regarded as the time at which the Highland forests began to lose their primeval innocence.

Exploitation of the Pinewoods

With the accessible Lowland forests severely depleted, the people of Scotland looked to the Highlands for their timber. Although the extensive forests of the Highlands were relatively inaccessible, labour was cheap and the nation needed timber urgently. In spite of well-meant forest legislation in the 15th and 16th centuries, the replacement of the Lowland forests was negligible.

The demand for charcoal and fuel for iron smelting had steadily increased during and since the Iron Age, and it is interesting to note that by 1609 Parliament (Anon. 1814-72) was sufficiently concerned about the consumption of forests by the iron industry to enact legislation restricting activities of iron mills responsible for ''. . . the utter wasting and consuming of the said woods, which might be reserved for many better uses''. This concern about the effects of the iron industry was well founded. Fell (1908) estimated that, in 1613, 180,000 tons of iron were smelted per year in Britain; this would require about 3.6 million tons of trees annually for charcoal (Carlisle and Brown 1967). This timber drain was tremendous and, although it was concentrated in the Lake District, Sussex Weald and Severn Valley in England, many iron bloomeries existed in Scotland, even as far north as Strath Naver in Sutherland and Loch Maree in Wester Ross (Blaeu 1654; Anon., 1814-72).

In spite of the 1609 legislation controlling iron smelting, Sir George Hay, a man of great power, was able to continue his iron smelting operation beside Loch Maree on the lands of Letterewe which he acquired in 1607. A large iron works was erected at Furnace on the north side of the loch (Anon. 1814-72; Dixon 1886; Macadam 1887) and we can only guess at the huge timber consumption and the probable devastation of the deciduous forest at Letterewe, the natural pine on the loch's islands, and the pine on the south east side of the loch. Oak and birch were favoured for charcoal, but the pine also would be used as fuel. We do not know a great deal about which other indigenous forests were exploited for the iron industry, but it is known that, during the 17th and 18th centuries, birch and other trees were felled at Speyside and Loch Etive to produce charcoal for iron smelting. A great deal of timber was taken from the Highlands to fuel the large Carron Iron Works at Falkirk (Macadam 1887; Mackay 1914; Ritchie 1920; Steven and Carlisle 1959).

About the same time that the iron industry was gaining momentum at Loch Maree, Crown surveyors were examining the forests of the Highlands and reported (in 1600) the presence of large pine trees suitable for the masts of ships, particularly at Loch Arkaig and Ardgour in Inverness-shire, where superb stems were floated down the rivers to the sea lochs (Speed 1611).

During the middle and closing decades of the 16th century, early travellers, particularly Timothy Pont, penetrated the Highlands. If one can decipher Pont's curious English laced with strangely spelled contemporary Scottish terms, a fascinating picture emerges. He describes great pine forests around Loch Eil, oakwoods north of Kinlocheil, fourteen miles of pine forest on Loch Arkaig, and a ''fair oaken wood'' in the same glen. Pont commented upon pines 60 to 80 feet high suitable for masts by Loch Maree, and oak yielding planks 4 to 5 feet (1.2 to 1.7 metres) broad in the same area. Pont's data was used to construct Blaeu's Atlas (1654), and this Atlas gives a useful picture of forest distribution. In Pont's diaries, it is clear that he looked at these Highland forests with a practical, commercial eye, very much aware of their potential value (Macfarlane 1908).

From the 17th century onwards, the pinewoods were extensively exploited, and they would have disappeared very rapidly but for their remoteness and difficult terrain. Extraction was particularly difficult, and problems were encountered in floating logs down even the larger rivers like the Spey and Dee. As the nation grew and floating techniques were improved, demands on the natural pine forests were considerable.

By the middle of the 18th century, the forests of the Highlands were showing signs of devastation, and after the unsuccessful 1745 rising, when many Highland estates were forfeited to the Crown, the new masters attempted to repair some of the devastation by felling limitation, enclosure, grazing control, seed sowing and tree planting at, for example, Rannoch and Barisdale. However, in spite of these attempts at conservation, exploitation of the pine forests reached a peak in the late 18th century and early 19th century, particularly in Speyside, Deeside, and Rannoch during the Napoleonic Wars (Steven and Carlisle 1959).

No account of the history of land use in the natural pinewoods in the 18th century would be complete without mention of the information available in the voluminous Forfeited Estates Papers lodged in the archives of Register House in Edinburgh. These Papers consist of a vast number of letters, reports, notes and accounts relating to the estates confiscated by the Crown for treason after 1745. Some of the material about forests is in easily accessible batches — particularly those relating to the Black Wood of Rannoch, or Strowan as it was called at that time — but a great deal is thinly scattered in the documents and much patience is needed to find and interpret the data. Some of the most valuable material is contained in the meticulous reports of Crown factors and other agents employed as surveyors. These papers provide a detailed picture of land use and costs, and also describe people's attitudes, motives and weaknesses, which do not seem to have changed a great deal in the last two centuries. There is still a lot of material in these archives that has not been tapped.

After the middle of the nineteenth century, the pace of exploitation slackened, although there was still considerable local activity. The trees that were left were the parents of many of the current pine of the 100-150 year age classes. There was a resurgence of felling in the natural pinewoods during the 1914-18 War, and again during the Second World War 1938-45, leaving us with what we have today.

The Ecological Impact of Man

Man's most important activities in the Highland pinewoods have been, and still are, felling, burning, grazing and planting, and all of these have affected the structure of the pine stands, vegetation succession (including pine regeneration), the pine gene pool, soil fertility and wildlife populations. In some forests, such as the Black Wood of Rannnoch — where canals, locks and log collection basins were constructed to facilitate extraction of pine during the Napoleonic Wars—man also influenced the local topography.

Stand structure and regeneration

The natural structure of many pinewoods is that of being uneven aged by groups. Also, where the forest grows on the irregular topography of lateral moraines, there is a ridge and hollow pattern, with the pine on the ridges. In the major pinewoods of Scotland, this situation still obtains today and has only been affected by man in that the pine are fewer and some pine forests, such as Rhiddorch, have virtually disappeared. The distribution of the age classes, however, has undoubtedly been affected by man, firstly by the felling and extraction of the larger, old stems and also by the destruction or regeneration by increased grazing pressure and a greater frequency of both intentional and accidental fires. These grazing and burning activities have been particularly effective at the forest margins. Scots pine *(Pine sylvestris* L.) will not tolerate a great deal of shade, and the most successful regeneration is on clearings with a sparse tree cover, and at the forest margins. In the natural condition, the pinewoods tended to shift their positions as the marginal regeneration spread. On hillsides, the upwards movement of the trees is often limited by climate and lateral movement is often prevented by man, particularly through his moor burning and grazing activities. Many existing pine forests are artificially contained by man, and must rely upon regeneration within their own boundaries.

The problem of success and failure of pine regeneration is a controversial topic. Although there have been surveys of regeneration and many empirical trials, we still know very little about the dynamics of regeneration of these forests. Consequently we just have to speculate and use common sense on a basis of the meagre known facts.

Many natural pinewoods, particularly those in the east, are regenerating very well locally; Glentanar and Rothiemurchus are good examples. Many other pinewoods would regenerate well if the grazing pressure were to be reduced. In all pinewoods, there are a great many pine seedlings, but, for one reason or another, these often fail or go into check. The check can be edaphic, due to reducing soil conditions and inhibition of nutrient uptake (Brown, Carlisle and White 1966), or to failure of the seedlings' roots to penetrate the raw humus, or to grazing, or vegetation competition.

If regeneration is to succeed there must be enough seed, the soil surface must be in a receptive state, there must not be excessive competition from other vegetation, and grazing must be at an acceptable level. All these conditions must be met at the same time. In the natural situation, nature is concerned with survival and not with timber productivity and is in no great hurry; she can afford to wait for a century or more for the right conditions to occur. Today, foresters are necessarily more impatient, faced as they are by the urgent need to renew a dwindling resource. The forester

regenerating the forests naturally, therefore, has the task of imitating nature by increasing the frequency of occurrence of the right conditions for regeneration. The trouble is that we are not quite sure what these "right conditions" are; sometimes everything looks ideal and the regeneration fails.

A clue to these right conditions is afforded by the records of pinewood history. Scanning the histories of individual forests (Steven and Carlisle 1959), one gets the general impression that the pine regeneration has benefited from natural and man-made disturbance. The early records contain repeated references to large quantities of regeneration coming in after felling and burning, with the greatest regeneration success following fires, with or without felling, in areas that were well drained. The picture emerges of Scots pine being a partially fire-dependent species in the natural condition. This fire dependence is not as extreme as that of Jack pine *(Pinus banksiana* Lamb.) and Lodgepole pine *(Pinus contorta* Dougl.) which need high temperatures to open their serotinous cones, but resembles the situations of Red pine *(Pinus resinosa* Ait.) and White pine *(Pinus strobus* L.) which need fire to create the best regeneration conditions in the vegetation and on the soil surface. The success of Scots pine natural regeneration appears to depend upon the coincidence of a good seed year and vegetation that is neither too tall nor too dense. Fires can create the right vegetation condition, but whether or not they stimulate cone production by suddenly providing a great deal of potash for the surviving trees of seed-bearing age is still a point in question. However, the relationship between past fires and past regeneration is fairly well documented, and we must give thought as to whether or not man's recent protection of the forests from fires is reducing the opportunities for effective pine regeneration. It is only in recent years that foresters have begun to lose their fear of fire and to consider using fire as a silvicultural tool. In Canada and the U.S.A., better fire control techniques and a better understanding of forest fuel behaviour enable foresters to use fire as a silvicultural tool with increasing confidence. Burning is becoming a part of National Park policy in the U.S.A. in an attempt to regenerate and maintain fire-dependent ecosystems (Kilgore and Briggs 1972). Perhaps consideration could be given to using controlled fires in the Highland pine forests in order to imitate nature.

Gene Pool

A great many trees have been taken out of the native pinewoods in Scotland and it is necessary to consider what the effect has been upon the gene pool. In the 17th century, the forests were exposed to high grading, the best trees being taken out for ships' masts; since then fellings have only been selective to the extent that trees that had fairly straight stems suitable for sawing were taken and the coarse trees were left. It does not seem likely that this has greatly affected the gene pool of the remaining larger forests at least so far. In order to shift appreciably the population mean of an attribute controlled by several genes (such as tree form and growth rate) in a large forest, selection has to be very intensive. Even though good trees were felled, they would have made their gene contribution in seed and pollen before they were felled. If stands were to be selectively thinned over a long period, there could be a shift in the population means of form and growth, but this has never been the case in the indigenous pinewoods.

Most of the best regeneration in these pine forests has come from very old, gnarled trees left after logging or fire. This regeneration is frequently of good form, so that these twisted old trees are probably just poor phenotypes rather than poor genotypes. Man's activities, however, have led to the virtual destruction of some of the pine forests. For example, very few pine remain in Rhiddoroch and Glen Einig today, yet quite a large quantity of pine was sold from the area in 1725 (Lang 1898). Where pine forests have nearly disappeared, obviously the gene pool has been depleted, and full use of the few remaining trees should be made to preserve these genes. Unfortunately, the smallness of the remaining populations makes it likely that there will be a high degree of selfing.

The greatest genetic hazard to which these pine forests have been exposed has been not the genes that man has taken out so much as those that he has introduced. Prior to about 1950, there were many instances of Scots pine of unknown or doubtful origin being planted in or adjacent to the native pinewoods. We can only guess at the influence of these introduced genes on the natural gene complement.

Soil fertility

Extraction of tree stems, burning and grazing can all affect soil fertility. On the relatively infertile, acid pinewood soils with their low available nitrogen and base status, and low ion exchange capacity, any nutrient loss is potentially serious. However, the Scots pine appears to be well adapted to these poor soils and we do not often see evidence of marked nitrogen or base deficiency, except in reducing soil conditions or on some of the very poor, granite or quartzite gravels. The logging operations must have taken out a great deal of nitrogen, phosphorus and the bases, but the rainfall in these forests was probably sufficiently high to replace nitrogen and the bases, but not phosphorus (Carlisle, Brown and White 1967). Burning woody vegetation repeatedly causes a considerable drain of nitrogen and sulphur (Allen 1964), but, again, the nutrient content of the rainfall will have replaced a great deal of what was lost; rainfall is probably the main source of nitrogen replacement, as it is not very likely that, with the soil pH being frequently well below 5.0, there would be appreciable nitrogen fixation by soil organisms. The main potential soil nutrient loss due to logging is phosphorus, which is not readily replaced by rainfall or soil mineral weathering on these sites. The problem is that we do not really know what the soil nutrient levels would be in the absence of man's activities; we have no real control or reference point. In the management of natural or semi-natural ecosystems, one is reluctant to use fertilizers, but we must also ask ourselves whether or not we are trying to maintain natural ecosystems on un-naturally degraded soils.

Wildlife

In prehistoric times, the mammalian fauna of the Highlands was much richer than today and included deer, elk, caribou, bear, lynx, wildcat, wolf, fox, Pine marten, polecat and badger – all essentially forest species (Steven and Carlisle 1959). Some of their descendants still live today in the pinewoods, for example deer, foxes, wildcats, Pine martens and badgers, but many, such as the elk, caribou, bear, lynx , wolf and polecat are now extinct.

In early times, man needed to hunt for both food and protection, and hunger and fear are not good breeding grounds for sound wildlife conservation policies. It must be remembered that, during the millennia following the Ice Age when man was active in Scotland, there were considerable climatic and vegetation changes, and these doubtless affected wildlife populations. There is little doubt, however, that the extinction of the bear, lynx and wolf can be laid at man's door.

Deer conservation and control measures have been taken in Britain since feudal times and still go on today. In the pinewoods of Scotland, measures taken range from fencing deer out of pine forests to protect regeneration, fencing deer in the forest to provide accessible shooting, control of deer populations by shooting, provision of corridors to allow deer movement from low ground to high ground and *vice versa*, and the protection of deer from all shooting. To completely exclude deer from forests denies them the use of vital winter shelter; fencing deer in the forest destroys pine regeneration; and protection from all shooting can lead to overpopulation and starvation. Control of deer populations, and possibly in some cases deer movement, is essential both for the well-being of the deer, and for successful pine regeneration. We still need to know what grazing intensity different types of forest can stand and yet regenerate successfully.

It is difficult to generalize about man's effect on deer populations as we do not know what the populations would be without man's interference. When these pinewoods were surveyed by the author between 1950-1956, woodland management policies had led to abnormally high deer populations in some areas such as Ballochbuie and Amat, and relatively low populations in fenced areas like Glentanar – not that fencing in these areas was all that successful in keeping out deer in winters when the snow was deep. In most areas where deer, cattle and sheep were grazing, although deer and cattle ate some pine regeneration, the main damage was done by sheep.

Today, man's chief targets are game species and the predators which affect his recreation and agricultural livestock. The fox is a prime target, but in spite of shooting and even poisoning, it continues to thrive; otters are still killed to protect fishing on many waters. Wildcats, with the predilection for grouse and other small game, are regarded by many as vermin to be shot, although most of the cats that people see and shoot in the pine forest are feral rather than the true *Felis sylvestris*. Gamekeepers on grouse moors and many farmers till regard raptors as nuisances to be destroyed at every opportunity, resulting in local reductions of hawk and falcon populations; the losses are accentuated by the pervasive effects of pollutants such as DDT. Hooded crows still seem to thrive in spite of man doing his best to destroy them in sheep grazing areas both within and outside the pinewoods. Although Black grouse and capercaillie are picturesque components of the avifauna of the pine forests, their habit of eating pine shoots does not endear them to foresters concerned with growing straight trees, with the consequence that these birds are shot; the present populations are probably abnormally low.

A great deal of man's impact on the pine forest wildlife in the past has been due to the use of forests and their margins for commercial forestry, agriculture (including grazing and moor burning) and recreational shooting and fishing. The wildlife has been managed — or perhaps a better word is 'controlled' — to favour these activities rather than to preserve the natural pinewood fauna. If the prime goal were to be total forest ecosystem conservation, the activities of species such as capercaillie and Black grouse would be acceptable, since the main objective would not be to grow straight trees. Deer and fox activity would also be acceptable within the forest provided populations were not excessive, although adjacent farmers would not look on these animals with favour. There will always be some degree of conflict between conservation and commercial interests if the species being preserved are detrimental to the adjacent land use, or this land use interferes with the species being preserved. We cannot expect to get successful marginal regeneration of pine or effectively preserve wildlife if conflicting forest margin land use continues. Consideration should be given to preserving or gaining control over marginal areas and including them in the native pinewood conservation plan.

One of the most attractive features of the indigenous pinewoods is that one can often come into close contact with locally distributed or relatively scarce creatures such as Pine martens, wildcats, Crested tits and crossbills. The pinewoods are refuges for these animals and should be managed as such. Although many of the native pinewoods have been heavily exploited by man and are now artefacts, they still have very strong natural characteristics and a primeval atmosphere that can at times be sinister and oppressive. A visitor to the pinewoods in the winter often feels that early post-glacial times are not far away and that, to quote Professor H.M. Steven, "to stand in them is to feel the past" (Steven and Carlisle 1959). These pinewoods are well worthy of preservation both for science and as part of Britain's historical heritage.

Conclusions

1. Although man has been grazing, burning and cultivating since Neolithic times, and was doubtless responsible for deterioration of many upland soils in Britain, his effect on the indigenous pine forests of Scotland was probably not very great until after the Lowland forests were exhausted in the 16th and 17th centuries and man turned to the remoter Highlands for timber.

2. The depletion of accessible Lowland woods, an increased demand for timber for building, and a growing iron industry resulted in surveys of the pine forests being made in the 16th and 17th centuries with a view to assessing the value of these Highland forests as sources of timber.

3. The pine forests were saved from complete destruction by their inaccessibility and the consequent problems of timber extraction However, increasing demands for timber and the improvement of timber floating techniques resulted in extensive exploitation that began in the 17th century and continued until the middle of the nineteenth century, with a peak of activity during the Napoleonic Wars. Since then there have been periods of heavy exploitation during two World Wars.

4. The main effect of man on pinewood stand structure has been on the number of trees and the age class distributions. The basic pattern of the forests is uneven-aged by groups often on a ridge and hollow topography, and this probably has not changed a great deal in the larger remnants of the forests.

5. In spite of high grading in the past, the selection intensity has been so low that it does not seem likely that, at least in the larger forests, the Scots pine gene pool has been greatly depleted. Some small pine forests have been virtually destroyed and their gene pool depleted, and the genetic purity of some forests has been threatened by planting pine of unknown or non-local origin in or adjacent to the indigenous pine forests.

6. Regeneration of the pine forest has been associated with major site disturbances by logging and fire, particularly the latter. Scots pine in the natural state appears to be partly fire dependent. The successful control of fire in recent times may be the reason for some regeneration problems we face today. Consideration should be given to using controlled prescribed fires to regenerate these forests in good seed years. Regeneration failure is also due to excessive grazing levels. We need to know much more about pine regeneration dynamics.

7. Scots pine seems to be well adapted to the relatively infertile soils of the native pinewoods. Logging and burning have probably caused a considerable loss of

macronutrient elements from the soil, but, except in the case of phosphorus, most of these have probably been replaced by rainfall nutrients. We do not know what these pinewood soils would be like without man's interference. Even though there is not much evidence of nutrient deficiencies in the pine of these forests, except on reducing peats and poorer gravels, increment in the forests is often very low, and we may be dealing with un-naturally degraded soils.

8. Since Palaeolithic times, several large mammals (elk, caribou, bear, lynx and wolf) have become extinct in Scotland, due to both man and changes in climate.

Today man tends to shoot species which interfere with his recreation, agriculture, and timber production, so that populations of raptors and such pine-damaging birds as capercaillie and Black grouse are probably lower than the forest can support. Some species, such as foxes and Hooded crows, are very resilient to man's active hostility. Control of fox and deer populations will probably always be necessary.

9. Although man has greatly affected these forests, they still have many natural characteristics and a primeval atmosphere, and are well worth preserving for science and as part of Britain's historical heritage.

Literature Cited

ALLEN, S.E. (1964). Chemical aspects of heather burning. *J. appl. Ecol.,* **1**, 347-367.

ANON. (1814-72). *Acts of Parliament of Scotland,* 1- 8. H.M.S.O.

ANON. (1837). *Liber Sancte Marie de Melros,* edited by C. Innes. Edinburgh.

ANON. (1868). Facsimiles of National Manuscripts of Scotland. *Ordnance Survey.*

ANON. (1878-93). *.Exchequer rolls of Scotland,* 1-14.

ANON. (1956). Map of Roman Britain, 3rd ed. *Ordnance Survey.*

ASHE, G. (1971). *The quest for Arthur's Britain.* Paladin.

BLAEU, J. (1654). *Atlas.* Lib. 12. Tom. 5: *Scotia quae est Europeae.* Amsterdam. Blaeu.

BROGGER, A.W. (1929). *Ancient emigrants.* Clarendon.

BROWN, A.H.F., CARLISLE, A. & WHITE, E.J. (1966). Some aspects of the nutrition of Scots pine on peat. Physiology in Forestry. *Forestry,* **39**, suppl., 78-87.

CALLENDAR, S.G. et al. (1927). Preliminary reports on caves containing palaeolithic relics near Inchnadamph, Sutherland. *Proc. Soc. Antiq. Scot.,* **61**, 169.

CARLISLE, A. & BROWN, A.H.F. (1967). The influence of forest practices on woodland nature reserves. In: *Biotic effects of public pressures on the environment,* 69-81. Nature Conservancy. (Monks Wood Symposium no. 3).

CARLISLE, A., BROWN, A.H.F. & WHITE, E.J. (1967). The nutrient content of rainfall and its role in the woodland nutrient cycle. *Congr. int. Un. Forest Res. Org.* 14th, **2**, 145-158.

CHADWICK, N. (1972). *The Celts.* Penguin.

CHILDE, V.G. (1947). *Prehistoric communities of the British Isles.* 2nd ed. Chambers.

CLARK, J.G.D. (1972). *Excavations at Star Carr; an early Mesolithic site at Semar near Scarborough, Yorkshire.* Cambridge Univ. Pr.

DIMBLEBY, G.W. (1962). *The development of British heathlands and their soils.* Oxford Univ. Pr.

DIXON, J.H. (1886). *Gairloch, its records and traditions.* Edinburgh: Cooperative Printing Co.

FELL, A. (1908). *The early iron industry of Furness and district.* Cass.

GODWIN, H. (1956). *The history of the British Flora.* Cambridge Univ. Pr.

GRAHAM, A. (1953). Archaeological gleanings from dark-age records. *Proc. Soc. Antiq. Scot.,* **85**, 64.

KILGORE, B.M. & BRIGGS, G.S. (1972). Restoring fire to high elevation forests in California. *J. For.,* **70**, 266-271.

LACAILLE, A.D. (1954). *The Stone Age in Scotland.* Wellcome Inst. Hist.

LANG, A. (ed.), (1898). *The Highlands of Scotland in 1750 from manuscript 104* in the King's Library, British Museum. Edinburgh.

MACADAM, W.I. (1887). Notes on the ancient iron industry of Scotland. *Proc. Soc. Antiq. Scot.* N.S., **9**, 89.

MACFARLANE, W. (1908). *Geographical collections relating to Scotland,* edited by Sir A. Mitchell and J.T. Clark, 1-3. Edinburgh: Scott. Hist. Soc.

MACKAY, W. (1914). *Urquhart and Glen Moriston, olden times in a Highland parish.* 2nd ed. Inverness: Northern Counties Publ. Co.

MOVIUS, H.L. (1942). *The Irish Stone Age.* Cambridge Univ. Pr.

MULLER, C. (1883). *Claudii Ptolemaei Geographia.* Paris.

MURRAY, J.M. (1935). An outline of the history of forestry in Scotland up to the end of the nineteenth century. *Scott. for. J.,* **49**, 1-19.

PATON, H.M. (ed.), (1957). *Accounts of the Masters of Works for building and repairing royal palaces and castles.* 1. 1529-1615. Edinburgh: H.M.S.O.

PIGGOTT, S. (1949). *British Prehistory.* London: Oxford Univ. Pr.

RAHTZ, P. (1972). Glastonbury Tor. *In Ashe, G.* 1972, 111-122.

RITCHIE, J. (1920). *The influence of man on animal life in Scotland.* Cambridge Univ. Pr.

RYLANDS, T.G. (1893). *The geography of Ptolemy elucidated.* Dublin: Rylands.

SKENE, W.F. (ed.), (1872). John of Fordun's Chronicle of the Scottish Nation. *Historians of Scotland,* **4**, Edinburgh.

SKENE, W.F. (ed.), (1976). *Celtic Scotland.* Edinburgh.

SPEED, J. (1611). *History of Great Britain.* London: Hall & Beale for Sudbury & Humble.

STEVE, H.M. & CARLISLE, A. (1959). *The native pinewoods of Scotland.* Oliver and Boyd.

STRABO (1854). *The geography.* Translated by H.C. Hamilton and W. Falconer. London: Bohn.

THORPE, L. (ed. and transl.), (1966). *Geoffrey of Monmouth. History of the Kings of Britain.* Penguin.

WADE-EVANS, A.W. (1938). *Nennius' history of the Britons.* Church Hist. Soc. London.

WAINWRIGHT, F.T. (1955). *The problem of the Picts.* Nelson.

WILSON, D.M. (1972). *The Anglo-Saxons.* Penguin.

The Native Pinewoods of Scotland: The current state of the resource

R. Goodier, Nature Conservancy Council, Edinburgh
R.G.H. Bunce, Institute of Terrestrial Ecology, Merlewood Research Station

1. Introduction

In their classic work on the native pinewoods of Scotland, Steven and Carlisle identified 35 native pinewoods in Scotland by investigating all the areas that had been considered, at various times, native and natural. Several criteria were used by Steven and Carlisle to determine the status of these sites. First, they consulted historical records, mainly from the 18th century, but sometimes going back to the 17th or 16th centuries. If the woods were old, and reputed to be natural pinewoods at that time, it was thought that it was unlikely that they, or their predecessors, had been planted. An uneven age structure, the characteristics of the field vegetation and a wide range of morphological variation in tree type were also regarded as indicative of naturalness. Finally, the remoteness and inaccessibility of some sites rendered it unlikely that the woods had been planted.

When evaluating the current state of the resource, three main categories of information need to be considered.

a) The area of forest that remains
b) The structure of the tree layer, its age and potential longevity
c) The dynamics of the forest, involving assessment and prediction of likely ecological trends.

In the present paper, these categories will be considered separately, using the information provided by Steven and Carlisle and from investigations commenced in 1971 by the Nature Conservancy, and continued to the present time jointly by the Institute of Terrestrial Ecology and the Nature Conservancy Council. In the studies initiated in 1971, it was assumed that the major native pinewood sites had been correctly identified. The aims of the initial survey were to provide a more precise definition of the range of ecological variation, to look again at the groupings produced by Steven and Carlisle, and to ensure that any conservation strategy finally produced took account of this range of variation. The results of this part of the survey have been described by Bunce in an earlier chapter. The second aim was to see what was happening to the forests, what changes had taken place inside them, what regeneration was taking place and what felling had occurred. The long-term aim was to devise conservation programmes for the individual forests that would ensure their continuity as forests with as little interference as possible from man. Some early attempts at this long-term aim are described by Forster and Morris in a later chapter.

2. The area of native pinewood

With the exception of Dulnan, all the major pinewoods were outlined on maps in Steven and Carlisle (1959), and these were used as a basis for the 1971 resurvey of the pinewoods. The other eight sites consist only of scattered trees.

There are considerable difficulties involved in obtaining an estimate of the acreage involved, particularly in determining when a forest becomes moorland with scattered trees, and whether areas of bog incorporated into the forest matrix should be included in the total acreage. As a first estimate, the areas shown as pine and mixed birch/pine by Steven and Carlisle were measured directly from their published maps. This estimate gave a total of 26,800 acres, a figure which is one of the same order of magnitude as the estimate of 22,000 acres given by Innes and Seal (1972). However, field visits and inspection of aerial photographs showed some anolmalies, mainly due either to the problems of defining a site mentioned above, or because felling and planting had taken place since Steven and Carlisle's original survey. The procedure for the 1971 survey has been described in an earlier chapter and involved 416 plots being placed randomly within the boundries of the pinewoods as defined by Steven and Carlisle, representing an unbiased sample. The sample is small, however, and the errors in estimates of the various parameters could, therefore, be quite large. Nevertheless, a comparison of these estimates with interpretation from aerial photographs of the extent of the forest suggests that an acceptably accurate picture of the extent of the pinewoods was obtained, even though, in individual cases, there are anomalies and such cases need more accurate future study. The initial results of the survey showed that the 26,800 acres, obtained by measuring the area of pinewood and mixed birch/pine on Steven and Carlisle's maps was not all, dense "well stocked" woodland. Thus, of the 416 plots, only 197 contained Scots pine, and 66 of these also contained birch. A further 79 plots contained birch alone and the remaining 140 plots contained no trees at all. To illustrate the relatively small amount of comparatively dense pine forest within the individual sites, and for the resource as a whole, we have estimated from the sample plots the acreage of basal area of Scots pine above that for the general yield class 60 for 80 year old Scots pine, a density which is considered to be about a minimal stocking level appropriate to forest management for timber production. The results of this calculation for the individual sites are shown in Table 1, column c, and the total is only 3,182 acres. A further indication of the relative density of woodland in the different sites is to be found in Table 2, where the total number of trees and the basal areas of Scots pine and birch, recorded from sixteen 200 metre square sample plots in each site, are listed. As Millar has emphasised (in a later chapter) such estimates are approximate and more accurate figures could be obtained by detailed comparisons of aerial photographs from individual forests. Table 2 serves to indicate that the maps in Steven and Carlisle give an over-optimistic picture of the extent of native pinewoods because of the different densities included within the boundaries in the original maps. Thus, the high density figure for Glenmore is due to the relict area being a relatively dense nucleus of old Scots pine left within the surrounding plantations, and some of the plots placed within the boundaries given by Steven and Carlisle for the Glenmore forest fell within recent pine plantations. 58 plots of the 416 came within plantations of exotic species planted since the original survey. However, the data from Table 1, column 3, and Table 2 confirm that the area outlined by Steven and Carlisle represents forest of very varying density, ranging, on the one hand, from closely-grown mature pines to, on the other, extensive areas of open bog, with only small stunted pines around the margin.

An analysis of the vegetation of the 4lb sample plots distinguished four geographically distinct site types in which there are marked differences in both the density and the extent of the Scots pine trees. The forests of the east are extensive and not only have a high proportion of pine, but also, in general, have a relatively high density of trees. The two western types showed not only a low density of pine (with the exception of the Loch Maree Islands), but are also very restricted in area. These are the sites where pine is under most stress and at the limit of its distribution and, in one sense, of particular interest. The rarity and interest of these extreme types, therefore, needs emphasis; on the other hand, the sites are under less risk of commercial exploitation that the larger and more valuable eastern forests.

Aerial photographs are now being used to produce maps of ten key sites from the four groups, mainly to show the detailed distribution of the stands of pine, but also to show density and size class distributions. In the three detailed surveys completed so far, the total acreages correspond well with those taken from the maps of Steven and Carlisle. The respective comparisons were:

Glentanar 2,133 (2,195); Ballochbuie 2,124 (2,349) and Rannoch 918 (612) (discrepancy due to planting).

However, these three forests have clearly delineated forest boundaries, whereas in other forests (e.g. Mar and Coulin) the definition of boundaries is more difficult. There are, therefore, important details to confirm on the major stands, but the general distribution of the forest is now well known. Further data are required on particular sites for the production of detailed management plans.

In summary, the total extent of the remaining forest depends mainly on the definition of what constitutes a forest: if a broad definition is given, the total area is about 26,800 acres; if only relatively dense stands are included, the total area is about 4,000 acres.

3. Forest structures

The structure of any forest contains information on its past history as well as its present state. The general structure of the individual forests is well described by Steven and Carlisle and the results from the recent survey confirm their findings, but indicate that further changes have taken place.

The girth class distribution of all the trees recorded in the survey is given in Figure 1. The high frequency of small trees is misleading as many of the younger trees were recorded from a very few plots — as shown in Figure 2. Few plots contain large numbers of trees, with 97 out of the 155 plots having below 20 trees per plot (i.e. 100 trees per hectare).

The distributions for individual sites (Figure 3) provide further emphasis that the forests consist largely of old trees with few younger specimens, as Steven and Carlisle indicated. Some forests, e.g. Loch Maree and Abernethy, have reasonable distributions, but others, such as Ballochbuie and Mar, are badly skewed towards the older (larger) classes. The forests of Glen Moriston and Glen Garry require particular comment; much of the forest at these two sites has been replanted with Sitka spruce and the younger trees are regenerating in small gaps among the plantations, suggesting the effects of removal of grazing.

Having emphasised the open nature of these forests, many of the less-disturbed Scandinavian forests are also open and, as may be seen from the photographs in this volume, they appear similar to those in Scotland in that few young trees are evident. Further comparisons are, however, required before a realistic interpretation of the girth class distribution can be made. There are few natural forests remaining in Europe on which to base such comparisons and little is known of the natural structure within these forests. One major feature of most natural forests is the high proportion of dead and dying trees. In Britain, most of the woods are intensively managed and are relatively young. In the survey, only 6 per cent of the total sample of pine was dead, and although some dead trees may have been removed, this small proportion suggests that, while the forests consist largely of old trees, the death rate is still low.

The relationship of size with age has been further investigated in nine of the forests and the correlations of age with diameter are given in Table 3 and two examples of the scatter diagrams in Fig. 4. Only two of the forests do not have significant linear correlations and it is reasonable to consider diameter as an indication of age. The regressions for age on diameter are currently being calculated for the different forest types.

The structure of the forest does not depend solely upon the diameter distribution of the trees, but also on their height and on the other species present. The forests of the east tend to have taller (and probably more vigorous) trees, whereas those of the west contain more stunted trees because of the factors associated with the depth of organic matter (peat) on the sites. The proportion of birch also varies, and has a critical effect on the populations of birds and of insects. The birch tends to grown on brown earths less well-suited to pine and therefore often forms a mosaic, although, under certain conditions, there is a mixture of both species. The contribution of other hardwood trees is generally small and largely confined to the water courses or where there is surface water. However, at one or two sites, oak grows in close proximity to pine, notably at Ardgour and Barisdale. The former extent of such an overlap is not fully known, and the original contribution of the hardwood species can only be guessed, although there is some evidence that the range of species was greater. The shrub layer is generally absent, although juniper occurs locally in dense groups, and perhaps represents a considerable retraction from its original range.

Where pinewoods have been fenced, e.g. Rannoch and Crannach, the effect is immediately to diversify the structure of the forest, with seedlings of rowan, birch and pine rapidly developing into saplings, and willow developing in wetter areas. The abundance of rowan on fenced sites, as compared with its frequency as a tree in the survey (35 out of 416 plots), is surprising, but where grazing is limited, rowan would probably contribute significantly to a more diverse structure than at present.

The present structure of the pinewoods is probably less diverse than if it were under less pressure from grazing and exploitation. Existing evidence suggests that, with suitable control of grazing, a more diverse structure could be evolved quite rapidly. Carlisle (personal communication) noted, during the Symposium excursion, some widespread changes in both Rothiemurchus and Abernethy compared with his surveys of 20 years ago. The forests have more extensive regeneration than formerly and birch is now more widespread, due probably, in part, to a change in the condition of *Calluna,* and, in part, to a change in grazing patterns, although these may not be independent factors.

4. Dynamics of the forest

The discussion of regeneration is fundamental to this section, although many other factors are also involved.

The success and failure of natural regeneration of pine has been the subject of much debate and of extensive research. A detailed review of such work is urgently required and it is hoped to prepare one in due course. The numbers of seedlings, saplings and regeneration counted during the 1971 survey (Table 4) emphasise the differences between the seedling and sapling stages. Although many factors may inhibit regeneration and control its density, the overriding factor is believed to be grazing by wild and domestic animals.

Whilst there is much research still to be done on the factors controlling regeneration, limitation of grazing pressure in a forest should stimulate regeneration in due course, although the location of the regeneration is not predictable. Moreover, where seedlings are growing in adverse environmental conditions, grazing is more likely to be inhibiting than where conditions favour regeneration. The ages of seedlings less than 4'3'' (1.3 metres) in height have been analysed for seven forests and these forests show wide differences in the frequency distribution of age classes of seedlings, depending partly on grazing pressures and partly on size characteristics. Many such "seedlings" can often be of considerable age, the oldest recorded being 29 years but many others were more than 15 years old, and no evidence was found of large numbers of seedlings resulting from "seed years".

When regeneration is present, it is often patchy and can, therefore, easily be missed during casual observation. Furthermore, such patches are often outside the present boundaries of the trees, emphasising the danger of concentrating studies of regeneration too narrowly within the present margins of forest cover.

If the grazing pressure is removed or moderated, then other factors may become limiting, the most likely being the availability of suitable micro-sites for the establishment and subsequent growth of seedlings to a sapling stage. The relative availability of such sites will vary widely between east and west.

Five hypotheses about dynamic changes in natural pinewoods occur in discussions, either individually or in combination:

i)   **Fire** Fire, perhaps started by lightning, may be a necessary sequence in a natural pine forest and may play a vital role by burning the ground layer vegetation and preparing the seedbed.

ii) **Windthrow** Strong winds occurring at, say, approximately 300 year intervals may lead to widespread destruction, upturn of mineral soils and thus create suitable conditions for regeneration.

iii) **The 'moving' forest** Downwind movement of seed may lead to leeward regeneration of forest, with subsequent reduction of the forest area to the windward.

iv) **Natural sequence between pine and hardwood species** The birch may colonise open areas, followed by pine, which in turn is followed by other hardwoods. Comparable sequences have been noted in North America and Sweden.

v)   **Pine forests as the end point** In a succession from glacial times, pine may be the final stages before a return to open moorland as a result of soil degradation.

Although all these hypotheses are relevant to consideration of the dynamics of the pinewoods, and examples can be found where all these processes are apparently feasible, there is still too little information firmly based on direct observation and measurement. The current knowledge of the dynamics of the pinewoods is incomplete, as has been emphasised throughout this volume. There is some evidence to suggest that the least disturbed forests, with their associated diversity of species of many groups, are the fullest expression of a pinewood ecosystem, as they support the largest number of species that would be expected under pinewood conditions. These areas are among the most important for conservation as they can only be re-created over a long period of time, and are also important in any long-term studies of ecosystem dynamics.

There is little evidence of changes in the species composition of the tree layer in the pinewoods, and, although rowan occurs as a coloniser, it rarely becomes part of the tree layer. The strong correlation between the composition of the tree layer and the site conditions suggests that a balance exists, but there is considerable variability. Certainly, there is not sufficient information to enable us to predict the species likely to colonise a given area. The site conditions will have changed considerably from those of the original forest, whose composition has been established by pollen analysis.

5. Conclusions

Whether we take the 4,000 acres of denser pine stands, or the 26,000 acres which include much sparse scattered pine, the total area occupied by the natural pinewoods is small, and less than 1/25th of the area of pine plantations in Britain. Yet this native pinewood was the habitat within which much of the character-istic highland wildlife evolved in Scotland, and which, in spite of its rarity and the depredation it has suffered, still contains features of interest, whether they be the old pines themselves, or the rich vertebrate and invertebrate fauna. Many of these features are not reproduced in the pine plantations, or are only found there in a degenerate form. Despite their well documented importance for wildlife conservation in Britain, the pinewoods are vulnerable — in part, to felling for the valuable timber they contain, and, in part, to replanting with exotic species. The latter is perhaps more serious, as the old pinewoods have frequently recovered their character after felling, but planting with exotic species or non-local strains of pine, particularly accompanied by ploughing, produces more serious changes in the ecosystem. While it is undoubtedly true that regeneration, with the present heavy grazing, is absent from many of the forests, it nevertheless seems likely that the immediate, rather than the long-term, threat comes from the direct activities of man and his exploitation of the forest. Indirectly, overgrazing is also exploitation. The losses in the resource over the last ten years are mainly due to felling and planting of exotics rather than to death of trees, which, despite the age of the forest, accounts for only a small proportion of the total number.

References

INNES, R.A. & SEAL, D.T. (1971). The native Scottish pinewoods. *Forestry,* **44,** suppl., 66-73.
STEVEN, H.M. & CARLISLE, A. (1959). *The native pinewoods of Scotland.* Oliver and Boyd.

Table I Area of sites included in the survey, measured from Steven and Carlisle.

	A PINE		B MIXED		C	
	acres	(ha)	acres	(ha)	acres	(ha)
Glentanar	2,133	863	378	153	157	64
Ballochbuie	2,124	860	72	29	685	277
Mar	1,026	415	297	120	83	34
Abernethy	2,043	827	1,134	459	990	401
Rothiemurchus	2,304	932	846	342	197	80
Glenmore	160	65	50	20	32	13
Glen Feshie	711	288	387	157	138	56
Rannoch	918	372	388	157	75	30
Meggernie	324	131	234	95	105	42
Glen Moriston	198	80	180	73	48	19
Glengarry	801	324	62	25	54	23
Barisdale	451	183	117	47	—	—
Arkaig	405	164	486	197	—	—
Ardgour	324	131	504	204	52	21
Glen Affric	1,755	710	270	109	127	51
Glen Cannich	747	302	234	95	—	—
Glen Strathfarrar	504	204	297	120	200	81
Guisachan and Cougie	630	255	63	25	43	17
Coulin	351	142	72	29	—	—
Achnashellach	320	130	9	4	20	8
Shieldaig	126	51	360	146	—	—
Amat	243	98	441	178	—	—
Loch Maree	396	160	306	124	176	71
Black Mount	135	55	126	51	—	—
Glen Orchy	135	55	81	33	—	—
Tyndrum	162	66	72	29	—	—
Total......	19,426	7,863	7,466	3,021	3,182	1,288

A = Pine = Area shown as pure Pine
B = Mixed = Area shown as mixed Pine/birch on the maps, or scattered trees
C = Estimates of the acreage of Scots Pine, general yield class 60, 80 year old, obtained from the proportion of plots in each site, that had a basal area above this figure

Table 2 Total basal area of Scots pine and birch, recorded from the sixteen plots in each site (200 m² plot)

	PINE		BIRCH	
	Individuals	Live B.A. (sq. m.)	Individuals	Live B.A. (sq. m.)
Glentanar	61	3.16	—	—
Ballochbuie	44	7.31	7	0.15
Mar	14	4.27	2	0.08
Abernethy	219	6.16	8	0.08
Rothiemurchus	134	2.66	9	0.78
Glenmore	249	4.41	11	0.06
Glen Feshie	58	3.57	5	0.65
Rannoch	50	2.04	70	1.12
Meggernie	21	3.84	10	0.61
Glen Moriston	69	1.11	133	0.28
Glengarry	108	3.98	40	1.39
Barisdale	11	0.97	24	0.66
Arkaig	3	0.47	17	0.64
Ardgour	3	1.27	46	1.18
Glen Affric	95	4.97	31	0.68
Glen Cannich	12	0.73	25	0.74
Glen Strathfarrar	29	6.47	36	1.82
Guisachan and Cougie	38	2.14	71	1.74
Coulin	12	1.64	11	0.55
Achnashellach	36	2.35	50	0.75
Shieldaig	40	2.15	67	0.98
Amat	7	0.85	19	0.83
Loch Maree	108	5.03	13	0.01
Black Mount	57	1.07	15	0.42
Glen Orchy	1	0.005	22	0.65
Tyndrum	14	1.99	12	0.49

Table 3 Correlation coefficients between age and diameter in nine native pinewoods

	N	r	Significance level
Glentanar	38	.676	● ● ●
Ballochbuie	23	.484	●
Rannoch	30	.834	● ● ●
Glen Affric	22	.345	NS
Loch Maree	30	.784	● ● ●
Shieldaig	30	.815	● ● ●
Amat	28	.712	● ● ●
Tyndrum	30	.530	● ●
Barisdale	30	.025	NS
Eastern type	61	.580	● ● ●
Central type	52	.636	● ● ●
North-western type	60	.794	● ● ●
South-western type	58	.599	● ● ●
Eastern + Central	113	.616	● ● ●
North-western + South-western	118	.723	● ● ●
Overall	231	.679	● ● ●

Table 4 Frequency of seedlings, larger seedlings, saplings and trees recorded in the sixteen plots from all sites

	Seedlings		Larger Seedlings (over 25 cm under Breast Height)		Saplings (over Breast height, under 5 cm DBH)		Trees	
	Scots pine	Birch	Scots pine	Birch	Scots pine	Birch	Scots pine	Birch
Glentanar	10	3	6	2	2	—	11	—
Ballochbuie	6	10	—	1	—	—	12	2
Mar	3	6	2	3	—	—	8	1
Abernethy	9	7	5	4	5	3	14	3
Rothiemurchus	4	3	3	—	3	—	8	1
Glenmore	4	5	3	2	5	2	9	3
Glen Feshie	6	8	2	—	1	—	7	2
Rannoch	4	9	5	5	3	2	7	7
Meggernie	1	14	—	2	—	—	6	4
Glen Moriston	9	14	9	11	7	7	5	5
Glengarry	4	9	9	6	5	3	10	3
Barisdale	4	13	—	5	—	2	5	8
Arkaig	2	13	2	14	1	2	3	6
Ardgour	3	9	1	7	—	1	3	8
Glen Affric	3	7	7	11	3	3	8	6
Glen Cannich	7	8	5	7	—	2	5	3
Glen Strathfarrar	5	12	2	6	—	1	7	7
Guisachan and Cougie	6	11	7	11	5	6	7	11
Coulin	7	10	3	8	—	1	6	8
Achnashellach	4	8	5	7	4	3	9	5
Shieldaig	9	9	8	11	1	9	8	9
Amat	3	9	1	5	—	2	3	8
Loch Maree	11	6	10	5	5	3	8	—
Black Mount	2	9	8	—	1	1	4	5
Glen Orchy	3	12	1	4	—	—	—	9
Tyndrum	5	14	—	3	—	—	7	7

Figure 1. 5 cm diameter class distribution of all Scots pine trees recorded in the survey (from 4lb sample plots)

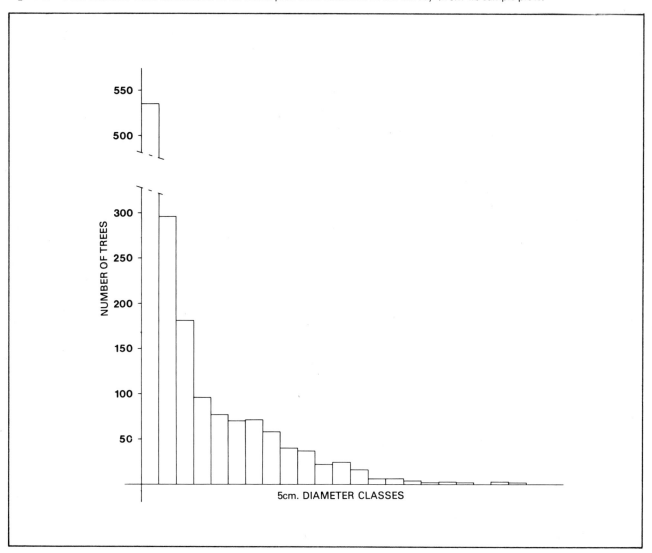

Figure 2. Frequency of plots containing different numbers of trees (from 4lb sample plots)

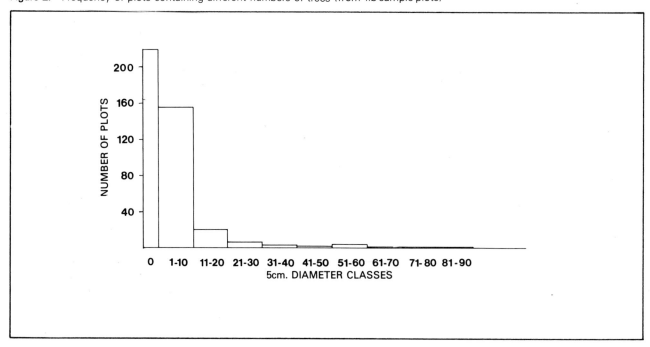

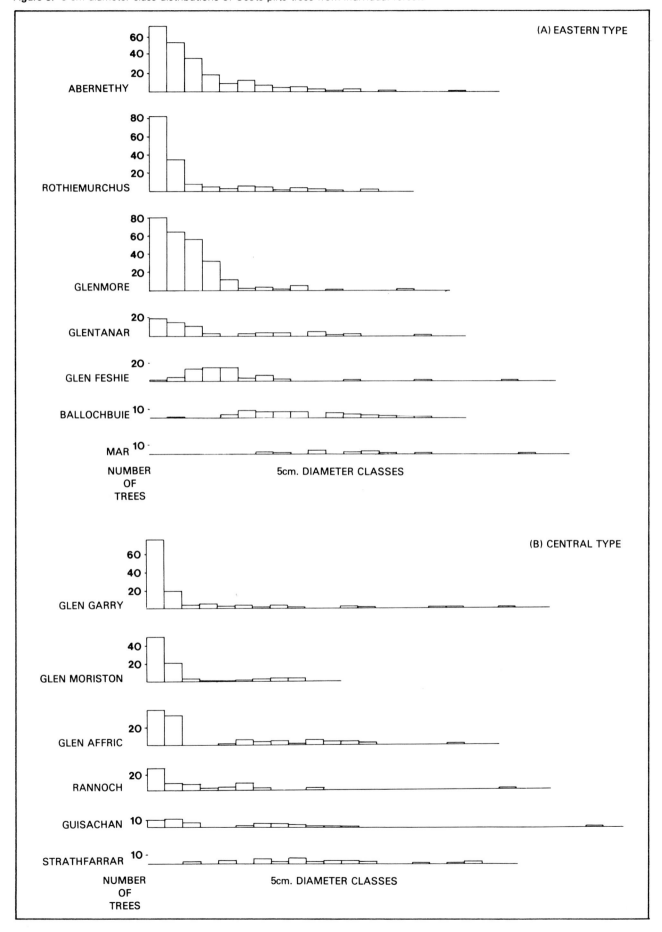

Figure 3. 5 cm diameter class distributions of Scots pine trees from individual forests

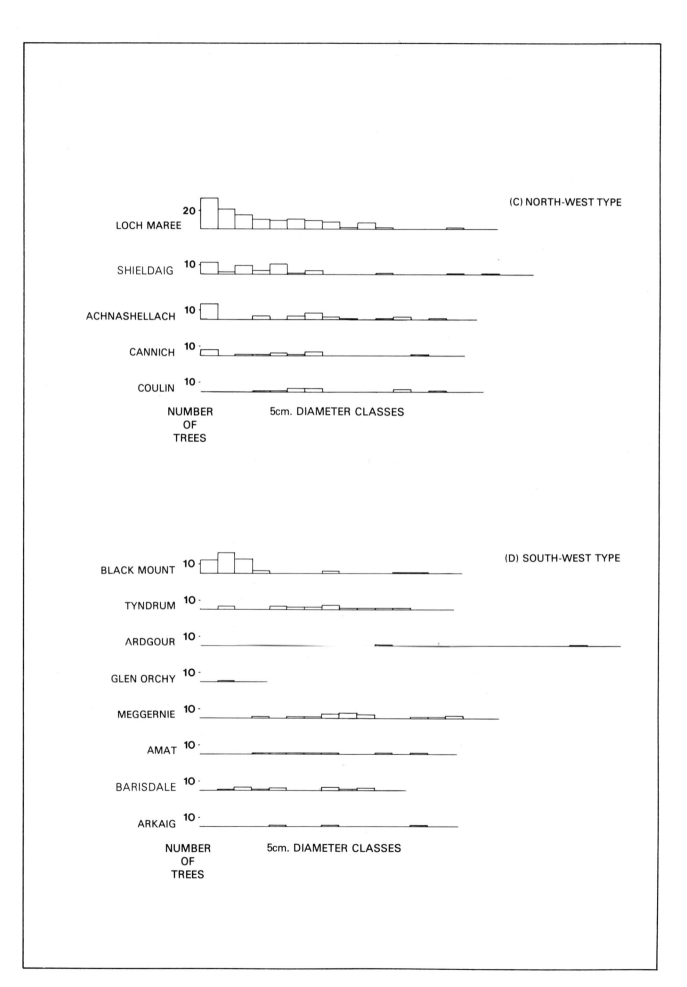

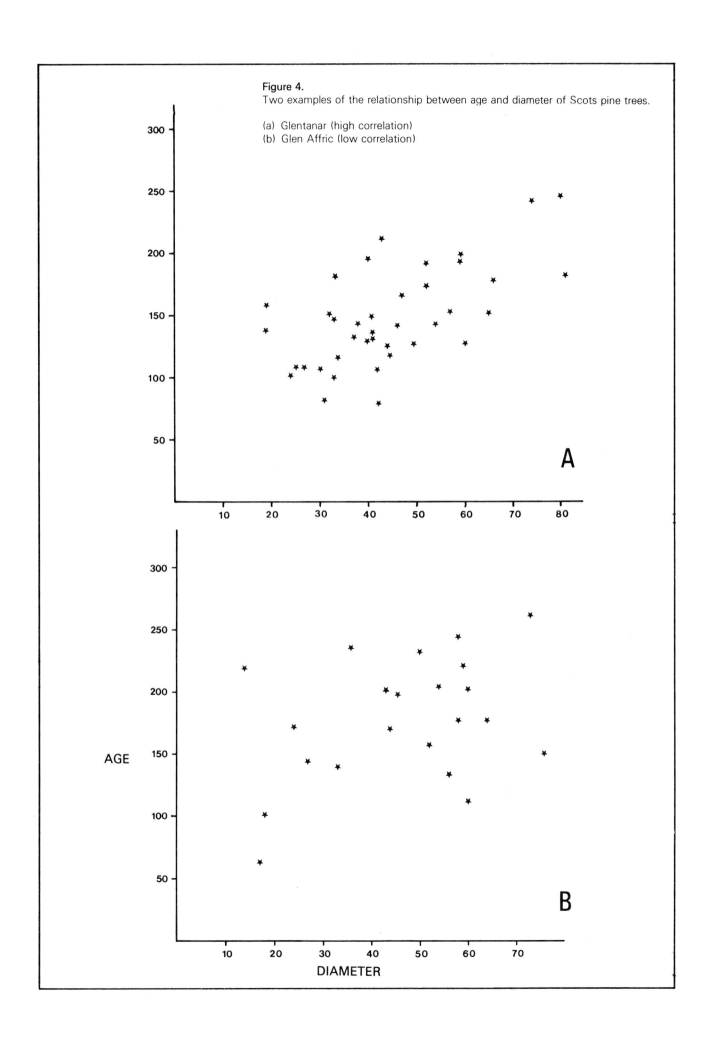

Figure 4.
Two examples of the relationship between age and diameter of Scots pine trees.

(a) Glentanar (high correlation)
(b) Glen Affric (low correlation)

A

AGE

B

DIAMETER

The structure and conservation of native pinewoods in Northern Fennoscandia

Yrjö **Vasari** Department of Botany, University of Oulu,
SF-90100 Oulu, Finland

The zonal pattern of the forest vegetation in northern Fennoscandia is described following the lines of Finnish forest botanists. Special attention is devoted to the forest types dominated by pine. The problems connected with modern exploitation of pinewoods and their rational conservation are presented. In any conservation policy, the nature reserves and protected areas are of decisive importance.

Fennoscandia forms the western extension of the vast northern belt of North Eurasian coniferous forests. By far the greatest part of Fennoscandia is covered by coniferous forests composed of Scots pine (*Pinus sylvestris* L.) and Norway spruce (*Picea abies* (L.) H. Karst.).

In addition to coniferous forests, two other major biomes cover parts of Fennoscandia, viz. temperate forests in the south (temperate and hemiboreal zone in the map of Ahti et al. 1968) and treeless arctic-alpine vegetation ("tundra") (hatched area in the map, Fig. 1). The floristic poverty of the Fennoscandian forests and the relative evenness of the peneplain plateau lend the landscape a fairly uniform and monotonous character over wide stretches. In an area like this there is, however, an excellent opportunity for the vegetational pattern to express the climatic zonality. Special attention has been devoted to this question of climatically based regional pattern in vegetation by Professor Aarno Kalela and his co-workers in Finland (cf e.g. Kalela 1958 and 1961).

For the main part, Finnish forestry and forest-botany rests upon the concept of "forest types" as originally defined by Professor A.K. Cajander at the beginning of this century (cf. Cajander 1909, 1926, 1927, 1949, also Cajander and Ilvessalo 1921). According to Cajander's hypothesis, a forest type is a complex concept comprising not only the stands which in their mature state are distinguished by the same floristic composition and the same ecological-biological character, but also all stands (areas burnt or cut or disturbed for any other reason) where the natural succession will lead to the same end result. Thus, for example, all immature successional phases of the same potential type are included in one and the same forest type. The typifying of the forest stands is based mainly upon the elements of the vegetation, other than trees, which are believed to reflect more truly than trees themselves the characteristics of the ecological factors prevalent within the particular area in question. In this way, forest type comes to include all the successional phases within a given place — for example, the deciduous trees of young forests, birch, Grey alder, aspen etc. following disturbance (e.g. a forest fire) and finally the mature woods composed of coniferous trees, Scots pine and Norway spruce. The fundamental significance of this concept of Cajander in forest classification has been recognized by

scientists from other Fennoscandian countries too (cf. e.g. Sjors 1965, p. 62).

The forest types form a series, from dry heaths to luxurious grass-herb forests. They can be grouped into three major categories: 1) dry heath-forests, 2) damp heath-forests and 3) grass-herb forests. These groups follow each other in succession with the improvement of edaphic conditions. They correspond more or less closely to the associations described by Aune on page 5. Studies on the vegetation have shown that the forest types are not the same throughout the coniferous forests of Fennoscandia, but minor differences exist among types which, if taken superficially, would be grouped together, and that it is possible to distinguish several zones of different forest vegetation. These zones can be divided into smaller sections by differences in the oceanity-continentality degree of climate. Climate has been observed to have a pronounced influence upon the vegetation, although one that is secondary in importance to that of the gradient in the south-north direction. (The zonal and sectional pattern of the Fennoscandian vegetation is given in Fig. 1).

The forest resources in Finland have been the subject of intensive and regular studies during most of this century. Within the field of forestry, major accomplishments have been the evaluations of five countrywide surveys of forest resources in which the line-survey method has been employed. The third survey, in the years 1951-53, was particularly interesting in that biologists were employed in the teams of surveyors. During the course of the survey, parallel lines in a southwest-northeast direction were run in the main part of the country (Southern and Middle Finland) at intervals of 13 km, in southern parts of Northern Finland at 16 km, and, in the northern-most part of the coniferous forest zone. at intervals of 20 km. The method itself has been described by Professor Ilvessalo in several publications (e.g. Ilvessalo 1956); the methods and results of the biological observations have been presented by Professor Kujala (1964). The main results, from the point of view of the foresters, have been published and illustrated in the form of numerous maps by Ilvessalo (1960, 1952).

In the present context, Northern Fennoscandia has been limited roughly by the 64 N lat. By far the largest areas in this part of Fennoscandia belong to the middle and northern forest vegetation zones, and to the domain of treeless arctic-alpine vegetation, which does not belong to the scope of our present treatment.

Within the northern parts of Fennoscandia, pine is the dominant tree species in the forests. As can be seen from the map by Ilvessalo (1952, Fig. 2), the proportion of forests dominated by pine exceeds 50 per cent in most parts of Northern Finland and the same is roughly true of the rest of Northern Fennoscandia within the forest zone. Only in Northern Norway is pine a relatively rare tree species (cf. Ronning 1960, p. 51).

Ecological differences seem to govern the local relationships between forests dominated by spruce and pine respectively. The distribution of forest stands dominated by these trees may well be "chiefly related to soil texture but also reflects some features of regional type. – – In many valleys of Northern Sweden, pine prevails in the valleys, with their drier climate and coarser soils, and spruce on the hillsides and upland, with a moister climate, excessive snow and, above all, more fine-grained material in the tills" (Sjors 1965, pp. 60-61). The mutual importance of these factors is fairly clearly visible in, for example, the map of Ilvessalo (1951, Fig. 2): the extensive areas of coarse glaciofluvial material are dominated by pine; on the other hand the upland areas of Kuusamo-Salla and Kalnuu as well as the "Lapland triangle", where the bedrock is rich in basic rocks, stand out as areas rich in spruce.

The Scots pine is not morphologically uniform within the whole vast area of Northern Fennoscandia. Two major taxa are usually distinguished, obviously representing end stages of clonal variation, southern race ("P. septentrionalis" Schott) and a northern one, the "Lapland pine" (**P. silvestris** var. **lapponica** (Fr.) Hartm.). The approximate limit between these two races follows roughly the 66 N lat. This type occurs, however, also south of this limit in upland areas (Sarvas 1964, pp. 371-372). Typical features of the northern var. **lapponica** are a long and narrow crown, short branches and very straight trunk. The existence of this morphologically well-defined northern race lends the northern pine forest a peculiar appearance of their own. The forests composed of this variety are also very slow-growing and sparse.

The sructure and character of the forests change gradually in the south-north direction. The structure of the woods within different forest vegetation zones has been excellently described by Professor Kalela (see e.g. Kalela 1961). Perhaps the main characteristics of the change when moving northwards are: 1) an increase in the dwarf-shrubs usually associated with peaty soil (**Betula nana, Vaccinium uliginosum, Ledum palustre**); 2) the forests become lighter and sparser) and 3) a general increase of the lichens in the bottom layer.

The forest types of different vegetation zones are listed in Table 1. Scots pine is the dominant tree in the climax stage of the extreme dry, dry, and moderately dry heath forests, with the exception of Fjeld Lapland, where birch (**Betula tortuosa**) has this position.

It is not at all certain whether the present limit of the pine forests in the north represents the true natural limit. It has been maintained, evidently with good reason, that by selective cuttings man has created the boundary as it is at present by forcing pine to retreat from the positions it had held before the intervention of human exploitations (cf e.g. Hustich 1961). In fact, the birch-dominated heath forests of northernmost Fennoscandia show hardly any fundamental differences – with the exception of the dominant trees! – when compared with the pine forest further south (cf e.g. Hamet-Ahti 1963 a and b).

The extent of the pine-dominated, wooded peatlands, is not covered by this survey. Roughly one-third of the total area of Finland consists of mires and more than 40 per cent (on average) of these peatlands in Northern Finland contain pines (cf. Ilvessalo 1960, maps 13 and 15).

The year 1956 was one of fundamental importance in Finnish nature conservation policy. Before the war there were, in all, 10 nature reserves in Finland, created for the protection of original features of the Finnish landscape. Six of these reserves were lost in the peace treaty following the wars. The biologists, forest scientists and other people interested in active nature protection were all aware of the significance of this severe loss, and preparations were made to establish new nature reserves. As a result of intensive preparatory work, a law was passed in 1956 resulting in the immediate creation of 19 new nature reserves, seven national parks (open to the general public) and 12 nature parks (reserved for scientific research) (cf. e.g. Soyrinki 1961 and Mikola 1973). This law was passed in the spirit of complete unanimity by the Finnish Parliament, and it was believed that such a large-scale scheme for the establishment of nature reserves would effectively solve the protection problems. This belief was supported by the fact that full-scale exploitation of the forests in the far north was not considered as a possibility, and that the vast peatlands were certainly not under any threat of exploitation.

The situation has, however, changed fairly rapidly as the increasing demands of progressive industrialization caused the disappearance of the so-called zero-limit of profitableness which until then had protected the forests and peatlands of Northern Finland, and heavy pressure began to concentrate upon them in the form of increasing demands for raw material. This demand led to an over-exploitation of the forests in Northern Finland during the fifties' and sixties'. Even the Director General of the National Board of Forestry in Finland, Mr. P.W. Jokinen, has admitted recently that, during the years 1945-66, the cuttings in the State forests in Northern Finland exceeded the productivity by about 20 million cubic meter or roughly 1 million cubic meter per year! (Jokinen 1975). The seriousness of this admission is emphasised by the fact that the forest resources in the north are relatively small and that their regeneration rate is slow.

Together with the heavy exploitation of the northern forests, drastic measures were taken to increase the speed of forest regeneration. Vast clear-cuttings, effected nowadays by heavy machines, were followed by ploughing, artificial regeneration from either seed or seedlings, application of fertilizers and use of poisons against young underbrush. The optimistic expectations of these techniques were largely based upon the experience gained from the favourable climatic period of the late 30's. In many cases, the expectations have indeed proved to be over-optimistic and unrealistic — the total timber resources of Finnish Lapland, for example, have now been estimated to be 41 million cubic meter less than in 1953, while the annual growth has declined by 0.5 million cubic meter! (cf. Joutsamo 1975).

At present, however, the errors of the past are being increasingly recognised and measures are being taken to prevent harmful treatment of the forests. The state owns considerable areas in Finnish Lapland and the National Board of Forestry, which has responsibility for the care of state forests, has decided that all the areas north of the limit of the 800 effective temperature will be excluded from artificial methods of regeneration. In other words, the economic exploitation will be limited to the degree permitted by the natural productivity of the forests. Special consideration will be given to areas above 300m and near the forest limit in the north, where few, if any, cuttings will be allowed (cf. e.g. Jokinen 1975). The National Board of Forestry also protects, in many other ways, the forests under its control. Of special significance from the point of view of conservation are the so-called "primeval forests" which are entirely protected from cutting etc. but which are open to the public. These measures in themselves will have a great positive influence upn the forests of Northern Finland. In addition, however, an improvement of the network of natures reserves has been suggested by the Advisory Board for Environmental Conservation, established immediately after European Conservation Year 1970. According to this plan, several new nature reserves will be established and existing reserves will be enlarged. The existing nature reserves — National Parks and Nature Parks — comprise 2360 km , or 0.8 per cent of the land area of Finland, and the total suggested area of the new scheme will be 5600 km , or 1.8 per cent of the land area :Hayrinen 1973). Figure 5 represents the scheme of nature reserves for Finland showing the existing and proposed reserves. Some of the proposed reserves are designed to conserve peatlands which have become threatened to a degree that was hard to foresee only about 20 years ago. — The whole question of the peatland protection is a separate story — a report of the plans concerning it has been given by Hayrinen and Ruuhijarvi (1969).

By far the largest of the planned nature reserves, Koilliskaira National Park in eastern Lapland, on the Venno-Soviet border, will be 2900 km² in area. A heated debate has arisen about this Koilliskaira National Park — the opponents to it stress the consequences in the field of employment, local economy etc. whereas the proponents underline the importance of establishing a nature reserve which would keep the largest area of existing primeval forests in Finland intact for future generations. If established, it would be one of the largest, if not the largest, nature reserve in the whole of Europe. The conservation of this area has also been recommended by a joint Internordic body for the protection of important biotopes (Luonnonvarainhoitotoimisto tiedottaa 1973b).

The next largest nature reserve in Finland is the Lemmenjoki National Park, 1330 km² in area. It is particularly interesting in the present context as the northern limit of pine forests runs through the reserve. About one third of its area is covered by pine forests, another third by fjeld birch forest and the remaining third by more or less open oroarctic vegetation. On the Norwegian side of the frontier, another national park (Ovre Anarjokka — 1120 km²) has been planned, although not yet established. As it is now, Lemmenjoki should be the fifth largest National Park in Europe. Three National Parks larger than this are also situated in Northern Fennoscandia — a Soviet park in the western part of the Kola peninsula and the Padjelanta-Sarek double park in Northern Sweden (cf. Virallinen luonnonsuojelu — Nature Conservation Office 1971).

The National Parks are open to the general public and an important part of their function is intended to be recreation. In this respect, they share the difficulties of many other frequented areas in Northern Fennoscandia. The dry heaths — as well as fjeld heaths — are extremely susceptible to human erosion, but this threat has only recently been recognised (cf. e.g. Hoogester 1974). Adequate means for protecting the susceptible vegetation from human erosion have not yet been found, and this problem is still being studied. However, the tourists will usually follow good paths and use cooking sites, etc., if they have been properly constructed. Certain plants seem to tolerate trampling better than others, and thus it seems possible that a protective plant cover can be formed of native species. The plants of dry pine heaths are, however, in particular danger as their toleration of trampling is extremely low. The protection of dry heaths — favourite tourist grounds — has proved to be an especially difficult task, demanding much consideration and work.

Naturally, the strictly protected Nature Parks, where scientific work can be performed with special permission, are likely to preserve the susceptible pine forests for future generations. It is our task to see that this conservation works, so that there will remain a chance for people (scientists included!) to see what the pine forests of Northern Fennoscandia have been like in the past, more peaceful, times.

References

AHTI, T., HAMET-AHTI, L. & JALAS, J. (1968). Vegetation zones and their sections in north western Europe. *Ann. bot. fenn.,* **5**, 169-211.

CAJANDER, A.K. (1909). Uber Waldtypen. *Acta for. fenn.,* **1** (4), 1-176.

CAJANDER, A.K. (1926). The theory of forest types. *Acta for. fenn.,* **29** (3), 1-108.

CAJANDER, A.K. (1927). Wesen und Bedeutung der Waldtypen. *Tartu Ulik. Mersaosak. Toim.,* **10**, suppl.

CAJANDER, A.K. (1949). Metsatypit ja niiden merkitys. (Forest types and their significance). *Acta for. fenn.,* **56**, 1-71.

CAJANDER, A.K. & ILVESSALO, Y. (1921). Ueber Waldtypen II. *Acta for. fenn.,* **20**, 1-77.

HAMET - AHTI, L. (1963a). Zonation of the mountain birch forests in northern-most Fennoscandia. *Ann. bot. Soc. Zool. Bot. Vanamo,* **34** (4), 1-127.

HAMET-AHTI, L. (1963b). Pohjois-Euroopan metsanrajakoivikkojen asemasta kasvillisuuden vyohyke-jarjestelmassa. *Luonnon Tutk.,* **67** (5), 157-163.

HAYRINEN, U. (1973). Vanhojen metsien asema ja merkitys: Metsaluonnon suojeluohjelma (The role of the mature forests: A conservation plan for forest ecosystem). *Suom. Luonto* 2/1973, 82-93, 112.

HAYRINEN, U. & RUUHIJARVI, R. (1969). Pohjois-Suomen soiden sailytyssuunnitelma. *Suom. Luonto* 4/1969, 1-31.

HOOGESTEGER, M. (1974). Saariselkakin kuluu (Saariselka is getting damaged). *Suom. Luonto* 3/1974, 161-162, 179.

HUSTICH, I. (1961). Forest and tree lines in northern-most Fennoscandia. *Arch. Soc. Vanamo,* **16** (suppl.), 111-113.

ILVESSALO, Y. (1952). Forests and Forestry. In: *Suomi, a general handbook on the geography of Finland. Fennia,* **72**, 472-494.

ILVESSALO, Y. (1956). Suomen metsat vuosista 1921-24 vuosiin 1951-53. Kolmeen valtakunnan metsien inventointin persutuva tutkimus. *Metsatiet. Tutkimuslait. Julk.,* **47**, 1-227.

ILVESSALO, Y. (1960). Suomen metsat kartakkeiden valossa (The forests of Finland in the light of maps -Die Walder Finnlans im Licht von Karten). *Metsatiet. Tukimuslait. Julk.,* **52** (2), 1-70 + 1-30 maps.

JOKINEN, P.W. (1975). Lapin metsataseen epatasapaino (The Imbalance of Northern Forestry). *Suom. Luonto* 1/1975, 8-10, 61.

JOUTSAMO, E. (1975). Lapin metsein kasittely luonnonsuojelun kannalta (Conservation and exploitation of the Lappish Forests). *Suom. Luonto* 1/1975, 3-7, 61.

KALELA, A. (1958). Uber die Waldvegetationszonen Finnlands. *Bot. Notiser,* **111**, 353-368.

KALELA, A. (1961). Waldvegetationszonen Finnlands und ihre Klimatischen Paralleltypen. *Arch. Soc. Vanamo,* **16** (suppl.), 65-83.

KALLIOLA, R. (1973). *Suomen Kasvimaantiede.* Porvoo.

KUJALA, V. (1964). Metsa- ja suokqwvilajien levinneisyys ja yleisyyssuhteista Suomessa. Vuosina 1951-1953 suoritetun valtakunnan metsien III linjaarvioinnin tuloksia. (Deutsches Referat: Uber die Frequenzverhaltnisse der Wald - und Moorpflanzen in Finnland - Ergebnisse der III Reichswald-abschatzung (1951-1953). *Metsatiet Tutkimuslait. Julk.,* **59**, 1-137 + 1-196 maps.

LUONNONVARAINHOITOTOIMISTO TIEDOTTAA (1973a). Virallinen luonnonsuojelu; Suomen kansallispuistoverkon kehittaminen. *Suom. Luonto* 3/1973, 140-159.

LUONNONVARAINHOITOTOIMISTO TIEDOTTAA (1973b). Virallinen luonnonsuojelu; Pohjoismainen yhteistyotoiminta luonnonsuojelukysymyksissa. *Suom. Luonto* 6/1973, 272-176.

MIKOLA, P. (1973). Muistelmia luonnon- ja kansallispuistojen perustamisvaiheista (Recollections about the creation of the present national parks and nature reserves). *Suom. Luonto* 1/1973, 8-11.

RONNING, O. (1960). The vegetation and flora north of the Arctic Circle. In: *Norway North of 65,* edited by O. Vorren, 50-72.

SARVAS, R. (1964). *Havupuut. - Porvoo - Helsinki.*

SJORS, H. (1965). Forest regions. *Acta phytogeogr. suecica,* **50**, 48-63.

SOYRINKI, N. (1961). Nature Conservation in F inland. *Arch. Soc. Vanamo,* **16**, (suppl.), 120-126.

VASARI, Y. (1965). The vegetation of Northern Finland - past and present. *Inter-Nord,* **13**, 17-36 (in print).

VIRALLINEN LUONNONSUOJELU - Nature Conservation Office: Lemmenjoen kansallis-puistoa on laajennettu (Lemmenjoki National Park has been expanded). *Suom. Luonto* 2-3/1971, 62-64, 96.

Fig. 1—*The vegetation zones in Fennoscandia mainly according to Ahti & al. (1968).* The section limits (-----) are only marked within Finland. 0 suboceanic, 0 slightly oceanic, OC indifferent (neither oceanic nor continental), C slightly continental. The numbers denote the sections within the northern boreal zone. 1 Perapohjola, 2 Forest Lapland, 3 Fjeld Lapland, 4 Fjord Lapland (begins only outside Finnish territory).

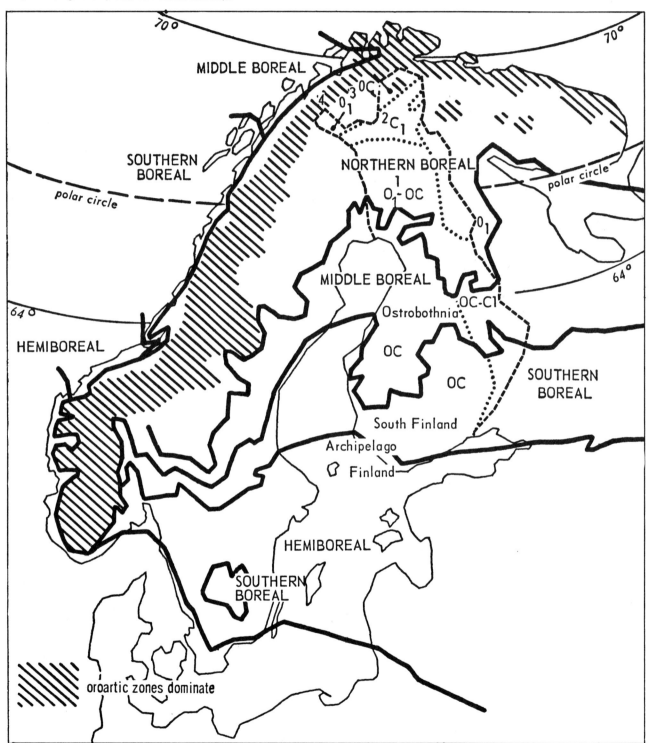

The remainder of Northern Finland, with the exception of a few treeless areas (not all of them!) is included by Ahti et al. (1968) in the northern boreal zone. It is a noteworthy feature of their classification that they regard the birch forests which physiognomically form a characteristic part of Northern Fennoscandia as marking only oceanic sections of the northern boreal zone rather than an independent zone (Ahti et al. 1968: 198). In this respect they differ fundamentally from the earlier concept of Kalela (e.g. 1961 b, cf. also Kalliola 1973: Fig. 140) and thus adhere to a line of thought which has been expressed earlier by, e.g. Zoller (1956).

A major contribution brought forward by Ahti et al. (1968) was that of paying attention to the climatic gradient which exists from the oceans to the interior of continents and its manifestation in terms of vegetation. They suggested the term section for the parts of vegetation zones which are distinguished by those characters of the vegetation that are caused by the degree of oceanity or continentality in Lapland and this causes the vegetation to attain a different lusher character. Within the forest zone damp heath forests. sometimes even grass-herb forests are common (Kalliola 1973: 221-222).

The natural boundaries between birch forests and the barren areas, orohemiarctic and oroactic alike, are often difficult to define in Northern Fennoscandia. The influence of man has been very strong and long-lasting in the northern sparsely wooded areas and has led to widescale destruction of former forests, which in many places occupied even the seashores. It is, however, not only direct human influence which has affected the balance between birch-forests and the treeless vegetation but also several other factors including fires and outbreaks of insect pests (ef. Ahti et al. 1968: 199-201 and the literature cited therein; Hustich 1961).

Table 1 According to a model of Kalliola (1973), based on the studies of Kalela (1961b) Combination of forest types within different forest vegetation zones, and Hamet-Ahti (1963a).

+ = insignificant in the vegetation zone in question, not much studied.

Vegetation zone / Forest type group	Southern Finland	Ostrobothnia-Kainuu	Perpohjola	Forest Lapland	Fjeld Lapland
Extreme dry heaths	Cladina type (CIT)	Cladina type (CIT)	Cladina type (CIT)	Cladina type (CIT)	Sub-alpine Empetrum-Lichenes type (sELiT)
Dry heaths	Calluna type)ct)	Empetrum-Calluna type (ECT)	Myrtillus-Calluna-Cladina type (MCCIT)	Uliginosum-Vaccinium-Empetrum type (UVET)	Sub-alpine Empetrum-Lichenes-Pleurozium type (sELiPIT)
Moderately dry heaths	Vaccinium type (VT)	Empetrum-Vaccinium type (EVT)	Empetrum-Myrtillus type (EMT)	Uliginosum-Empetrum-Myrtillus type (UEMT)	Sub-alpine Empetrum-Myrtillus type (sEMT)
Fresh heaths	Myrtillus type (MT)	Vaccinium-Myrtillus type Deschampsia-Myrtillus type (VMT) (DeMT)	Hylocomium-Myrtillus type (HMT)	Ledum-Myrtillus type (LMT)	+
Rich heaths	Oxalis-Myrtillus type (OMT)	Geranium-Oxalis-Myrtillus type (GOMT)	Geranium-Myrtillus type (GMT)	+	+
Grass-herb forests	Oxalis-Maianthemum type (OMaT), etc.	Geranium-Oxalis-Maianthemum type (GOMaT), etc.	Geranium-Dryopteris type (GDT) etc.	+	+

Fig. 2 Map of the nature reserves (existing and planned) in Finland within the framework of biogeographical provinces. Numbers denote National parks and Nature parks bigger than 50 km in size. Letter symbols: A – Archipelago and Coastal land, SW – South Western Finland, FL – Lake Finland, SS – Suomenselka (Western watershed), O – Ostrobothnia, MS – Maanselka (Eastern watershed), TK – Tornio-Kainuu, PP – Perapohjola, FoL – Forest Lapland, FjL – Fjeld Lapland.

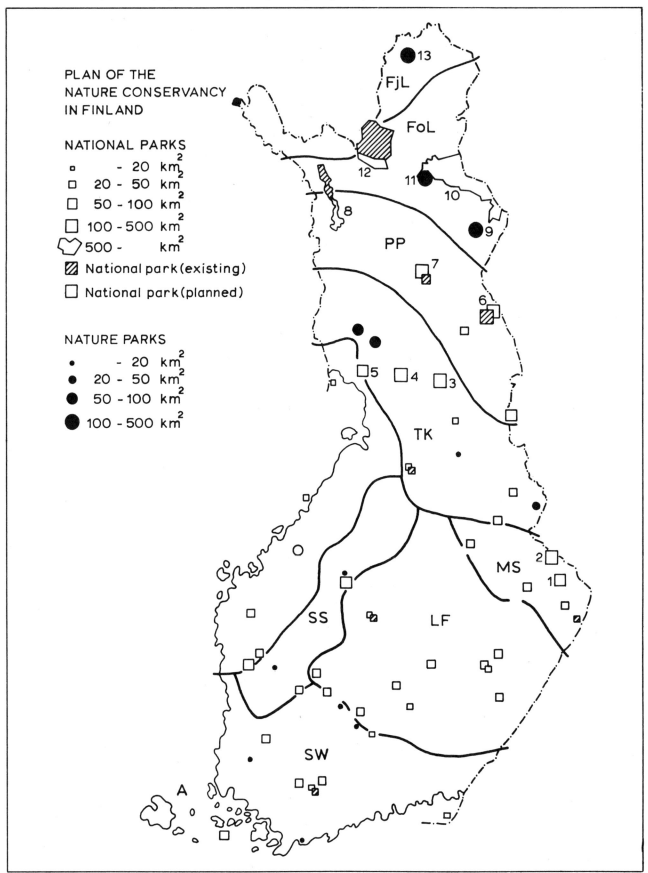

Plate 1 Extreme dry heath forest of the *Cladina* type (CIT). Forest Lapland, Sodankyla, Vuotso.   Photo Y. Vasara.

Plate 2 Dry heath forest of the *Empetrum-Calluna*-type (ECT). Kainuu, Sotkamo, Vuikatti.   Photo Y. Vasari.

Plate 3 Modern forest management in Northern Finland (Perapohjola, Kuusamo). In the foreground ploughing of the forest soil.   Photo Y. Vasari.

The gene-pool of Caledonian Scots Pine — its conservation and uses

By **R. Faulkner** Forestry Commission

Introduction

In the preface to their book 'The Native Pinewoods of Scotland', Steven and Carlisle (1959) stated the need for conservation thus — 'The native pinewoods are also of practical importance to the forester today. He wants the best strains of the different tree types he uses and the pines in these woodlands have persisted through successive generations, often under adverse conditions, and retained their health and vigour. . . . Not all are useful from the silvicultural point of view, but some are and will form part of our future woodlands in other parts of the country and indeed in other countries. They remain important and valuable tree material which should not be contaminated by non-indigenous strains. From every point of view, therefore, these woodlands should be preserved and perpetuated'. Steven and Carlisle were writing twenty years ago about remnant native pinewoods up to 300 years old. Since then, most of the woodlands — and so most of the available gene-pools — have become smaller and less well stocked due to windthrow and felling, and they are now much more costly to replace. Fortunately, some native pinewood areas have been naturally regenerated or extensively restocked with plants derived from seed produced in the native pinewoods.

Because of the longevity of trees, any extensive areas of natural regeneration should provide adequate gene reserves for any foreseeable future needs and at least until the next cycle of regeneration (Barber *et al* 1974). In contrast, those artificially regenerated areas where choice of seed trees has been limited because of the small amount of planting stock required, and where there has been a bias towards parent trees with good stem-form and vigour and with better potential for commercial forestry, will not adequately represent the parent gene-pool. Furthermore, future thinning in privately-owned, and many state-owned plantations, will almost certainly favour those phenotypes which have the best long-term commercial value for sawn-timber.

In many cases, the original woodlands were felled. Where complete fellings were followed by extensive natural regeneration, it is reasonable to assume that the natural regeneration will reflect the original geno-type of the stand. However, it is usually impossible to ascertain whether fellings were complete or not and, therefore, whether the present stands really do reflect the original material. Some remnant woodlands have been subjected to very intensive dysgenic selection in which trees of high commercial value have long since been removed — except, perhaps, for a few exceptional places where felling and log extraction were too difficult to execute. Such remnant native pinewoods certainly do not represent the original stock which can never be restored. Coupled with this is the fact that all existing native pinewoods are subject to some degree of contamination by migrant wind-borne pollen from non-native sources. Any action the conservationist might take will inevitably involve some degree of selection which must produce some bias and, thus, be a further step away from the goal of re-creating and perpetuating the pinewoods even as they exist today.

The value of the native pinewoods for commercial forestry

Among the range of conifers which can be grown in Britain, Scots pine is one of the least productive and so one of the least attractive to commercial forestry. The area of Scots pine planted annually has dropped over the past two decades from more than twenty per cent to less than five per cent of the total national planting programme. Furthermore, the Scots pine provenance experiments, in which the performance of plants derived from seed collected from different sources are compared, have shown that seed from native pinewoods produces less vigorous plantations than seed from other selected plantations growing in Britain, or from some seedlots imported from central Europe (Lines 1964, 1965). Likewise, individual tree progenies from selected, vigorous, and well-shaped 'plus' trees in native stands are almost always inferior, and particularly in rate-of-growth in volume, when compared with progenies derived from plus trees selected in fast-growing, non-native stands with good stem form.

Out of 73 native plus trees currently represented in progeny tests, only five appear to have sufficiently outstanding merit to warrant their inclusion in a breeding population from which to develop commercial cultivars. Thus, there is little to encourage the breeder to further explore the existing native pinewood gene-pool for additional breeding material.

Conservationists often argue that the existing pinewoods are a potentially valuable source of unexploited genes which succeeding generations of breeders will be glad to tap in order to remedy problems which are not encountered at present, the assumption being that components of the present stands and their progenitors have withstood potentially destructive insects, fungi, adverse climatic effects and soil conditions for several thousand years. While this *might* be so, it can also be argued that the native pinewoods are not more likely to contain genes for resistance to new pests or diseases, or mutant forms of existing ones, than, say, the 253,000 hectares of alien provenances or semi-native populations already in existence elsewhere in Britain. Breeding for resistance to specific pests and diseases requires several cycles of intensive selection, breeding and testing, and what might take a cereal breeder ten years to accomplish will take ten to twenty times longer for the Scots pine breeder because of the long breeding cycle. In the event of a calamitous new disease appearing, the forester would, therefore, have to change from Scots pine to another species for some considerable time in order to circumvent the problem.

Thus, from a timber grower's view-point, there is little incentive to conserve the existing native pinewoods as potential gene-pools. The commercially-oriented tree breeder cannot justify an intensive selection and breeding programme in the numerous, highly variable and slow-growing remnant populations, when there are already available several valuable and higher-yielding base populations, or alternative species. For these reasons, the conservation argument must have a different basis.

Why conserve the native pinewood gene-pools?

Conservationists must define objectives which are reasonable, practicable and feasible within the limits of the financial support that can be mustered now and in the future.

The case for conserving the native Scottish pine gene-pool, in whole or selected parts, is undoubtedly strong, and might be argued on the following grounds:

1. The Scottish pinewoods developed to form separate ecotypes after gene migration from continental sources was reduced or stopped by submersion of the land-bridge between England and the Continent some 7,000 years ago. Subsequently, the species successfully colonised a wide variety of sites, including deep peats, sands and gravels, and has persisted under a wide range of climates. The pinewood populations have thus proved themselves to be highly adaptive (Steven and Carlisle, *Op cit* p. 20-38).

2. Collectively, the pinewoods are composed of several island populations which have been subjected to high selection intensities and, within very short distances, have grown on a wide variety of sites. The extremes include: a population at Shieldaig, at the extreme western limit of the whole range of Scots pine and down to sea level under very mild maritime conditions, with fairly high-rainfall (1525mm, 60in) favoured by the Gulf Stream. 110km (70 miles) south-east of Shieldaig is another extreme island population growing up to 615m (2050ft) at Rothiemurchus, and under near-continental sub-alpine conditions. The most easterly population, at Glentanar, occurs at 180m (600 ft) and where the annual rainfall is but 890mm (35in).

3. The Scottish pinewoods are unique in the number of variants which they contain, but the proportion of these variants now present has been markedly influenced by the dysgenic selection which took place in historic times.

4. Many successful intra-specific hybridisation programmes on trees and other out-breeding plants, such as the grasses, depend upon crossing populations at the extreme ends of the species range, particularly where the variation between populations exceeds that within populations. Although many foresters in Britain do not regard Scots pine as a conifer of high future commercial importance, the Scottish pinewoods could be of major importance to other European countries whose forest economies depend upon Scots pine. The Scottish native pinewoods might play a useful role in foreign breeding programmes, just as British foresters are finding value in slow-growing, island populations of *Pinus contorta* in Alaska for hybridisation with more southerly 'Coastal' or 'Inland' populations.

5. Up to the present time, landscape artists and planners have paid scant attention to the amenity potential of Scots pine, but there is growing interest in the indigenous tree species, and greater interest in Scots pine can be expected. This could manifest itself in a growing demand for variants for such special attributes as bark colour, crown shape, foliage colour, slow growth, and so on. Dwarf and other extremely slow-growing variants may also find a ready use in urban areas as air pollution, which at present precludes Scots pine in many towns, diminishes.

Which populations should be conserved?

This question cannot be answered satisfactorily without a reliable indication of the size of the gene-pool available. Guiding principles which can be suggested, and in their order of importance, are:

1. Concentrate on the populations occupying the extreme geographical limits of distribution, since these are most likely to contain the widest variation. Thus pinewoods at Amat, Shieldaig, Glen Falloch/Tyndrum, and Glentanar should be considered first.

2. Concentrate on the largest populations, where risk of contamination by pollen from outside unrelated sources is likely to be least as, for example, in the pinewoods at Affric, Rannoch, Abernethy/Rothiemurchus and Loch Maree.

3. Include some larger remnants in the central area which were probably centres of gene-migration in the past, for example Ballochbuie and Glengarry.

Methods of Gene Conservation

There are numerous ways of conserving genes and each has its own peculiar benefits and disadvantages. Methods practical in some situations can be impractical in others. Any method which involves raising and cultivating plants in special isolated seed production units must be duplicated to reduce the risk of loss through fire. Protection against grazing and browsing animals also is essential.

1. **Pollen:** Conservation of genes in the form of pollen collected, cleaned, vacuum-dried to a suitable moisture content for storage, sealed in suitable containers and held under deep-freeze (-20 C) conditions until required has been suggested (Harrington, 1970).
Pine pollen has been stored in this manner, but with some loss of viability, for fifteen years (Stanley *et al,* 1960), and, with improved techniques, longer storage periods might be feasible. Although providing a good practical tool for the tree breeder, this method is unsuitable for the conservationist as there must be a guarantee of female flowers on populations of trees of native origin to pollinate. If these exist, then pollen will also be available.

2. **Seed:** Scots pine seed can also be stored for

periods of 10 to 20 years, but this period is of little value to the gene-conservationist, whose time-scale is in centuries rather than decades. Seed stored for short periods can, however, assist the gene-conservationist who uses artificial regeneration as his principal method.

3. **Vegetative propagation:** This is a reliable method of preserving existing genotypes. It assumes that mutations have not occurred since the parent tree developed from the original seed, or that a mutation will not occur in the propagated plants after vegetative propagation. It is costly and can only be considered in special situations. For example, the entire southern-most population at Glen Falloch, where only approximately sixty trees remain and where the trees are so widely scattered that an effective inter-breeding population no longer exists, could be preserved by vegetative propagation. In this situation, and in the absence of nearby plantations of other Scots pine, even low densities of foreign pollen in the atmosphere will result in a relatively high rate of contamination and any resultant natural regeneration will not represent the parent stand.

Old trees are virtually impossible to propagate by rooted cuttings, and grafting success is normally low because of the small size of the scions and the associated difficulties of preparing a suitable cut face to provide a satisfactory union with the stock plant. When 8-12 years-old, grafts can readily be used for artificial pollinations from which new populations can be derived (see 5 below). Grafted plants usually produce large cones and seeds from which very vigorous one-year-old seedlings can be obtained.

4. **Clonal seed orchards:** Balanced mixtures of grafted plants from 100-150 randomly selected trees (or whole populations if small) can be established in well-isolated clonal orchards to provide seed for re-stocking a pinewood area. They do not guarantee a balanced mixture of genes from all different clonal components because of the variation between clones in flowering times, the amounts or proportions of male and female flowers, the different cycles of peridicity in flower production between years and the variation between-clones in average yields of seed per cone. Although clonal seed orchards do not ensure panmixis between large groups of clones, they do allow the parent material to be moved well away from sources of pollen from unrelated sources.

5. **Artificial pollinations:** This is only feasible on grafted plants. The method is to collect and to use a balanced mixture of pollen from 100-150 randomly selected parents to pollinate artificially isolated female flowers on each clone. Seed is separately harvested by clones and mixed in equal amounts from each parent to obtain a suitable balance of the components. There is no guarantee that one pollen source in the original pollen mixture has not been more effective in fertilisation than the others. The method is costly and would be completely impractical for the mass-production of

commercial quantities of seed. It could be a useful intermediate stage in producing a mixture of seedlings to be planted at wide-spacing and for later conversion to a special seed plantation (see 7 below) in which subsequent thinnings are made randomly.

6. **Natural regeneration:** Natural regeneration has been attempted in some pinewoods, but with only partial success and that mainly on low-elevation sites and areas where surface peat deposits are relatively shallow and ground disturbance has taken place. It can be accomplished where the stocking of seed trees is adequate, and for this reason is not practical everywhere. There must be an adequate seed crop and the surface peat and moss layer of the forest floor must be largely removed by burning, or by some form of semi-intensive cultivation such as ploughing or heavy disc-cultivation. Protection must be given to the young regeneration which usually will grow in mixture with birch and rowan in particular. Dense patches of regeneration will, in the course of time, have to be thinned and the competing species removed.

Natural regeneration obtained in this way will be subject to both natural and artificial selection pressures. Natural selection will favour those genotypes which grow fastest and can withstand competition. Hybrids formed between the native trees and pollen from foreign sources are likely to succeed better than pure native pinewood material because of the faster growth-rates. Artificial selection resulting from the selection of seed trees will be minimal if seeding fellings occur after a good seed-crop has been noted, i.e. 12 months *after* pollination, but, should the natural regeneration fail, a further irreplaceable in-road will have been made into the gene-pool. Successful seedlings will be those which grow best under the conditions of the artificially prepared sites and which are retained by the conservationist during any thinning operations.

Because of the very low stocking in most native pine-woods, particularly in those at high elevations, the generally poor seed crops on over-mature trees, the high risk of failure of regeneration and the high protection and management costs, natural regeneration is not a reliable and suitable way of conserving many of the remaining gene-pools.

7. **Special seed plantations:** A relatively inexpensive and practical way for conserving the gene-pools and, at the same time, providing easily collected and regular supplies of seed for artificial regeneration is through the creation of special seed plantations. These could be achieved for each selected pinewood, or, in some cases, a group of pinewoods, by the use of recent aerial photographs of the pinewood(s) to plan one or more transects across the area adequately to sample those parts most remote from artificial plantations during the main pollination period preceding a good seed year. Meteorological records of the principal wind-direction and speeds during the main pollination period, together

with estimates of local topographic influences on wind-direction, are used to assist in choosing areas most likely to be least contaminated by important foreign pollen sources growing within one kilometre of the pinewood area. Flowering in Scots pine is delayed by 3 to 5 days for every 100 m rise in elevation and native pines often flower later than pines introduced from more southerly origins. Contamination at higher elevation is, therefore, unlikely.

Seed plantations of four hectares are the minimum size for developing a satisfactory pollen cloud (Koski 1975) and, when in full seed production, such a plantation will yield 30-40 kg of seed per annum. Four thousand plants will stock a four hectare seed plantation, using an initial spacing of 3 m between plants, and this requires some 15,000 seeds for sowing. Assuming ten full seeds per cone in a good seed year, 1,500 cones should provide sufficient planting material for a seed plantation. Ten cones per tree from 150 sample trees distributed at random along the predetermined transects will provide a population with a very wide genetic base since countless pollen parents are involved. 1,500 cones could be collected by shooting down cone-bearing branches for the cost of perhaps 700-1000 cartridges loaded with L.G. shot and could be completed in a few days. After extraction, seed should be sown and the seedlings lined-out, with minimal selection, to produce the planting-stock.

The transplants should be planted in an area of low risk from fire and pollen contamination, and managed with minimal selection to form a gene-pool which, after 10-12 years, could be managed as a special seed plantation to provide seed for restocking parts of the parent pinewood, as and when required. Thinnings in the special seed plantation should be non-selective, that is, mechanical, and seed from it, used for raising plants for re-establishing pinewood areas, would be collected from randomly chosen trees.

Further cycles of special seed plantations could be cheaply established, or young stands artificially created on the parent pinewood areas from the first seed plantation could be used as secondary seed sources.

The seed plantation method pre-supposes that panmixis will occur along the transects and that all sample trees will produce equal amounts of pollen, cones and seeds per cone. In practice, this will not occur and it is not possible to obtain the necessary data on which to weight samples from the different trees in proportion to their contribution to the total seed crop. The method is, however, cheap and practical and gives the greatest scope for gene-conservation. It is a better way of obtaining planting material to perpetuate the existing gene-pools than the current practice of making tiny and costly collections of seed from a handful of trees to support the very modest annual planting programmes in the few forests where re-stocking of native material is attempted.

Recommendations

It is recommended that: —

1. In small populations where satisfactory cross-pollination is unlikely to occur, or, in larger populations, where contamination from outside sources is a threat, the whole population, or a random selection of at least 100 phenotypes, should be vegetatively propagated by grafting. When old enough, the grafted trees should be artificially pollinated, using a balanced mixture of pollen from all the components so as to generate a seedling population which can later be used as a special seed plantation.

2. In large populations, where the risk of contamination from outside pollen sources is low, seed derived from wind-pollinations should be collected from about 150 randomly selected trees. Equal amounts of seed from each tree should be mixed together and used to form a special seed plantation to provide seed and plants for artificially restocking the pinewoods from which they were derived.

References

BARBER, J.C. & KRUGMAN, S.L. (1974). Preserving forest-tree germ plasm. *Am. Forests,* **80,** 8-11 and 42-43.

HARRINGTON. J.F. (1970). Seed and pollen storage for conservation of plant gene resources. In: *Genetic resources in plants their exploration and conservation,* edited by O.H. Frankel and E. Bennet. Blackwell.

KOSKI, V. (1975). Natural pollination in seed orchards with special reference to pines. *Bull. For. Commn. no.* **54,** Chap. 8.

LINES, R. (1964). The East Scotland Scots pine provenance trial of 1952. *Rep. Forest. Res. Lond. 1963,* 127-133.

LINES, R. (1965). Results of some older Scots pine provenance experiments. *Rep. Forest. Res. Lond. 1964,* 174-194.

STANLEY, R.G., PETERSON, J. & MIROV, N.T. (1960). Viability of pine pollen stores 15 years. *Res. Notes Pacif. SW Forest Range Exp. Stn,* no. **173.**

STEVEN, H.M. & CARLISLE, A. (1959). *The native pinewoods of Scotland.* Oliver and Boyd, p.v., 90-91, 298-301.

The appreciation of pinewoods in the countryside

Miss V.M. Thom Countryside Commission for Scotland.

This chapter inevitably differs substantially from all the others in the volume. It must do so on two accounts — first because it deals with a topic which cannot really be treated as a scientific study and second because, unlike most of the other chapters, it is not based on an intensive examination of one particular aspect of our native pinewoods. Rather, it is concerned with applying the principles of what is known as countryside interpretation to the question of increasing appreciation of pinewoods.

In the concluding chapter of their classic text on pinewoods, Steven and Carlisle wrote "The first thing needed to ensure the future of the native pinewoods is the appreciation by as many of their owners as possible that they are a unique natural heritage". Hopefully, the pinewood owners are now awake to their responsibilities and are taking appropriate action. Since that statement was made, several significant developments have taken place. The so-called leisure revolution has resulted in a vast up-surge in the numbers of people making use of the countryside for recreation — a fact of which residents in areas of outstanding scenery are only too well aware — and, rather more recently, the influence exerted by pressure groups and public opinion has increased greatly. There has also been a marked growth of interest in wildlife and, where public sympathy has been successfully invoked — as in the case of the osprey — in its conservation. I suggest, therefore, that this is an appropriate time to amend Steven and Carlisle's sentence so that it reads *"One of the things* needed to ensure the future of the native pinewoods is appreciation, by as many *people* as possible, that they are a unique natural heritage". That premise is really my starting point and is fundamental to all that follows.

At this stage, I am going to refer to the Oxford Dictionary and its definition of the world "appreciate". The definitions given include "be sensitive to" and "esteem highly", both of which are relevant to this discussion. In my opinion "sensitivity to" equates with "awareness" and "esteem highly" with "consider worth looking after". In countryside interpretation, which is really a painless form of conservation education aimed at the casual visitor to the countryside, we are concerned with both these concepts and also, as an intermediate stage between them, with understanding. There is a much-quoted phrase which goes "Through interpretation, understanding; through understanding, appreciation; through appreciation, protection". Referring back to our two definitions of appreciation, I would amend this phrase to read "interpretation aims at developing awareness and progressing from awareness to understanding; from understanding to esteem; and from esteem to protection". The theory is attractive, but just how does one progress through these stages in practice?

By inserting the extra rung in the interpretation to protection ladder, we have, I believe, clarified the situation somewhat, as we have distinguished between the creation of awareness and the development of understanding. The first may simply involve stimulating interest, catching attention, arousing curiosity — the second must necessarily involve the acquisition of knowledge, and the absorption of information which will lead to understanding. Only where the first stage is successful can there be any real prospect of the interpretation process reaching the esteem and protection stages. All stages are, of course, utterly dependent upon effective communication — a fact which sometimes, regrettably, appears to be overlooked by would-be interpreters.

In the Countryside Commission for Scotland, we have developed guidelines to the planning of interpretive programmes. These guidelines focus attention on the various steps that must be taken in preparing an interpretive plan and the points at which major decisions must be taken. I think it would be useful to draw attention to certain parts of our guidelines and to discuss these in relation to interpretation of the pinewoods.

First, at what we call the "inventory stage", we consider it essential to carry out three very different exercises:

i) to explore the interpretive potential of the resource;

ii) to consider the conservation and safety constraints; and

iii) to investigate visitor characteristics.

These exercises should help us to answer the questions:

> *What* are we going to interpret?
> *Where* are we going to interpret?

And, *for whom* are we going to interpret?

It is only when we have these answers that we are really in a position to define clearly our interpretive objectives.

Let us look at these three questions a little more closely and consider the relationship between the answers we give and subsequent stages in the planning process. Take the "who for" first. We need to know something about the kind of people in whom we are going to try and arouse curiosity or stimulate interest. What kind of background do they come from? How much contact have they had with the countryside? Do they really *see* what is around them? One of the basic precepts of interpretation is that it should relate what is being displayed or interpreted to something within the experience of the visitor — and, unless you have taken the trouble to find out something about that visitor, you cannot hope to achieve this.

So the content of interpretation, in terms of the way the story is presented, should be determined by the type of visitor expected — and so too should be the "level" of the interpretation — by which I mean the complexity of the information put across and the vocabulary used.

I would hazard a guess that on Speyside, where the prospective customers are more numerous than in any other pinewood area, the appropriate level of interpretation would be rather different from what might be acceptable in the Black Wood or by Loch Maree.

The second part of our inventory exercise is concerned with constraints. In relation to the native pinewoods, these are obviously more likely to be considerations of resource conservation than of visitor safety. It is necessary to decide, for example, whether the increased risk of fire damage makes interpretation within the real, naturally-regenerating pinewoods a totally unacceptable hazard or whether, as suggested earlier, the presence of more people in the forest reduces the fire risk. If the setting aside of a portion of forest for this purpose *is* considered acceptable, then which portion would it be most appropriate to use; which area would be most easily isolated from the main forest in the event of fire and yet be sufficiently accessible for visitors? Considerations such as these must determine not only which forest areas are chosen for interpretation, but also exactly where visitors can be allowed to go.

The third part of the inventory exercise is concerned with the exploration of interpretive potential—a bringing together and sifting of all the available information about the area or the site and its component parts. We have heard a great deal about the native pinewoods as seen through the eyes of specialists, and such information would obviously form part of the interpretive potential of the pinewoods. It would be a pity, however, to consider the scientific aspects as the dominating interest and to take insufficient account of the aesthetic appeal of the pinewoods and of the fascinating history of their use by man. In exploring interpretive potential, we are seeking not only to build up a comprehensive dossier on the site, but also to identify the significance of the resource, the "something special" that makes one particular place different from any other, and to identify a suitable theme or story line which will help to convey this significance to the visitor. What, then, is "special" about the native pinewoods?

I am sure that many people must enjoy the contribution that pine trees make to the appearance of the countryside, without any greater degree of awareness than the knowledge that these trees satisfy the eye. Perception of the environment is a topic for numerous research studies nowadays, but it is not a subject in which I can claim to be at all well-informed and I have no intention of discussing the psychology of perception. To me, pines are often important features in the landscape because they provide striking colour contrasts with species such as birch and because they evoke a feeling of ruggedness and strength. This is as true of solitary specimens and of planted groups as it is of the native forests—so we must delve further in our search for "significance". The flora and fauna associated with pinewoods do not really help a great deal—there are no birds or mammals completely dependent on the native forests, and anyway the prospect of seeing animals is often poor and the visitor has often to be content with simply seeing signs of their presence. Even flowers, such as *Linnaea borealis* and *Goodyera repens,* which are described as typical of pinewoods, occur in planted woods as well as in the native forests.

When I was preparing this paper, I contrived to escape from the office for a day in the Black Wood of Rannoch, where I conducted my own private visual and atmospheric appraisal of one particular patch of forest. It was a warm sunny day and, being alone, I was able to enjoy to the full the atmosphere of the place, the compound of sights, sounds and smells that can only really be experienced when you are entirely on your own and which is often largely ephemeral and cannot therefore readily be interpreted to a mass of visitors—and certainly cannot be interpreted by any means other than a guided walk. During my visit, I was struck by the fact that it was not only possible but was even easy to see out of or through the forest—the variations in tree height allowed glimpses of distant hills and the irregular spacing of the trees gave vistas through the forest itself. Two aspects of the Black Wood made a particularly strong impression on me. First, the totally unregimented appearance of the natural pine wood and the tremendous variety in character of the trees. It seemed to me that, in an age of serried ranks and increasing uniformity, this lack of regimentation was an aspect of the native pinewoods which would appeal to, and be appreciated by, many whose surroundings are monotonously orderly, and which could be used as an introduction to a closer look at the individual variations between trees and to a conservation message concerning the importance of ensuring the continued survival of this variation.

The second very strong impression I got was of continuity—the complete mixture of trees of all ages, from the smallest seedling to huge old trees long past their prime—the mosaic that has been referred to in several previous chapters. That this continuous succession has gone on for around 9,000 years is a staggering thought—and is not a particularly easy concept for people to grasp because it is difficult for most people to comprehend a time-scale of that magnitude. Certainly, it is possible to try to explain about pollen analysis or to use the peat overlying buried stumps as an indicator of the time that has passed since the tree was alive and growing. However, as it is during historic times that real damage has been done by man to the pinewoods, would it not be better to focus attention on the threat to continuity resulting from man's activities in the comparatively recent past?

Even in a fairly superficial search of the literature, I have been struck by the amount of material available for illustrating interpretation based on man's use of the forests. There are old maps, for example, and contemporary documents and records of various kinds.

Some of these are especially likely to arouse interest because they relate to situations or experiences with which modern man can readily identify himself: records of things like wages and prices, for example: old photographs that can help to bring alive working conditions in the forest many years ago—and the progressive mechanisation of the timber trade.

There are lots of descriptive snippets, too, that give ideas for possible story-lines:

In relation to regeneration: the proposal to use swine to break up the ground in the Black Wood so that the seeds from cones scattered afterwards would have a better chance of survival.

In relation to fire damage, which is no recent problem: "some idle boys and herds carried fire early one morning to the back of the Black Wood and there kindled muir burn and went home." The date was 1763. Again, in 1770, it was recorded that 500 men were summoned, by means of the Fiery Cross, to fight a fire in Abernethy.

In relation to the living conditions of forest workers in the past: "they lay down for the night in their wet clothes, each man's feet to the fire, each man's plaid round his chest, a circle of wearied bodies, half stupefied by whisky, enveloped in a cloud of steam and smoke".

There must be many more such snippets to be found, given time to really search through old estate records, but it takes a lot of time to do the job thoroughly, to check on details so as to ensure that your representation of the past is as accurate as it is possible to make it. It takes time also to work out the most effective way of communicating the story—whether this story is based on history or scientific data. Which do *you* think is the most important thing, ensuring complete accuracy in every detail, or getting the message over? Is it permissible to simplify, provided that the result is not misleading, even if it is not "the whole truth"? Is it permissible to use conjectural illustrations

of the past if these will help commmunication? These are questions one frequently finds oneself asking when preparing interpretive plans.

To sum up:

I have suggested that interpretation, by leading visitors to the countryside towards awareness and understanding of the forests and esteem for them, *could* assist in the future conservation of our native pinewoods.

I have indicated the stages that should be gone through in the planning of countryside interpretation. I have pointed out that the native pinewoods are sufficiently rich in interpretive potential to permit the development of several different story-lines. There is, therefore, no need for a repetition of the same story at different pinewood sites—a modicum of consultation, co-operation, and perhaps restraint, is all that would be needed to prevent such duplication occurring.

We are still left, however, with two major questions to be answered:

First—is it possible to interpret the native pinewoods adequately without taking people into them? In my opinion it probably is not — but some readers will possibly disagree with me.

Second—is the potential benefit from greater public appreciation of the pinewoods sufficient to justify permitting some parts of the "real" pinewoods to be used for interpretation? It is those responsible for the care and the future of the native forests who will have to make this decision.

Finally, I would like to put one question to those directly involved in work on the pinewoods. Would it be practicable, given time, to re-create a natural-looking and feeling forest in an area that at present holds only scattered pines? Gimingham has already suggested that it would be practicable—in which case, would this not be a very suitable place in which to present to the public a sotry of pinewood conservation?

Figure 1 Countryside Commission for Scotland guidelines to planning an interpretive programme

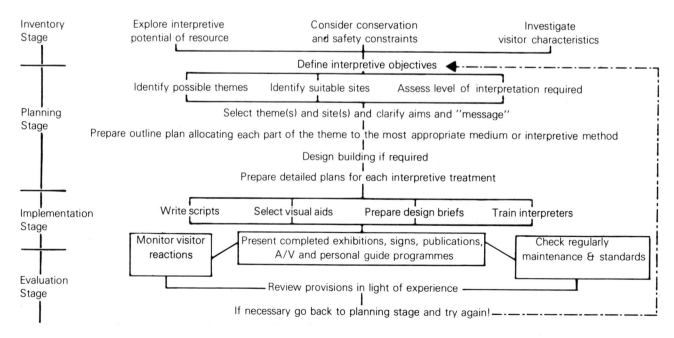

Pinewoods as habitats for mammals

V.P.W. Lowe Institute of Terrestrial Ecology

Introduction

Almost all the areas of what was formerly the forest zone in Britain are now artefacts of management by man, and most of them are treeless. It is therefore no longer possible to determine exactly how any of the British mammals related to the pinewoods in former times. Moreover, as the remaining fragments of pinewoods are mostly small and isolated, one cannot expect to find many of the mammals still associated with these woods and persisting with their former patterns of adaptive behaviour. Therefore, instead of attempting to discuss only the British pinewoods as habitats for mammals, this paper aims to describe how just two species of mammal found in Britain relate to the more extensive coniferous forests in other parts of the world. One, the Red squirrel (*Sciurus vulgaris* L.) is restricted to woodland habitats at all times; the other, the Red deer (*Cervus elaphus* L.) uses the pinewoods in Scotland largely as a result of the changes in its more natural habitats effected by man.

Except for the Red squirrel, only the Pine marten (*Martes martes* L.) among British mammals is associated in many people's minds with Scots pine (*Pinus sylvestris* L.), which at one time formed such extensive forests in Scotland. Little is known about the Pine marten but it should be noted that this species is not in fact restricted to pinewoods (Brink 1967) or even to woodland (Southern 1964).

In America, Marshall (1951) noted that the American marten (*Martes americana* (Turton)), like the European 'Spruce marten' as he called it, preferred spruce and fir woods, only making use of pine woods (*P. ponderosa*) where these were adjacent to woods of these other species.

In Scotland, Lockie (1964) found that the marten was an omnivore which exploited any temporary abundance of diverse foods. The principal species of vertebrate prey proved to be the Short-tailed vole (*Microtus agrostis* L.): in this respect the feeding habits of the marten appear to be universally similar, small rodents, berries and birds probably being the most important constituents throughout the New as well as the Old world (Marshall 1951).

Whilst marten may not have changed their feeding habits in Scotland when adapting to their new, and in some cases, treeless habitats, the deer, both Red deer (*Cervus elaphus* L.) and Roe deer (*Capreolus capreolus* L.), have had to make considerable adjustments. In England, for instance, both species tend to be crepuscular or nocturnal in their grazing activities, remaining under cover of woodland by day. In Scotland, the same species graze both by day and by night; they also flourish in areas without any woodland cover. These differences suggest that at least some of their behavioural characteristics in Scotland must have been acquired after their habitat was deforested, as large areas of grassland, heath and moorland could not exist for long without man's assistance (Gimingham, 1971).

Steven and Carlisle (1959), although noting the presence of most of the species of Scottish mammal in the pinewoods from time to time, with the exceptions of Red deer and Red squirrels, were unable to relate any of them to the Scots pine specifically. In the case of the badger (*Meles meles* L.) for instance, which was found but rarely, they suggested that, when present, it usually occupied ". . .the birch woods within their boundaries" (p. 80). However, with regard to the Red deer and Red squirrel, they did note that both appeared capable of modifying the pinewoods and were thus economically, as well as ecologically, important. They did not consider the Red squirrel to be a serious pest at the present time but noted that, previously, this species had caused considerable damage to Scots pine. With regard to Red deer, they were surprised that "Deer do not only eat Scots pine as a last resort; they were seen browsing on young pine in Strathfarrer with ample grass pasture, within twenty yards,..."

Similar observations are frequently made by foresters, and as natural regeneration of Scots pine is one of the most vital parameters in the conservation of the pinewoods, I have attempted to explain in this paper why these two species, particularly the Red deer, are likely to continue to frustrate the aims of the conservationist. The paper concludes by considering these implications and suggests some alternative plans for woodland management.

Scots pine and the coniferous forests

The Scots pine is one of the most widely distributed conifers in the world. In the extreme north, in the Taiga Zone, it is usually associated with fir (*Abies* sp.), larch (*Larix* sp.) and spruce (*Picea* sp.). It also occurs in the belt of mixed forest to the south of the Taiga in association with various hardwood species such as oak, lime (*Tilia* sp.), hazel (*Corylus* sp.), birch and aspen (*Populus* sp.), and, further south again, in the broadleaved forests in association with oak, ash (*Fraxinus* sp.), sycamore (*Acer* sp.), elm (*Ulmus* sp.) and beech (*Fagus* sp.). In fact, it is absent only from north east Siberia and the desert or semi-desert regions (Tseplyaev 1961). The most significant aspect of its distribution in relation to the mammals is as Walter (1973) writes, "There is no sharp boundary between deciduous forest zone and coniferous forest zone; instead, a transitional boreo-nemoral zone is inter-calated between the two . . . ."(p. 191). This transitional zone consists of pure and mixed stands of various species of tree depending on site conditions, but pure and isolated stands of Scots pine rarely occur.

In Scotland, the only 'natural' coniferous woods consist amost entirely of Scots pine, and are usually small and tend to be isolated, like the pinewood in Glen Derry illustrated in Plate 1a. Moreover, the ground flora are usually suppressed through grazing, as in this illustration, or through shading and are rarely rich in their diversity, being remnants of former forests on sites which were too poor to be put to any other use. As McVean (1964) notes, the surviving species composition and structure in any of the major types of woodland probably reflect management or land use by man rather than the original forest cover. At the same time, enough remains to suggest that, originally, there must have been a zonal arrangement with pine occurring naturally as a belt between the oak (*Quercus* sp.) on the lower ground and birch (*Betula* sp.) on the higher slopes, and in this way forming a natural extension to the west European transition from temperate deciduous forest through coniferous forest to the boreal deciduous forest.

The Red squirrel and its habitat

Both the Red squirrel (*Sciurus vulgaris* L.) in Europe and the Red squirrel (*Tamiasciurus hudsonicus* Erxleben) in Canada are said to prefer coniferous forest to deciduous woodland (Shorten, 1954, 1962; Southern 1964; Brink 1967; Tittensor 1970; MacClintock 1970). Soper (1973), however, has suggested that mixed forest may be its optimum habitat in Alberta, Canada, and Shorten (1954) has also stated that, when present, other species of pines, larches and spruces improve the coniferous habitat. My own experience certainly shows that Red squirrels may sometimes be much more numerous in mixed deciduous woodlands than in pinewoods. For instance, in one of the woodlands so typical of the limestone fells in the Lake District of north-west England (O.S. sheet no. 89, ref. 43851) in which the dominant tree species are oak, ash, sycamore, birch, hazel and yew (*Taxus baccata* L.), I was able to locate at least nine pairs of squirrels in an area of approximately 1 sq km, in the years 1968-75, with as many as 22 squirrels being seen on one occasion. By contrast, in a similar but larger strip of pinewood (c. 3 sq km) on Kinveachy in Speyside, Inverness-shire (O.S. sheet no. 37, ref. 8713), no more than five pairs were ever located during the years 1964-74 and most of these occurred in or near blocks of larch planted within the forest. Elsewhere, in Speyside, most of the Red squirrels appear to be concentrated in areas where larch, spruce and pine have been planted together, mainly in people's gardens. In some areas, even when the pine has an admixture of birch, the Red squirrel is scarce or even absent altogether, as in Glen Affric (F.M. Macrae, pers. comm.).

In Finland, the Red squirrel is found throughout the country except in the northern mountain birch forests, where it is found only sporadically (Lampio, 1972). According to a study covering the winters of 1968-73, Pulliainen (1973) found that ". . . squirrels showed a clear preference for spruce forests (mixed or pure). . ."; he also found no trace of squirrels in the pure birch forests. However, he did observe squirrels moving into the pine forests in larger numbers in certain years, e.g. the winter of 1972-73, a poor year for both quantity and quality of spruce seed.

The Red deer and its habitat

Dzieciolowski (1969) evaluated the habitat requirements and food resource of the Red deer in Poland. He concluded that the Red deer is a browser rather than a grazer by nature, but is very adaptable and flourishes in a great variety of environments. The most important plants were trees and shrubs, with the Scots pine the most important and sought after of all the trees, followed by the hornbeam (*Carpinus betulus* L.), birch, oak, alder and other hardwoods in that order. Grasses, sedges and rushes were the least preferred foods and failed to reach even 20 per cent of the Red deer's diet in the best habitats. But in the poorest habitats — young conifer plantations — the diet consisted principally of dwarf shrubs, grasses and graminids and forbs (89 per cent).

Flook (1964), discussing the range requirements of elk (*Cervus canadensis* Erxleben) in the Banff and Jasper National Parks, Alberta, stressed the adaptability of the species. He also suggested that, in the poorer habitats, this species became a grazer; in these two parks, this was due to the inadequate control of elk numbers in the 1930's and 1940's. In the richer habitats of Elk Island Park, Alberta, and Riding Mountain Park, Manitoba, by contrast," . . . browse and forbs together comprise the major part of the summer diet, and browse alone makes up most of the winter diet" (p. 125). These differences in feeding behaviour, correlated with both habitat structure and population density, are also reflected in the wide range in fertility of deer. Cowan (1950), for instance, reported ratios as low as 15-24 calves per 100 cows in the overbrowsed Banff National Park where the deer had become grazers. Knight (1970) noted a ratio of only 18 calves per 100 cows in the 1963/64 winter in the Sun River elk herd — again, an area in which the deer were grazers. In Scotland, where most Red deer have access to the shrub, heather (*Calluna vulgaris* L.) but not to trees, an average ratio of 39.4 calves per 100 hinds was observed by a survey team over the years 1952-59 (Lowe, 1961). In Holland, under similar conditions, Eygenraam (1962) observed a ratio of 45 calves per 100 hinds. In Germany where trees were available as food for the deer, Ueckermann (1960) found a calving percentage of 64.8 per cent, whilst Raesfield (1964) calculated the average calving figure to be of the order of 70 per cent.

Red deer are not the only species to prefer the deciduous and open mixed forest habitat. In a study, similar to that of Dzieciolowski (1969), Thilenius (1972) classified the various habitats within the Ponderosa pine forest of the Black Hills in South Dakota (USA), according to the use made of them by White-tailed deer (*Odocoileus virginianus* Zimmermann) and Mule deer (*O. hemionus* Rafinesque). The two most preferred habitats were the low-ground mixed forests with oak the dominant tree species and the very open pinewoods with *Symphoricarpos occidentalis* the dominant shrub. The two least preferred habitats were the pure Ponderosa pine forest on limestone with juniper (*Juniperus scopulorum*) the chief shrub, and the dry grassland with scattered pines. Roe deer also prefer habitats with a good shrub layer; in fact Vladyshevskii (1968) found considerable competition between Red and Roe deer and noted that "... the basic winter plant diet for red deer and roe deer is almost identical. The only exceptions are the juniper, whose shoots the roe deer very seldom eat, and the pine, which the red deer like as a food much more than roe deer".

If the world distribution of Red deer is compared with the vegetational zones figured by Walter (1973) (see Figure 1), these preferences for deciduous and mixed conifer/deciduous woodlands are shown to be universal. The only zones besides deciduous forest occupied by Red deer are mixed conifer/deciduous woodland and the montane forests adjacent to hotter and drier deserts or semi-deserts. However, only in western Russia (Lithuania, Latvia and Estonia), Sweden, Norway, Scotland and in eastern Siberia in the USSR (areas with less continental climates) do Red deer occur naturally in forests of mixed conifers and hardwoods. Red deer do not inhabit the boreal coniferous zone. and. therefore, with the possible exception of the Yakutia region in eastern Siberia (Egorov 1967), they do not overlap with reindeer or caribou (*Rangifer tarandus* L.) in their distribution. However, the coniferous forests, whether they consist of pine or mixed species, tend to be used by deer of one species or another wherever they occur. In the extreme north, for instance, the caribou in summer (May-September) inhabit the tundra, but, after the rut, they migrate southwards and by November they are mainly in the taiga forest for the winer (Parker 1972). The adult males move farthest south and winter deep in the boreal forest zone. Further south again, in mountainous country, what the caribou accomplishes latitudinally, the Red deer accomplishes in a vertical direction. In the spring, Red deer move upwards through the different forest zones until they reach the alpine pastures above the timber line. Then, in the same way that the caribou move between tundra scrub, taiga and open tundra during the summer months and prefer to calve on the higher ground (Kelsall 1968), so Red deer also tend to calve on the higher ground and use the forest about the tree limit for cover and shelter up to the time of the rut in late September/early October. After the rut, the deer descend the hills, passing through the different forest zones until they reach the hardwoods in the valleys, where they spend the winter. Again, like the caribou, the old Red stags winter below the hinds and calves. In Scotland, the forest zones are largely missing, but the seasonal movements appear to have remained unchanged (Darling 1937; Lowe 1966). In Switzerland, where all the montane coniferous forest zones are still preserved, as in the Swiss National Park (plate 1b), but the low ground deciduous woodlands are missing, the problems of deer management

are very similar to those in Scotland.

Red deer started to colonise the Swiss National Park (168 km^2) around the year 1915, and, being few in number, in the early years they mainly overwintered in the pine, spruce, and larch forests within the park. By 1930, their numbers had increased to 136 animals. Shortly afterwards as the deer continued to increase in numbers they ate out their food supply to such an extent that by the 1950s only odd animals still remained in the park during the winter months (Schloeth and Burckhardt 1961). Today, the park is able to carry the deer only during the summer months, May-October.

Discussion and Conclusions

The native pine forests of Scotland are the last fragments of the original forest system; many of them have survived only because they are remote or happen to be growing on soils too poor to be put to any other use. As a result, they are generally small, isolated and consist predominantly of only the one species of tree. In their present form and distribution, they are almost valueless to mammals. The effect of this imbalance between habitats, with too little woodland and too large an area of grazing, is reflected by the so-called 'damage' done to the pinewoods, not only by squirrels and deer but also by sheep and cattle, for none of which do they constitute a necessary part of their natural habitat. On the Continent, where the Scots pine forms an important component of the forest for certain mammals, it is invariably mixed with spruce and/or larch in the coniferous woodlands, or is mixed with these and various hardwoods in the mixed deciduous/coniferous forests, and these support a far greater variety of mammals than we have in Britain.

The Red squirrel thrives in both types of forest on the continent, but, when in blocks of woodland consisting predominantly of Scots pine, it invariably has access to trees of a different species, in adjacent blocks, whether these be conifers or hardwoods.

Likewise, in North America the Red squirrels (*Tamisciurus hudsonicus* Erxleben) are found mainly in the mixed spruce and pine forests, but as MacClintock (1970) points out, it is only in these forests that they can "...flourish without competition from their cousins, the Gray and Fox squirrels" (p. 146) (*Sciurus carolinensis* Gm. and *Sciurus niger* L. respectively). This implies that, but for these competitors, the Red squirrels would also inhabit the deciduous forests.

Even the Abert squirrel (*Sciurus aberti* Woodhouse), with its apparent dependence on the Ponderosa pine (*Pinus ponderosa*) (Patton 1975), exploits the hardwoods for food when available. Stephenson (1974), for example, found that acorns from the Gambel oak (*Quercus gambeli*) could constitute as much as forty per cent of the diet of this species in autumn.

In Scotland, Red squirrels have also depended on one species of pine, but, for several centuries now, they have rarely had access to any hardwood species of tree which were useful for food. This lack of a supplementary diet may help to explain the excessive damage to some plantations in the late 19th and early 20th centuries (Ritchie 1920). In this context, it is also perhaps significant that since spruce, and particularly Sitka spruce (*Picea sitchensis* (Bong) Carr), was planted extensively in Scotland after the 1939-45 war, and larch was also often planted within or near plantations of pine, there has been little or no further damage of any economic importance. Of course it is possible that the squirrels involved had different ecological requirements since some, and perhaps all, of them were not of the British race, *Sciurus vulgaris leucourus* Kerr. The squirrels, which caused so much damage to Scots pine in Glen Tanar, for instance, during the period 1857-72, were descendants of the stock introduced by the Duke of Atholl on to his estate in about 1790. These had been imported from Scandinavia and therefore belonged to the race *Sciurus v. vulgaris* L. The damage caused to pine in the northern Highlands of Scotland was also brought about by descendants of imported squirrels; in this case, the original stock had been introduced into woods near Beauly, Inverness-shire, in 1844, but the race to which they belonged was not recorded (Ritchie 1920).

However, whatever may have been the reason for the damage to pine plantations in former times, these do not seem to have recurred, although descendants of the same races of squirrels are still present in these areas. The most likely explanation for this change in behaviour appears to be that extensive forests of Sitka spruce are now available and, whilst the overall fertility of the habitat has not been raised, large populations of squirrels at low density can be accommodated without excessive damage resulting to either species of tree. In this connection, it is important to note McVean's (1964) suggestion that the nearest equivalent to the pinewood *Vaccinium-Calluna* association on the continent might be among the spruce (*Picea* sp.) forest associations of Central Europe, because it is in these forests (also in those of the Nearctic) that the Red squirrels appear to be centred. Therefore, by creating a spruce/pine forest system, even if the spruce is mainly Sitka rather than Norway (*Picea abies* L. Karst), a broadly similar habitat has been produced.

Originally, the natural habitat of the Red deer appears to have been deciduous woodland or mixed coniferous/deciduous woodland, and in these woodlands they would normally have been browsers. In most countries, however, changes in land use by man have effectively removed much of the Red deer habitat, and the deer have survived only by becoming grazing animals. This transformation has been achieved by a reduction in their growth rate, stature and fertility.

In Scotland, since most of the ground below 300 m has been brought into cultivation by man, the Red deer has had to occupy a niche which elsewhere would be occupied by chamois or caribou, summering on al-

pine pastures above the tree line and migrating back into the forest zones each winter. The most important difference is that, while chamois and caribou normally winter in and are compatible with the coniferous forest zone (Baille-Grohman 1896; Brink 1967; Kelsall 1968; Parker 1972), the latter cannot support Red deer even when the forest is more or less natural and complete as in the Swiss National Park. In Scotland, the situation is further aggravated by the shortage of woodland of any kind. As a result it is no uncommon sight to see Red deer hinds and their followers wintering on the open hills and looking very much like caribou (see plate 2).

Where woodland is available to deer in winter, it will be used by them regardless of the species of trees in its composition. In a forest consisting predominantly of Scots pine with patches of birch such as that in Rothiemurchus (Inverness-shire), it is the areas of hardwood to which most of the deer are attracted for food (see plate 3); these areas are the nearest equivalent to the optimal wintering habitat of deer and provide most of the browse for them. Scots pine seedlings, in particular, are often plentiful in these more open areas and, apart from being the most preferred food of the Red deer, constitute one of the most important winter foods and are almost the only browse available apart from heather (*Calluna vulgaris* L.)

In other areas, where pine grow in dense stands and have a closed canopy, the trees may provide cover and shelter, but not food, as can be seen in plate 4a. Deer, and stags, in particular, use such pinewoods a great deal because of the cover they afford by day and the shelter they provide in times of storm and after heavy falls of snow, but they have to seek food elsewhere, in the glades or clearings within the woodlands, or in the fields and farmland or moorland adjacent to them. These pinewoods, and especially those parts occupying the higher ground, are used almost continuously for much of the spring and summer period as well as the winter, again partly for their cover but also for protection from flies, as demonstrated by the stags in plate 4b.

In most parts of Scotland, however, there are no woodlands of any kind in which the deer can winter. Therefore, the deer — stags in particular — tend to gravitate naturally to the low ground which would formerly have been covered with hardwoods or mixed conifer/deciduous woodland, and there compete with sheep for their grazings, or with other types of land use, in order to survive. These deer are usually termed marauders, and the species, like the squirrel, is viewed as a pest rather than as an asset by most of the people having to manage such land.

To sum up; having all but eliminated the Red deer's natural habitat and forced the species to adopt a mode of life more befitting the caribou or chamois, we now complain that they damage forestry, prevent regeneration, destroy farm crops and compete with domestic stock for their grazings. In addition, deer forest owners and sportsmen also complain that growth rates, fertility, overall size and quality of the trophies (antlers) of the deer have declined. It appears, therefore, that no one is satisfied with the present state of affairs and that the reform of the deer forest called for by Cameron (1923) is required even more today than it was after the 1914-18 war.

Implications for management of the native pinewoods

If the native pinewoods are to be conserved there appear to be few choices still open to us.

Largely by chance, and because it has been fashionable to plant spruce and larch extensively in Scotland since the 1939-45 war, there is now little likelihood of the Red squirrel again becoming a serious pest in the pinewoods in the foreseeable future. The same cannot be said of the Red deer.

Wherever woodlands are present and accessible to deer, the deer will inevitably use them. If these woodlands happen to be native pinewoods, all naturally regenerating Scots pine seedlings will be browsed each winter because this species is the preferred food of the Red deer (Dzieciolowski 1969). In many respects, this appears to be a universal problem; pine seedlings appear to be equally susceptible to browsing by deer in parts of the USA (Ross, Bray and Marshall 1970). Therefore, whilst the native pinewoods in Scotland remain available for use by deer, it is not realistic to expect these woodlands to remain viable entities. The only alternatives appear to be to reduce deer numbers drastically, to fence them out of the pinewoods, or to replace the Red deer with caribou (reindeer) or chamois, neither of which would prevent natural regeneration. Otherwise, if the present situation is allowed to persist, it can be only a matter of time before almost all the remaining fragments of the native pinewoods of Scotland will be destroyed completely.

Acknowledgements

Miss S.M.C. Robertson prepared the two maps in the figure and Mr. D.A. Kempson very kindly prepared all the monochrome prints for the plates. Dr. D. Jenkins and others of my colleagues helped in the preparation of the paper by discussion and criticism of earlier drafts.

References

BAILLIE-GROHMAN, W.A. (1896). *Sports in the Alps.* Lond. A. and C. Black, 356.

BRINK, F.H. VAN DEN (1967). *A field guide to the mammals of Britain and Europe:* Transl. Kruuk and Southern. Collins.

CAMERON, A.G. (1923). *The Wild Red deer of Scotland.* Blackwood.

COWAN, I. McT. (1950). Some vital statistics of big game on overstocked mountain ranges. *Trans. N. Am. wildl. Conf.,* **15**, 581-588.

DZIECIOLOWSKI, R. (1969). *The quantity, quality and seasonal variation of food resources available to red deer in various environmental conditions of forest management.* Warsaw.

EGOROV, O.V. (1965). *Wild ungulates of Yakutia.* Nauka, Maskva. (Israel Program for Scientific Translations, Jerusalem 1967).

EYGENRAAM, J.A. (1962). Leeftiydsopbouw en Reproduktie van eeen Nederlandse herten populatie. *Lutra,* **4**, 1-16.

FLOOK, D.R. (1964). Range relationships of some ungulates native to Banff and Jasper National Parks, Alberta. In: *Grazing in terrestrial and marine environments,* edited by D.J. Crisp, 119-128. Blackwell. (British Ecological Society Symposium no. 4).

FRASER DARLING, F. (1937). *A Herd of Red Deer.* Oxford Univ. Pr.

GIMINGHAM, C.B. (1971). *Calluna* heathlands: Use and conservation in the light of some ecological effects of management. In: *The scientific management of animal and plant communities for conservation,* edited by E. Duffey and A.S. Watt, 91-103. Blackwell. (British Ecological Socieety Symposium no. 11).

KELSALL, J.P. (1968). The migratory barren-ground caribou of Canada. *Can. Wildl. Serv. Monogr.* **3.**

KNIGHT, R.R. (1970). The Sun River Elk herd. *Wildlife Monogr., Chesterton,* No. 23.

LAMPIO, T. (1972). *Orava, Suomen Nisakkaat.* **1**, 246-270.

LOCKIE, J.D. (1964). Distribution and fluctuations of the pine marten. Martes martes (L), in Scotland. *J. Anim. Ecol.,* **33**, 349-356.

LOWE, V.P.W. (1961). A discussion on the history, present status and future conservation of red deer (*Cervus elephus* L.) in Scotland. *Terre Vie,* **108**, 9-40.

LOWE, V.P.W. (1966). Observations on the dispersal of red deer on Rhum. *Symp. zool. Soc. Lond.,* no. **18**, 211-228.

MACCLINTOCK, D. (1970). *Squirrels of North Ameria.* Van Nostrand Reinhold Co.

McVEAN, D.N. (1964). 'the forest zone'. In: *The vegetation of Scotland,* edited by J.H. Burnett, 144-168. Oliver and Boyd.

MARSHALL, W.H. (1951). Pine marten as a forest product. *J. For.,* **49**, 899-905.

PARKER, G.R. (1972). Biology of the Kaminuriak population of barren-ground caribou. Part 1: Total number, mortality, recruitment and seasonal distribution. *Can. Wildl. Serv. Rep. Ser.,* **20**, 1-93.

PATTON, D.R. (1975). Abert squirrel cover requirements in South Western Pondersoa pine. *USDA For. Serv. Res. paper RM-145.*

PULLIAINEN, E. (1973). Winter ecology of the squirrel *(Sciurus vulgaris* L.) in north eastern Lapland. *Ann. zool. fenn.,* **10**, 487-494.

RAESFIELD, F. VON (1964). *Das Rotwild.* Paul Parey, Hamburg.

RITCHIE, J. (1920). *The influence of man on animal life in* Cambridge Univ. Pr.

ROSS, B.A., BRAY, J.R. & MARSHALL, W.H. (1970). Effects of long-term deer exclusion on a *Pinus resinosa* forest in North-Central Minnesota. *Ecology,* **51**, 1088-1093.

SCHLOETH, R. & BURCKHARDT, D. (1961). Die Wanderungen des Rotwildes *Cervus elaphus* L. in Gebiet des Schweizerischen Nationalparkes. *Revue Suisse de Zool.,* **68**, 145-156.

SHORTEN, M. (1954). *Squirrels.* Collins.

SHORTEN, M. (1962) Squirrels: their biology and control. *Bull. Minist. Agric. Fish Fd.,* no. 184.

SOPER, J.D. (1973). The mammals of Waterton Lakes National Park Alberta. *Can. wildl. Serv. Rep. Ser.* 23.

SOUTHERN, H.N. (ed.), (1964). *The handbook of British mammals.* Blackwell.

108

STEPHENSON, R.L. (1974). Seasonal food habits of Abert's squirrels, *Sciurus aberti. J. Ariz. Acad. Sci.,* **9.**

STEVEN, H.M. & CARLISLE, A. (1959). *The native pinewoods of Scotland.* Oliver and Boyd.

THILENIUS, J.F. (1972). Classification of deer habitat in the Ponderosa pine forest of the Black Hills, South Dakota. *USDA For. Serv. Res. paper RM-91.*

TITTENSOR, A.M. (1970). The red squirrel (*Sciurus vulgaris* L.) in relation to its food resource. *Ph.D. thesis,* Edinb. Univ.

TSEPLYAEV, V.P. (1961). The forests of the U.S.S.R. Moscow. (Israel Program for Scientific Translations no. 2117, 1965).

UECKERMANN, E. (1960). *Wildstandsbewirtschaftung und Wildschadenverhütung beim Rotwild.* Parey.

VLADYSHEVSKII, D.V. (1968). Factors affecting the numbers of Europen Roe-deer *(Capreolus capreolus). Zool. Zh.,* **47,** 438-443. (British Library Transl. no. RTS 8943, 1975).

WALTER, H. (1973). *Vegetation of the earth in relation to climate and the eco-physiological conditions.* English Univ. Pr.

Figure 1 Map showing world distribution of A , boreal coniferous forest, decidous woodland and B , Red deer.

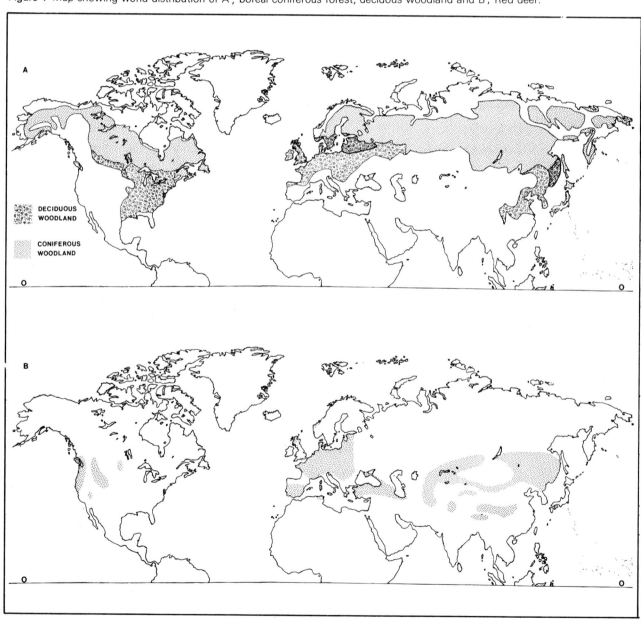

Plate 1a Typical fragment of pine wood in Glen Derry, Aberdeenshire, Scotland.

Plate 1b Conifer forest consisting largely of pines in the Swiss National Park.

Plate 2 A herd of hinds and followers wintering on Meall an Lundain above Glen Derry, Aberdeenshire, Scotland.

Plate 3 A herd of hinds and followers wintering in one of the mixed Birch/Pine areas within Rothiemurchus forest, Inverness-shire, Scotland.

Plate 4a A Roe deer (♀) in a mature pine forest with a closed canopy and almost no ground vegetation other than mosses.

Plate 4b Part of a herd of Red deer stags of all ages keeping cool and free from flies on a hot day in the Kinveachy pine forest, Inverness-shire, Scotland.

A review of the pinewoods managed by the Forestry Commission

T.C. Booth Silviculturist, Forestry Commission

Introduction

This paper begins with a summary of the organisation, staffing, and the policy of the Forestry Commission, and changes in these as they relate to the native pinewoods. This summary is followed by a review of the current position, to outline the Forestry Commission's attitude to this limited resource of which some 37% is under public ownership.

The responsibilities of the Forestry Commission are divided into two separate spheres, the Forest Authority and the Forest Enterprise. The latter is simply the running of the woodlands owned by the Forestry Commission. The former is more complex and pertains to the national responsibility for the carrying out of Government policy for Private Woodlands, the payment of grants, research and development and as a Government advisory body.

Work on both sides of Forestry Commission operations is carried out by the same staff, so that knowledge of both private woodlands and state-owned woodlands is widespread. Forest officers are trained at universities in a wide range of subjects. The suitability of training of Forestry Graduates for conservation and ecological posts can be seen by studying a list of posts taken by them both in this country and overseas. The forester grades are also trained in a wide range of skills in management and protection of forests, formerly at Forestry Commission training schools but now at the Cumberland and Westmorland Agricultural College at Newton Rigg. Staff are trained to manage according to the objects of management as laid down by Forestry Acts and Countryside Acts for conservation, amenity, recreation or timber production.

General Management

The widespread commitments of the Forestry Commission are covered by an intricate network of Districts and Forests, the staff of which can be called upon in the case of an emergency. This is most important when one considers the destruction that can be wrought over a short period of time even by natural hazards. Protection measures are essential and consume a large proportion of staff time whether it be purely conservation, woodland or commercial woodland. The following topics can all be covered by the general term 'protection'.

Fire

Although mentioned several times in this volume as being beneficial for producing a good seed bed for regeneration, it can also be disastrous to young plantations, and even more so in the case of the native pinewoods where it may have taken a tree 20 years to get its head above the heather. One fire every 30 years is sufficient to destroy all that has been gained by patience and diligence. Quick reporting and the application of both men and equipment are necessary to control an outbreak. In the case of the native pinewoods under Forestry Commission control, they are all part of larger blocks of forest covered by contingency plans

arranged with the local fire authority. The tragedy of not having such a system was illustrated at Shieldaig (Loch Torridon) where natural regeneration had been most promising, approximately 50% of the thicket stage crop being destroyed by a fire in March 1974. There is always a question of priorities in fire fighting and the local inhabitants gave top priority to saving the telephone exchange, which bore immediate effects, rather than the native pinewood with benefits in the far distant future.

Mammals

Grazing animals form one of the biggest hazards to regeneration, and the introduction of large flocks of sheep to the highlands has been selected by some as the beginning of the end of the native woodlands. Red deer and Roe deer are present in native pinewoods and have to be excluded by fencing. Fencing alone is not sufficient and a control by shooting is generally necessary in addition. This control entails a staff of wild life foresters and game wardens whose full-time job it is to keep damage to the crop to a minimum. Fencing is a costly operation and is at its cheapest when done in large regular-shaped units, and native remnants that are surrounded by commercial plantation can be protected at a reduced cost.

Insects and disease

Although no major incidence of pests and disease has been reported in a native pinewood, there is always a possibility of such a happening. Research specialists are always available to give advice on the treatment or the likely severity of such an outbreak. Constant surveillance is necessary in any large-scale management of a biological nature and this can be carried out most effectively when native woods are bounded by commercial plantations which provide a vital buffer to the generally small areas of native woods.

Forest policy

General

The policy to which the Forestry Commission works is defined by Government in a series of Forestry Acts, and this policy has changed with time. The creation of the Forestry Commission began in 1919, the purpose being to establish a reserve of timber in case of emergency and in the face of the difficulties of importing bulky cargoes through a blockade and the scarcity of woodlands. A similar background created the expansionist Post War Forest Policy 1947. The reduction in the possibilities of long-lasting blockades, due to changes in modern weaponry, brought about a change in policy in 1967, when it was decreed that the Forest Enterprise should be run on 'commercial' lines, that is make a profit. Conservation was only written into the policy in 1973 when there was a marked change in emphasis, and multiple land use, with conservation and recreation as major attributes for both Private and Commission woodlands, was defined for the first time (FC 1974).

Research

As would be expected, the objectives and the funding of research reflected the general forest policy. Several quotations obtained from R.F. Wood (1974) are pertinent here. From the Cabinet Committee in 1919 'that for research on other subjects in connection with forestry problems, and for fundamental research other than that directed to immediate economic benefit, the Commission should first refer to the 'appropriate authority' for the particular subject'. He also quotes Guillebaud as saying 'the function of the research branch was primarily to act as the handmaiden of the executive'. The position was quite nicely summarised 'perhaps also the atmosphere was unfriendly to 'impractical' treatments or levels of such treatments as a means of advancing knowledge, and it is fortunate that the early experimenters went well beyond the limit on occasions'. It was not until 1965, when the Natural Environment Research Council was established that long-term forestry research was specifically assigned to a Research Council. Fundamental forestry research only achieved its own institute in 1970 by the establishment of the Institute of Tree Biology. In the light of the general policy, the amount of research and conservation achieved by the early small group of researchers was truly remarkable. The bending of the rules was certainly carried out in the case of the native pinewoods.

Remnants of native pinewoods managed by the Forestry Commission

These areas are summarised in table 1 and the following notes.

Loch Arkaig, including Glen Mallie

This area contains scattered native pines, survivors of the 1942 fire, partly in young plantations and partly on ground not owned by the Forestry Commission. The pines have been retained for their landscape value. They are generally so widely scattered that any significant regeneration is unlikely.

Achnashellach

The denser parts of the native pinewoods on this area remain. They are protected by fencing erected when the present plantations were established. Planting, without restriction of species, has been done around, but not through, the denser natural pine areas. Scattered pines remain, but, except in gulleys, are now enclosed by plantations. Sitka spruce that have been planted through the area are to be removed.

Loch Maree (Eilean Ruaridh Mhor)

This area is subject to a management agreement with the Nature Conservancy Council.

Glenmore

The forest was largely exploited during the 1914-18 war, leaving only scattered pine over most of the ground. Planting, mainly of Scots pine of non-native and often uncertain origin, has been done over most of the area, and some of these trees are in the thinning stage. Some portions of the native woodland have been preserved near Loch Morlich and elsewhere. There is also a small 12-acre area which has been separately enclosed, and used for experiments and research since 1930. Seed trapping was carried out at Glenmore and a count of 653,000 seeds per acre was obtained. Of these, only 0.1% survived, 76% of the seed falling within 1 chain of the old crop.

Glengarry

When this site was acquired in 1930, the timber was not included in the sale, and felling was carried out after the acquisition. An agreement was reached with the timber merchant that seed trees should be left on a part of the area; 2.8 acres were enclosed and the fence has been maintained ever since. Vegetation maps were drawn in 1956 and 1966, and the pattern shows a decrease in *Calluna,* and *Vaccinium* and mosses dominating. There has been some birch regeneration but very few Scots pine, with what few there are approaching 1 metre in height after 30 years. Sowings were carried out in a similar enclosure without seed trees, the sowings being into mattock prepared trenches; a range of species were used, and these grew satisfactorily. A heavy attack of Pine shoot beetles was blamed for reducing the seedfall when the ground was still relatively free of weeds. Very dense birch regeneration was produced on the disturbed ground in the second enclosed area. The more inaccessible parts of the old wood were not felled and the denser parts of these remain untouched.

Glen Loy

Lord Robinson was involved in the setting aside of this area as an ecological reserve. It was fenced in 1930 and twenty years later there was minimal regeneration. Several experiments were tried in the 1940's without success. A new fence was erected in 1973 to exclude the deer in the hope that natural regeneration will take place on part of the area.

Glen Affric

This is the largest of the native pinewoods under Forestry Commission control and was acquired in 1951-53. From the beginning, special plans were drawn up to try and perpetuate the native pine wood; some 30 acres were felled per annum, and gaps were extended in the birch, with ground preparation to encourage regeneration. With the thought in mind that the area might be made into a Naitonal Forest Park, the work was mainly directed towards amenity. Following the publication of Steven and Carlisle's book

'The Native Pinewoods of Scotland', Professor Steven was present at Affric with an excursion of the Society of Foresters and he 'waxed elequent' on the reasons for the conservation of the pinewoods. The arguments he put forward were recognised as valid, and the management of the woods at Glen Affric were altered to implement Steven and Carlisle's recommendations.

Subsequent management of Affric is covered in detail by 'Innes and Seal' (72). In brief, 2,100 acres were ring-fenced to exclude deer and stock; subsequently, internal fences were erected to aid a strict control policy. Planting took place on a minor scale, always using plants of an Affric origin, and in later years ploughing and fertilisers were used to improve on the poor results of direct notching. The conclusion, reached in 1972 by the authors, that planting was necessary, would now probably be amended to say that natural regeneration is a strong possibility. The rigid policy of deer exclusion is having effect and a visit of the members of the Native Pinewoods Discussion group in 1974 saw the extremely happy state of increased natural regeneration, not only birch and rowan but also plenty of Scots pine. Within the pine reserve, the area of about 90 acres has purposely been left untouched since 1956.

Rannoch (Blackwood)

This is one of the better known examples of the native pinewoods, acquired by the Forestry Commission in 1947 and extended by further acquisitions to the west in 1959. The early work which took place under both local management and research had conservation as the paramount objective. The special nature of the area was recognised in 1972 when the area was scheduled as a Site of Special Scientific Interest by the Nature Conservancy Council. The early history of the wood is well documented, as is the management of the wood to the present time. All the research work in the native pinewoods has been summarised by McDonald (1952) and Henman (1961). Rannoch has several points of interest for future work. A 240 acre experimental reserve was established where there have only been minor intrusions for experimental work;

there are also 2 small fenced enclosures with minimal soil disturbance where natural regeneration of birch and rowan is abundant, and sown Scots pine survivors are few in numbers. There is also a famous small nursery site which previously bore a crop of potatoes where naturally regenerated Scots pine thrive. The main point of interest about Rannoch is the future management. After a series of meetings, field visits and site surveys a management plan has been drawn up and agreed with the Nature Conservancy Council (formally signed in November 1975). This involves the designation of 3 management areas.

1. Non-disturbance area   121 hectares
2. Minimum disturbance area   106 hectares
3. Conversion area   624 hectares
   Total   851 hectares

During the next 10 years no work will be carried out in the minimum disturbance area; during this period experiments are to be set up in the 'conversion area' to determine what is required to obtain regeneration by 'minimal interference'. The objective of management in the conversion area will be to convert the existing plantations, which include exotics, to a forest predominantly composed of pine and birch of local origin. In total, there is a substantial expansion on what was originally designed the 'Blackwood', especially so when a birch zone at the western end is included in the management area. Because this zone is subject to a farming tenancy, no direct intervention is at present possible.

Conclusion

While preservation is a better term for the management of the smaller remnants under Forestry Commission management, a most active conservation, and even some expansion, is being carried out in the major reserves. This is only possible because of a well distributed and equipped field staff who have a good ecological backing to their training. The research and conservation work carried out only took place because of a liberal interpretation of Forest Policy in the past, the most recent Forestry Act being an acceptance of what was taking place rather than a completely new line of approach.

References

HENMAN, D.W. (1961). 'Natural regeneration of Scots pine woods in the Highlands'. *Scott. For.,* **15**, 235-242.

FORESTRY COMMISSION *Annual Report 1973-74.*

INNES, R.A. & SEAL, D.T. (1972). The native Scottish pinewoods. *Forestry,* **44**, suppl., 66-73.

McDONALD, J.A.B. (1952). 'Natural regeneration of Scots pine woods in the Highlands'. *Rep. Forest Res., Lond.,* 1951, 26-33.

WOOD, R.F. (1974). 'Fifty years of forestry research'. *Bull. For. Commn.* no. 50.

Table 1 Remnants of native pinewoods managed by the Forestry Commission

North Scotland Conservancy		East Scotland Conservancy
Achnashellach	Glenmore	Rannoch (Blackwood)
Glen Affric	Glenmoriston	
Glen Cannich	Glenloy	West Scotland
Glen Einig	Guisachan and Cougie	
Glen Feshie	Loch Arkaig including Glen Mallie	Glenorchy
Glen Garry	Loch Maree	

Native pinewood conservation in North East Scotland

J.A. Forster, and D. Morris Nature Conservancy Council

1. Introduction

In recent years, the Nature Conservancy Council, Forestry Commission and private owners have been developing policies to promote the conservation of native pinewoods in Scotland. Effort has been concentrated on the larger pinewoods and especially on those in the Cairngorms area. From the experience gained in this work, we have attempted to put forward general guidelines for a conservation strategy.

Steven and Carlisle (1959) identified thirty-five pinewoods in Scotland that could be described as 'native', that is 'descended from one generation to another by natural means'. Nine of these are within the Cairngorms area and include some of the largest of the pinewoods, and one of the smallest. The Merlewood Survey (Goodier and Bunce, this volume) estimated the acreage of dense forest in twenty-six of the thirty-five native pinewoods, enabling the twenty-six to be ranked in order of size. The position of the Cairngorms' pinewoods, in the national series, is given below, along with the estimated acreage of dense pinewood in each forest.

Abernethy	1	160 ha
Ballochbuie	2	111
Rothiemurchus	4	32
Glen Tanar	6	26
Glen Feshie	7	22
Mar	10	13
Glenmore	16	5
Dulnain	-	-
Glen Avon	-	-

Dulnain is a large pinewood but was not surveyed by either the Steven and Carlisle or the Merlewood Survey. Glen Avon consists of only thirteen trees, according to Steven and Carlisle.

Although these nine native pinewoods must be the focus for a conservation strategy in the Cairngorms, we should, in the long term, also be prepared to extend the concept in two directions. We must take account of pinewoods which have been planted, in all parts of Britain, and now provide valuable tracts of wildlife habitat, and maintain various aspects of the pinewoods ecosystem — indeed such planting has occurred in recent years within the boundaries of the native pinewoods themselves. Secondly, we must consider sites and plant communities not now dominated by pine, but which are potentially capable of developing into pinewood, either permanently or as part of a cyclical process. Moorelands adjacent to native pinewoods can, for example, develop into forest through natural regeneration and this is evident in many parts of north-east Scotland. The dynamic relationship between heather moor and forest was well appreciated even in the 18th century when it was remarked "these highland fir-woods shift their stances" (Mitchie 1901). The role that other tree and shrub species play in this process is not known, but Gimingham (this volume) has suggested a long-term dynamic relationship between birch, pine and open heather moorland. Thus, the conservation strategies should aim to include all the species and processes characteristic of the pinewoods ecosystem.

2. The value of the pinewoods for nature conservation

The native pinewoods in the Cairngorms area are among the largest areas of semi-natural forest in Britain.

Size is of importance to nature conservation in a variety of ways (Streeter 1974). Quite apart from possessing more of the total pinewood resource, there are other ways in which the size of individual sites is important. Large sites are likely to cover a greater variety of terrain and therefore possess a greater variety of species than small sites. Certain species, for example goshawk, require large areas of habitat before they can maintain viable populations. Lastly, if a catastrophe strikes a forest, for example fire or severe windblow, it is probable that the larger forest will offer more chance for the survival of forest conditions over some part of it, and hence may be a refuge for plant and animal species.

There is good historical evidence from some of the forests in the Cairngorms area that they stand on sites that have been continuously occupied by forest cover since the end of the last glaciation (Birks 1970 ; O'Sullivan 1973). This continuous occupation is a rare feature in Britain and offers unique opportunities for the study of the response of trees to the environment over long periods of time. In some respects, therefore, these forests approximate more closely than any other in Britain to the climax condition. Despite man's undoubtedly heavy influence, they still may be regarded as relatively less disturbed than any other extensive area of forest in the U.K.

A great variety of structure occurs in the pinewoods, ranging from the open parkland types, with a few old scattered trees (eg Mar), to the dense stands in Ballochbuie and Abernethy.

Areas of deciduous woodland, natural regeneration, bog and mire communities, cliffs, screes, rivers and lochs all enhance this variety. Newton (this volume) has shown how a mosaic of habitats within the pinewoods can be important for bird species. High populations of Crested tit, for example, are favoured by the association of juniper and regenerating pine with very old mature trees (Watson 1969).

These pinewoods are also valuable for timber and as shelter and food for grazing animals, especially Red deer in winter, while Thom (this volume) has emphasised their role as a recreational resource of national importance. Related to all these aspects is the value of the pinewoods in supporting local employment for tourism, nature conservation, forestry and wildlife management.

3. Management for Conservation

The principal management objective for these pinewoods must be to ensure that the above values are maintained and enhanced. For nature conservation purposes, the objective should be to encourage the forest to develop with a minimum of interference for the following reasons:-

1. Steven and Carlisle specifically rejected forests that had been planted in the past.

2. Even though burnt, overgrazed and exploited for timber and, in some cases, lacking species typical of the ecosystem, the native pinewoods still remain less disturbed than any other woodland type in Britain.

3. Lack of knowledge of the natural structure of the forest and the requirements of dependent organisms supports the need for caution in management activities.

4. It is not possible to re-create a forest resembling a hypothetical "old forest of Caledon". Climate and soils have changed over the centuries, and the cumulative influence of man's past acitivities can never be removed. It may, however, be possible to encourage the development of more natural types of forest and eventually to develop towards the climax condition. Such a development, controlled largely by the interplay of soil, topography and climate, could only take place where management impacts were minimised.

5. The concept of minimal management in national park and nature reserve planning programmes throughout the world is assuming much greater importance (Lamprey 1974). It is essential that Britain should have at least some representative sites where minimal management is practised and, as Gimingham (this volume) has indicated, it is only possible for such management to take place in areas of substantial size which are protected from external processes.

6. The largest of the native pinewoods provide some of the best opportunities in Britain for wilderness-type recreation. Ratcliffe (1974) has stated:

"The British have ravaged their forest lands and, by our standards, these remnants of the 'Old' Wood of Caledon are superb. Quite apart from the wildlife, these forests have a fascination which can only be felt by wandering amongst them, and absorbing something of their atmosphere. There is here, at least in those parts where human activity is least in evidence, the quality of the real wilderness of the boreal regions'.

These values can only be maintained if management activities and impacts within the forest are of a low intensity.

4. The concept of "minimal management"

The development of "minimal management" policies is an essential ingredient to a conservation strategy for the native pinewoods. In areas where such an approach is feasible, management should aim to interfere only so far as is necessary to perpetuate and promote the development of natural forest.

Different methods must, however, be accepted in different forests, depending on the extent to which they have been subjected to detrimental impacts from man in the past. Experience of fenced plots in several forests — Glen Tanar, Mar, Glen Feshie, Rothiemurchus and Abernethy, and the results of surveys of regeneration throughout these woodlands, provide convincing evidence that the survival of the native pinewoods can be achieved by manipulating grazing pressures, and by excluding or reducing the number of grazing animals. Man may also have influenced the native pinewoods by reducing the incidence and extent of natural forest fires. It may, therefore, be worth simulating more natural conditions by burning small areas of heather moorland adjacent to forest stands.

It has been suggested by Fitzpatrick (this volume) that long-term soil degradation has occurred as a result of man's activities. However, there is no universal agreement on this issue and Scots pine is able to grow under low nutrient conditions in which other tree species will not survive. Before one could be justified in interfering with nutrient status or soil structure, one would need to be assured that there was general agreement so the past impacts of man on pine soils had been so detrimental. It appears that the present climate and soils of the Cairngorms area are adequate to enable the pinewoods to be perpetuated.

Regeneration of the forest using minimal management techniques may be satisfactory from a conservation viewpoint, but the density of trees produced may be unsatisfactory for commercial forestry. There are, therefore, often pressures to increase the stocking density by planting, but this has several major disadvantages.

Planting cannot re-create the pattern and density of trees that would occur in a natural forest; the choice of species to plant and the narrow spectrum of genetic variation in the seeds collected produces a severe bias in the future forest population; by rearing stock and then transferring it back to the hillside, at two, three or four years old, the normally severe selective forces that work during the establishment stages in the wild are bypassed. Thus, the gene-types growing to maturity are not those that would have been selected had natural regeneration alone been responsible for the seedling establishment. It must be recognised, however, that natural regeneration may take a long time to establish a new forest, and fencing may have to be renewed. In terms of the resource as a whole, if extensive tracts of forest are to be re-created over large areas of moorland, then large-scale fencing will be impractical. The direct reduction of the numbers of grazing animals by culling will be the only really effective technique. Fencing should be seen as a short-term emergency measure for small stands in danger of extinction by single catastroic events.

In most pinewood areas, the gradual re-establishment of forest through natural regeneration can be achieved by greater control of the burning and grazing pressure in, and around, the pinewoods.

It must be accepted that minimal management may on

occasion result in the forest dying out in certain areas or being replaced by other forest types, for example birch. If there is a sufficient representation of sites, then the local extinction in one site will be compensated by new growth in other sites.

There are sound nature conservation reasons for resisting the extraction of timber from much of the remaining resource. However, in some of the larger sites, timber extraction will have to be permitted because of the wider social and economic interests and the financial loss to the owners of pinewoods where they are unable to manage them by intensive forestry techniques.

5. Constraints on principal conservation management goals

Pinewood, whether it is required for timber or nature conservation, represents the same biological resource. This is an unusual situation in Britain, where it is more common to see competition between nature conservation and development for land, rather than the resource itself. At the national level, the remnant native pinewoods do not represent a significant timber resource compared to the 1¼ m ha of other production forest in Britain, and, nationally, we believe the benefits to be gained from conservation are greater. However, at the level of the individual estate or community, one must recognise that the management of the forest as a productive resource generates local income of importance to individual estates and provides sources of employment which have considerable value in areas of comparatively low population density and limited job opportunities. As the majority of native pinewoods are privately owned, no strategy can ignore the very real conflicts which will arise between national conservation goals and those which individual owners may wish to follow. These will include the extraction of the present timber crop and the conversion of semi-natural pinewoods to higher-yielding commercial forest stands.

There are also other non forestry objectives which may affect the land on which the native pinewoods are growing. The majority of the forests in north-east Scotland are used as wintering areas by Red deer. These occur in such large numbers that natural regeneration is often held in check, even in the most ecologically favourable sites. It is paradoxical that large numbers of deer are kept to provide a sufficient stock for sporting purposes and yet shooting intensity in recent years has generally not been sufficient even to keep the deer down to the levels recommended by the Red Deer Commission (1975). Unfortunately, in many of the forests, even to permit natural regeneration these levels would be too high. Thus, for practical purposes, it will be necessary to exclude Red deer by fencing, or reduce their numbers to such low levels that the sporting value of adjacent land may be reduced, at least in the short term.

6. Management techniques

The variety of goals and constraints to be taken into account in designing a conservation strategy requires a vigorous appraisal of the range of management techniques available and of their acceptability. Of crucial importance is the extent to which the use of a particular technique disrupts valuable ecological processes. The most undesirable are those whose effects last for the longest period of time, are irreversible, of wide as opposed to local impact, and bear least resemblance to an event that might have occurred naturally in the forest.

Ploughing, drainage and, to a lesser extent, screefing destroy soil profiles and field layer habitats and are virtually irreversible in their effects. Planting of exotic species is not acceptable, nor is planting of native species in areas developing as semi-natural or climax type forests. Although planting of Scots pine in areas around the native pinewoods is acceptable, providing extensive areas are still left for the native pinewood to expand by natural regeneration, only seed of local provenance should be used in order to minimise the level of genetic contamination. Timber extraction yields most of the income from the larger forests and does not have effects on conservation values which are as detrimental as any of the above techniques. Extraction should be permitted in some of the larger forests, provided it is carried out in such a manner that replenishment can be achieved by natural regeneration.

In the natural forest, the size of the forest would have been in better balance with the size of the grazing animal population and the forests would be continually replenished by natural regeneration. Changes in the rate of recruitment would reflect changes in grazing pressure brought about by climatic, habitat or predator fluctuations. Manipulation of grazing pressure is therefore the most acceptable management technique for the native pinewoods. More than any other technique it resembles in its effects the types of change that would have occurred in the natural forest. Ideally, grazing levels should be manipulated by direct culling or, as a second choice, by fencing to exclude the larger herbivores.

7. Zonation for conservation management

As a result of detailed studies on the native pinewoods and the many discussions which have been held in recent years to try to promote their conservation, it is believed that, in the larger forests, the aims of nature conservation and other forest interests can be accommodated within a system of zonation.

In most cases, subdivision of the forest into three types of zone would be adequate. These types are as follows:-

(i) Strict Natural Zone

In this zone, the primary object of management would be to maintain or develop a natural native pinewood ecosystem. The following management principles should be adopted:-

(a) Management should be restricted to the reduction of grazing pressure to the level at which natural regeneration is possible, control of fire hazards and the removal of any non-native species.

(b) There should be no unnecessary disturbance to wildlife, to soil profiles by ploughing, screefing or drainage, no timber extraction, and no tree planting. Windblown timber should not be removed.

(ii) Managed Natural Zone

Here the object of management would be the dual one of maintaining as near natural a forest as possible while still allowing extraction of timber for commercial purposes. The principles governing management should be:-

(a) Timber harvesting should be by selection thinning and felling of small groups to produce a forest structure of mixed age and capable of optimum timber production from a self sustaining resource.

(b) Replenishment of the resource should be by natural regeneration, unaided by ground treatments.

(c) There should be no ploughing or drainage and no tree planting. Windblown timber may be removed if it is commercially desirable, or if there is a danger of spread of disease or pests.

(iii) Planting Zone

Here the primary object of management would be the production of timber from the intensive management of Scots pine forest while, at the same time, optimising pinewood wildlife interest by the creation and maintenance of habitats resembling those in natural pinewoods. The principles governing management could be:-

(a) Commercial forest management practices should be used to obtain optimum production providing there are no deleterious effects on adjacent "strict natural" or "managed natural" zones.

(b) There should be no widespread application of fertiliser, presticide or herbicide which might affect adjacent zones.

(c) Only Scots pine of local provenance should be planted.

In the selection of zones, several important considerations have to be borne in mind. It is important that the Strict Natural Zones are of sufficient number and size to ensure viable examples of the main range of variation to tbe found within the resource. At the same time, it is necessary to ensure that these Zones are practical management units and are not so situated in relation to neighbouring land uses as to make their long-term survival unlikely. It is desirable that, in at least a few cases, these Zones are linked with open moorland into which natural regeneration can spread and are also associated with other vegetation types which make a natural sequence e.g. from valley bottom through a natural tree line to the montane zone. In general, Strict

Natural Zones will be chosen in forest areas where there has been least recent human interference. The Managed Natural and Planting Zones should be chosen to protect and complement the Strict Natural Zones. Thus, a Managed Natural Zone may be sited between the Strict Natural and Planting Zones. Similarly, a Planting Zone may be sited to buffer both Strict Natural and Managed Natural Zones against nearby plantations of exotic species or against excess grazing pressure.

8. Implementation

The success of achieving nature conservation aims through this type of zonation will depend on effective means of implementation. Some of the sites are already, or are likely to become, National Nature Reserves, but even in these the implementation will vary between those Reserves which are state-owned and those which are privately owned and subject to a Nature Reserve Agreement. Voluntary conservation bodies can play an important role; the high grade Abernethy Forest has recently been purchased by the Royal Society for the Protection of Birds and the last section of the Glenmore pinewood which has not been planted is now subject to a Reserve Agreement between the Forestry Commission and the Scottish Wildlife Trust. The important sites which are within the ownership of the Forestry Commission are the subject of detailed consultation between the Forestry Commission and the Nature Conservancy Council and for one of them, the Black Wood of Rannoch, a detailed plan of management, based on a zonation system, has been agreed between the Forestry Commission and the Nature Conservancy Council. On other sites, the possibility of grant-aiding private owners, has been explored, using the powers of Section 15 of the Countryside Act (1968). In the Tyndrum pinewood, the Nature Conservancy Council has assisted the owner to promote natural regeneration by fencing. While, however, the means of implementation are likely to be varied, it is important that it is carried out within the framework of a conservation strategy for the whole resource. We need to know if similar types of zonation can be applied to a wide variety of native pinewoods, including the smaller ones, and whether similar principles should apply to the four main groups of pinewoods identified by the Merlewood Survey (Goodier and Bunce, op. cit).

It has to be borne in mind that it is not the present generation that is the sole beneficiary of this development in conservation practice. The strategy, should therefore rely, in part, on resources that may be made available in the future. We should aim to prevent any further deterioration in the present state of our native pinewoods and plan for their gradual improvement over many years.

References

BIRKS, H.H. (1970). Studies in the vegetational history of Scotland. I. A pollen diagram from Abernethy forest, Inverness-shire. *J. Ecol.,* **58**, 827-46.

LAMPREY, H.F. (1974). Management of flora and fauna in National Parks, World Conference on National Parks, 2nd, 1972, 235-257. I.U.C.N.

MITCHIE, J.F. (Ed.), (1901). *The records of Invercould, 1547-1828.* New Spalding Club, Aberdeen.

O'SULLIVAN, P.E. (1973). Contemporary pollen studies in a native Scots pine ecosystem. *Oikos,* **24,** 143-50.

RATCLIFFE, D.A. (1974). The vegetation. In: *The Cairngorms: their natural history and scenery,* edited by D. Nethersole-Thompson and A. Watson, 42-76. Collins.

RED DEER COMMISSION, *Annual Report for 1975.*

STEVEN, H.M. CARLISLE, A. (1959). *The native pinewoods of Scotland.* Oliver and Boyd.

STREETER, D. (1974). Ecological aspects of oak woodland conservation. In: *The British oak, its history and natural history,* edited by M.G. Morris and F.H. Perring, 341-354. Classey.

WATSON, A. (1969). Preliminary counts of birds in Central Highland pinewoods. *Bird Study,* **16,** 158-163.